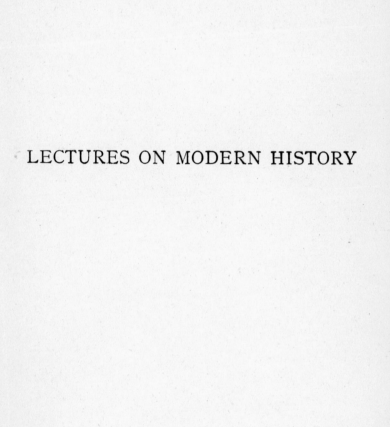

LECTURES ON MODERN HISTORY

LECTURES

ON

MODERN HISTORY

BY

JOHN EMERICH EDWARD DALBERG-ACTON

FIRST BARON ACTON

D.C.L., LL.D., ETC. ETC.

REGIUS PROFESSOR OF MODERN HISTORY IN THE UNIVERSITY OF CAMBRIDGE

EDITED WITH AN INTRODUCTION BY

JOHN NEVILLE FIGGIS, M.A.

SOMETIME LECTURER IN ST. CATHARINE'S COLLEGE, CAMBRIDGE

AND

REGINALD VERE LAURENCE, M.A.

FELLOW AND LECTURER OF TRINITY COLLEGE, CAMBRIDGE

MACMILLAN AND CO., LIMITED
ST. MARTIN'S STREET, LONDON
1952

PRINTED IN GREAT BRITAIN

PREFATORY NOTE

THE Lectures on Modern History were delivered by Lord Acton in his ordinary course as Professor in the academical years 1899-1900 and 1900-01. The Inaugural Lecture on the Study of History, here reprinted, was delivered on June 11, 1895. The document printed in Appendix I. is of great interest, as exhibiting the ideals of Lord Acton as a student and the aims of the undertaking which he planned and still bears his name.

It is hoped shortly to issue in another volume the Lectures on the French Revolution, and thus to complete the record of his work as Professor. The Introductory Essay deals exclusively with his Cambridge work. A more general account of his career will precede the volumes of essays and reviews. The editors wish to thank Professor Henry Jackson for his kind advice with regard to the Introduction.

The second impression differs from the first in that a few small errors in the text have been corrected. The editors desire to state that the Lectures are printed from the manuscript exactly in the form in which they were delivered.

J. N. F.

R. V. L.

CONTENTS

CONTENTS

INTRODUCTION

LORD ACTON AS PROFESSOR

IT was announced in February 1895 that John Emerich Edward Dalberg Acton, first Baron Acton, had been appointed to the Chair of Regius Professor of Modern History at Cambridge in succession to the late Sir John Seeley, who had held the office for upwards of a quarter of a century. Of the achievements of Acton's six years' tenure of the post, the present volume, together with that forthcoming on the French Revolution, will form the chief, though not the only monument. To those who found in the teaching of the late Professor inspiration as well as knowledge, the Lectures now published will serve at once to heighten and to relieve the sense, still so fresh, of personal loss. To the many friends and scholars who had known him in other spheres or for a longer space, they will be a fitting memorial of Acton's greatness in the realm of his unchallenged pre-eminence. Of all the previous occupants of the chair none is to be named with Acton for a career unique in interest, variety, and pathos.

Pathos indeed there was. The note was struck in the first phrases of the Inaugural Lecture. It was perhaps not unfitting that the severest rebuke to Anglican intolerance in the past should come from a man whose indignation knew no measure for the spirit of persecution within his own communion. Throughout those years at

Cambridge, from the pregnant address " Fellow Students ! "
which prefaced his Inaugural, Acton bore the manner of
one who was after many tempests "in the haven where
he would be." No one who reverenced so deeply the
scholar's calling could fail to be proud of this final if
belated recognition of his rightful place as a scholar
among scholars. But there were other things of which
he was proud. His delight in finding himself a
Cambridge man, his feeling for the College which adopted
him and made him an Honorary Fellow, his interest in
the young, even his pleasure in his rooms in Nevile's
Court, were the symbol of what he had lacked in early
days, and of the fact, elsewhere noted by himself, that he
never " had any contemporaries." The result was seen in
his willingness to take part in labours sometimes deemed
beneath professorial dignity, and in that freshness of
sympathy with which he would enter into the mind of
the youngest pupils—provided only they recognised that
History was a goddess, not a plaything. Perhaps also it
was shown in his keen desire to know everything about
people, for Acton's interest in human beings was no less
piercing than his love of books.

In this place, it is bare justice that the impression
made by Acton upon Cambridge should be decisively
recorded. This is the more needful, because there has
been in some quarters a tendency to belittle the activity
of the late Professor, a tendency which indicates the same
limited intellectual horizon as the denial that he was a
historian. As a matter of fact, when we remember that
Acton came to Cambridge at the age of sixty-one ; that
he bore within him the scars of an arduous and unsuccessful conflict ; that he was not, and, with his conception of history, could not be a recluse ; that he was
familiar neither with teaching nor examining, much less
with administration ; that his effective tenure of his office

was only six years, we ought to be amazed alike at the quantity of his achievement and the quality of his activity.

There are three fields which form the province of a University Professor—teaching, the organisation of his department, and research.   Under present conditions a professor of history who does nothing but research leaves unfulfilled half the duties of his office.   As Mill said of the House of Commons, his business is not so much to do things as to get things done.   He must take his place as head of a school and strive to guide the thought and work of younger students, besides inspiring a larger public by means of lectures.   The latter are, indeed, now an imperative duty, and no future occupant of the chair is likely to imitate the enthusiasm of Gray, Regius Professor in the mid-eighteenth century, who was thought to have shown unwonted conscientiousness in spending four years gathering material for an Inaugural, although he died without delivering or even writing it. On the other hand, the Professor should not limit his efforts to preparing undergraduates for a coming tripos.   Acton fulfilled his task to perfection.   His Lectures were not either in delivery or substance adapted to the assiduous note-taker ;   they might suggest, they would never diminish, the need of reading.   They were not so much a mine of instruction as a revelation of the speaker's personality.   Despite all his impartiality, his ideals were plainly evident, both in the matter and in the form of what he said ;   and not merely his ideals, but the intensity with which they possessed him.   One of his hearers has recorded these impressions :—

There was a magnetic quality in the tones of his voice, and a light in his eye, that compelled obedience from the mind.   Never before had a young man come into the presence of such intensity of con- viction as was shown by every word Lord Acton spoke.   It took possession of the whole being, and seemed to enfold it in its own

burning flame.   And the fires below on which it fed were, at least
for those present, immeasurable.   More than all else, it was perhaps this conviction that gave to Lord Acton's Lectures their amaz-
ing force and vivacity.   He pronounced each sentence as if he
were feeling it, poising it lightly, and uttering it with measured
deliberation.   His feeling passed to the audience, which sat
enthralled.   It was in truth an emotional performance of the highest
order, his lecture ; a wonderful work of art, such as in all likelihood will never again be witnessed.[1]

From the first his Lectures were crowded.   It must
be admitted that in the audience there were some who
were not serious students.   But it may be questioned
whether any one who heard even a single lecture could go
away quite unimpressed.   No one could fail to see how
the speaker's mind was possessed with the greatness of
human affairs, with the moral (or immoral) aspects of
political and ecclesiastical dexterity ; above all, with the
final supremacy of the soul over circumstance, as the real
ground for asserting the sacredness of truth and the
inalienable glory of Liberty.   It was this sense of the
fundamentally spiritual nature of his work which formed
the distinction, the difficulty, and the triumph of Acton.
His high seriousness gave him the influence which, despite
all detraction, he unmistakably wielded.   For Machiavelli
is more than the bane of politicians.   His principles are
the eternal snare of those who investigate their actions ;
while a flippant cynicism is the common homage paid by
youth to the duty of reflection.   Now no hearer, however
intelligent, no student, however anti-sentimental, could fail
to find in Acton's austere judgments, in the dignity of his
language, in the tones of his voice, a warning against any
treatment of history that was mean or utilitarian, and any
view of human nature that demands of it less than " may
become a man."

But it was in the direction of the school that Acton

---

[1] See an article by John Pollock on '' Lord Acton at Cambridge,'' in the *Inde-
vendent Review* for April 1904.

showed himself most markedly successful. Everything in his previous life appeared to point the other way. It might have been expected that he would withdraw from this part of his duties and become purely a man of the study, with neither desire nor capacity to influence his colleagues or to stir up interest in history among undergraduates. The very reverse proved the case. Probably no Professor was ever more accessible. He was willing to give advice to any one, and nobody who consulted him went empty away. If any student went to him for information he would be told more than he supposed his question to involve ; and would probably find on his arrival home that Acton's servant had preceded him with a pile of books in half a dozen languages, and a note stating that more would follow. It was all one to him, whether his energies were spent in understanding an undergraduate's difficulty or laying down the lines of a Fellowship Dissertation, or advising a lecturer, or suggesting authorities to a contributor. He was never too busy to write a list of books ; never too much bored to answer a question, and—perhaps it may be added— never too serious to pay a compliment with an edge.

In this connection one further point must be noted— the foundation of the Trinity Historical Society. Soon after Acton settled at Cambridge, suggestions were made to him that he might find in a company meeting unofficially for the reading and discussion of papers on historical subjects, a means of coming into touch with many who otherwise could hardly hope to know him. A conversation class in connection with his lectures on the French Revolution in the academical year 1895-96 was the first attempt of the kind, but was, however, not altogether a success, and Acton gladly welcomed the suggestion of the junior of the editors of these lectures that a College Society on the lines of other Societies then existing in Trinity for the discussion of theological, political, and literary subjects should be formed. The Trinity Historical Society was accordingly founded in the Michaelmas Term of 1896, and Acton became its first President. The Society met in the Professor's rooms, and was composed of Trinity men, but senior and junior men from other Colleges were welcomed. From the very first the meetings were a success and justified the interest which Acton continuously displayed. Not unnaturally some of the younger members were a little awed by their President's weight of learning. But their shyness soon wore off. Through these meetings many were enabled to enter more deeply into his mind, and to find that Acton was not merely a great scholar, but a man full of sympathy for the humblest learner. His criticisms of those who seemed to mistake rhetoric for knowledge were sometimes drastic and exercised a salutary influence. Nor did the effect stop here. In other Colleges, and on a smaller scale, the example set by Acton has been followed. The Trinity Historical Society still continues to flourish, and will ever be associated with his memory. It testifies both to the Professor's keen sympathy with youth, and to his desire to use every possible means to promote the growth of what may be called "historical mindedness."

So far as the purely administrative side of his office was concerned, it may be said that Acton fulfilled his functions as Tripos Examiner, was always ready with advice or criticism when lists of authorities were being drawn up, but that he took little part in academic controversies, although he felt very strongly against the action of the University of Fisher and the Lady Margaret in refusing to allow Edmund House the *status* which the Anglican Church had secured for Selwyn. He acquiesced in the scheme of 1895-96 for dividing the Historical Tripos into two parts, and spoke in its favour in the Arts school. But his own part in the change was not a very active one. On the other hand, the moment that there was any opportunity for advancing the discovery of truth his mind was on the alert. An acute observer, he was always interested in watching the development of character. He felt keenly the contempt with which some of those who "stood by the ancient ways" regarded history. For to Acton history was the master of political wisdom, not a pursuit but a passion, not a mere instrument but a holy calling, not Clio so much as Rhadamanthus, the avenger of innocent blood. That men who were themselves scholars, and therefore presumably lovers of truth, should regard what was to him the noblest of studies with indifference or hostility, he felt almost as a personal wrong. And certainly no one in Cambridge ever did more to remove the reproach from what the ignorant think of as the easiest of studies. His defect was, rather, that he overestimated the responsibility of his task, and that, with him as with Hort, the very sense of the value of knowledge diminished his additions to its stores.

Another valuable result of his professoriate was the orientation of the study. Acton, by his birth, his career, and his studies, and, above all, his detachment, was driven to regard history from a standpoint neither English nor German, but universal. As he told the contributors to the Modern History, "The recent past contains the key to the present time. All forms of thought that influence it come before us in their turn ; we have to describe the ruling currents, to interpret the sovereign forces that still govern and divide the world. By Universal History I understand that which is distinct from the combined history of all countries, which is not a rope of sand but a continuous development, not a burden on the memory but an illumination of the soul. It moves in a succession to which the nations are subsidiary. Their story will be told, not for their own sake, but in reference and subordination to a higher series, according to the time and the degree in which they contribute to the common fortunes of mankind."

The influence of this attitude was at once wholesome and profound. It is true that Seeley had expressly guarded himself against all views of history that were narrow and insular. But Acton was the incarnation of universal history. As a writer in the *Athenæum* put it :—

No glorified encyclopædia, no aggregate of unrelated facts confronted the inquirer who interrogated Lord Acton, but a soul in whom spoke, as it seemed, the wisdom of the ages, and from whose depths there issued the very oracles of history, shining with the light that comes of absolutely single love of truth, penetrating even the gloom of the future by an illuminative knowledge of the past. To be with Acton was like being with the cultivated mind of Europe incarnate in its finest characteristics. In the deep tones of his voice there seemed to sound the accents of history. In those unflinching phrases we heard the impersonal estimate of posterity weighing in unerring balance the thoughts and deeds of the actors of the present or past, with a knowledge that knew no gap. We do not of course mean that Acton knew everything, but that he thoroughly understood the operation of forces—religious, political, social, economic—which create from what without them would be the sandheap of individual caprice and personal interest, the enduring bonds of secular and religious society.[1]

Now it may safely be said that the main purpose of historical study, apart from any value it has as a mental gymnastic, is to produce this frame of mind. It is because he had it in a supereminent degree that Acton would remain a great historian, even though he had never written a line. And it was because he had it that he helped forward so materially the cause of truly historical thinking in Cambridge. His wide acquaintance among foreign scholars and his knowledge of Continental

[1] Cf. *Athenæum*, April 16th, 1904, Review of *Letters of Lord Acton to Mary Gladstone.*

Universities were but subsidiary though very valuable aids to the end. Acton as a teacher, as a lecturer, as a friend, inspired us all with the sense that history was something greater than before we had realised, that the student was engaged upon a task fundamentally sacred, and that while politics are unintelligible without it, yet, rightly understood, it is the surest evidence of religion in general, and "a schoolmaster to bring men to Christ." Such a view of history may be right or wrong, but it is assuredly that created by intercourse with Acton, breathing in every utterance he spoke and every essay he ever wrote.

His influence upon research is best exhibited in the plan of the Cambridge Modern History. That plan at once expresses the ideals of Acton as a historian, and affords the evidence that his conception of History was that of the development of civilised freedom and growth of European culture. In the original plan every chapter was to be written by the most competent available expert, wherever he hailed from ; nothing written at second hand was to appear. This was at last feasible, since "the long conspiracy against the knowledge of truth was at an end, and competing scholars all over the civilised world are taking advantage of the change." It might therefore be hoped that Cambridge would produce "the best history of modern times that the published or unpublished sources of information admit." But if each chapter was to be written by the man most thoroughly equipped with first-hand knowledge of its subject, it was idle to expect anything but a minute subdivision of labour. No man could be the first living authority save on a small period. At the same time Acton was here, as elsewhere, the foe of pedantry. That notion of history which reduces it to a form of orthography had no charms for him ; he had not, like Freeman, a horror of calling Charles the Great by his

B

popular name. As he pointed out, " Our principle should be to supply help to students, not material to historians. . . . It is intended that the narrative shall be such as will serve all readers, that it shall be without notes, and without quotations in ' foreign languages.' " With Acton's known views on impartiality, it was a matter of course that he should add, " We shall avoid the needless utterance of opinion and the service of a cause."

The book as planned was worthy of its first editor. Many universities and two continents were ransacked for contributors. Five chapters—none, alas! written—Acton had allotted to himself, and in the titles of the others (not always retained since) his personal characteristics received pregnant expression. In the practical work of editing, it must be admitted that he was less successful. His very fastidiousness prevented him from realising that there is a time when proof correcting must cease, and that even histories cannot be perfect. He was without the driving force needed to keep in line a heterogeneous body of specialists. The result was that his health broke down under the task, and although nearly two volumes were in type at the time of his surrender, the work when it actually appeared did so under different auspices, and expressed ideals not altogether the same.

What we have said does not fully set forth the nature and extent of Acton's influence at Cambridge. But it may serve to show that in the three forms of professorial activity—teaching, organisation, and research—his six years at Cambridge made a mark upon the school of history which will not soon be effaced. What we have here set down is a mere record of facts. But it was an act of piety to lay them before the reader, in order that he may understand something of the strange spell which the late

Professor exercised, and perhaps also discern the causes which made the life in Cambridge a beautiful and fitting close to a career illumined throughout its course by the love of truth. It is true that the work of these years tasked his energies, and at the last exhausted them. Yet we, who knew him, felt that he would hardly have had it otherwise. The glory of the sunset may take a sober colouring ; none the less is it glory.

J. N. F.
R. V. L.

INAUGURAL LECTURE ON THE STUDY
OF HISTORY *

FELLOW STUDENTS—I look back to-day to a time before
the middle of the century, when I was reading at Edinburgh and fervently wishing to come to this University.
At three colleges I applied for admission, and, as things
then were, I was refused by all. Here, from the first, I
vainly fixed my hopes, and here, in a happier hour, after
five-and-forty years, they are at last fulfilled.

I desire, first, to speak to you of that which I may
reasonably call the Unity of Modern History, as an easy
approach to questions necessary to be met on the
threshold by any one occupying this place, which my
predecessor has made so formidable to me by the reflected
lustre of his name.

You have often heard it said that Modern History is
a subject to which neither beginning nor end can be
assigned. No beginning, because the dense web of the
fortunes of man is woven without a void ; because, in
society as in nature, the structure is continuous, and we
can trace things back uninterruptedly, until we dimly
descry the Declaration of Independence in the forests
of Germany. No end, because, on the same principle,
history made and history making are scientifically in-
separable and separately unmeaning.

"Politics," said Sir John Seeley, "are vulgar when
they are not liberalised by history, and history fades into
mere literature when it loses sight of its relation to

* Delivered at Cambridge, June 1895.

practical politics." Everybody perceives the sense in which this is true. For the science of politics is the one science that is deposited by the stream of history, like grains of gold in the sand of a river ; and the knowledge of the past, the record of truths revealed by experience, is eminently practical, as an instrument of action and a power that goes to the making of the future.[1] In France, such is the weight attached to the study of our own time, that there is an appointed course of contemporary history, with appropriate text-books.[2] That is a chair which, in the progressive division of labour by which both science and government prosper,[3] may some day be founded in this country. Meantime, we do well to acknowledge the points at which the two epochs diverge. For the contemporary differs from the modern in this, that many of its facts cannot by us be definitely ascertained. The living do not give up their secrets with the candour of the dead ; one key is always excepted, and a generation passes before we can ensure accuracy. Common report and outward seeming are bad copies of the reality, as the initiated know it. Even of a thing so memorable as the war of 1870, the true cause is still obscure ; much that we believed has been scattered to the winds in the last six months, and further revelations by important witnesses are about to appear. The use of history turns far more on certainty than on abundance of acquired information.

Beyond the question of certainty is the question of detachment. The process by which principles are discovered and appropriated is other than that by which, in practice, they are applied ; and our most sacred and disinterested convictions ought to take shape in the tranquil regions of the air, above the tumult and the tempest of active life.[4] For a man is justly despised who has one opinion in history and another in politics, one for abroad and another at home, one for opposition and another for office. History compels us to fasten on abiding issues, and rescues us from the temporary and transient. Politics and history are interwoven, but are not commensurate. Ours is a domain that reaches farther than affairs of state, and is not subject to the jurisdiction of governments. It is our function to keep in view and to command the movement of ideas, which are not the effect but the cause of public events ;[5] and even to allow some priority to ecclesiastical history over civil, since, by reason of the graver issues concerned, and the vital consequences of error, it opened the way in research, and was the first to be treated by close reasoners and scholars of the higher rank.[6]

In the same manner, there is wisdom and depth in the philosophy which always considers the origin and the germ, and glories in history as one consistent epic.[7] Yet every student ought to know that mastery is acquired by resolved limitation. And confusion ensues from the theory of Montesquieu and of his school, who, adapting the same term to things unlike, insist that freedom is the primitive condition of the race from which we are sprung.[8] If we are to account mind not matter, ideas not force, the spiritual property that gives dignity and grace and intellectual value to history, and its action on the ascending life of man, then we shall not be prone to explain the universal by the national, and civilisation by custom.[9] A speech of Antigone, a single sentence of Socrates, a few lines that were inscribed on an Indian rock before the Second Punic War, the footsteps of a silent yet prophetic people who dwelt by the Dead Sea, and perished in the fall of Jerusalem, come nearer to our lives than the ancestral wisdom of barbarians who fed their swine on the Hercynian acorns.

For our present purpose, then, I describe as Modern History that which begins four hundred years ago, which is marked off by an evident and intelligible line from the time immediately preceding, and displays in its course specific and distinctive characteristics of its own.[10] The modern age did not proceed from the medieval by normal succession, with outward tokens of legitimate descent. Unheralded, it founded a new order of things, under a law of innovation, sapping the ancient reign of continuity. In those days Columbus subverted the notions of the world, and reversed the conditions of production, wealth, and power ; in those days Machiavelli released government from the restraint of law ; Erasmus diverted the current of ancient learning from profane into Christian channels ; Luther broke the chain of authority and tradition at the strongest link ; and Copernicus erected an invincible power that set for ever the mark of progress upon the time that was to come. There is the same unbound originality and disregard for inherited sanctions in the rare philosophers as in the discovery of Divine Right, and the intruding Imperialism of Rome. The like effects are visible everywhere, and one generation beheld them all. It was an awakening of new life ; the world revolved in a different orbit, determined by influences unknown before. After many ages persuaded of the headlong decline and impending dissolution of society,[11] and governed by usage and the will of masters who were in their graves, the sixteenth century went forth armed for untried experience, and ready to watch with hopefulness a prospect of incalculable change.

That forward movement divides it broadly from the older world ; and the unity of the new is manifest in the universal spirit of investigation and discovery which did not cease to operate, and withstood the recurring efforts of reaction, until, by the advent of the reign of general ideas which we call the Revolution, it at length prevailed.[12] This successive deliverance and gradual passage, for good and evil, from subordination to independence is a phenomenon of primary import to us, because historical science has been one of its instruments.[13] If the Past has been an obstacle and a burden, knowledge of the Past is the safest and the surest emancipation. And the earnest search for it is one of the signs that distinguish the four centuries of which I speak from those that went before. The Middle Ages, which possessed good writers of contemporary narrative, were careless and impatient of older fact. They became content to be deceived, to live in a twilight of fiction, under clouds of false witness, inventing according to convenience, and glad to welcome the forger

and the cheat.[14] As time went on, the atmosphere of
accredited mendacity thickened, until, in the Renaissance,
the art of exposing falsehood dawned upon keen Italian
minds. It was then that History as we understand it
began to be understood, and the illustrious dynasty of
scholars arose to whom we still look both for method and
material. Unlike the dreaming prehistoric world, ours
knows the need and the duty to make itself master of the
earlier times, and to forfeit nothing of their wisdom or their
warnings,[15] and has devoted its best energy and treasure
to the sovereign purpose of detecting error and vindicating entrusted truth.[16]

In this epoch of full-grown history men have not
acquiesced in the given conditions of their lives. Taking
little for granted they have sought to know the ground
they stand on, and the road they travel, and the reason
why. Over them, therefore, the historian has obtained an
increasing ascendency.[17] The law of stability was overcome by the power of ideas, constantly varied and rapidly
renewed;[18] ideas that give life and motion, that take wing
and traverse seas and frontiers, making it futile to pursue the
consecutive order of events in the seclusion of a separate
nationality.[19] They compel us to share the existence of
societies wider than our own, to be familiar with distant and
exotic types, to hold our march upon the loftier summits,
along the central range, to live in the company of heroes,
and saints, and men of genius, that no single country
could produce. We cannot afford wantonly to lose sight
of great men and memorable lives, and are bound to store
up objects for admiration as far as may be;[20] for the
effect of implacable research is constantly to reduce their
number. No intellectual exercise, for instance, can be
more invigorating than to watch the working of the mind
of Napoleon, the most entirely known as well as the
ablest of historic men. In another sphere, it is the vision
of a higher world to be intimate with the character of
Fénelon, the cherished model of politicians, ecclesiastics,
and men of letters, the witness against one century and
precursor of another, the advocate of the poor against

oppression, of liberty in an age of arbitrary power, of tolerance in an age of persecution, of the humane virtues among men accustomed to sacrifice them to authority, the man of whom one enemy says that his cleverness was enough to strike terror, and another, that genius poured in torrents from his eyes. For the minds that are greatest and best alone furnish the instructive examples. A man of ordinary proportion or inferior metal knows not how to think out the rounded circle of his thought, how to divest his will of its surroundings and to rise above the pressure of time and race and circumstance,[21] to choose the star that guides his course, to correct, and test, and assay his convictions by the light within,[22] and, with a resolute conscience and ideal courage, to remodel and reconstitute the character which birth and education gave him.[23]

For ourselves, if it were not the quest of the higher level and the extended horizon, international history would be imposed by the exclusive and insular reason that parliamentary reporting is younger than parliaments. The foreigner has no mystic fabric in his government, and no *arcanum imperii*. For him the foundations have been laid bare ; every motive and function of the mechanism is accounted for as distinctly as the works of a watch. But with our indigenous constitution, not made with hands or written upon paper, but claiming to develop by a law of organic growth ; with our disbelief in the virtue of definitions and general principles and our reliance on relative truths, we can have nothing equivalent to the vivid and prolonged debates in which other communities have displayed the inmost secrets of political science to every man who can read. And the discussions of constituent assemblies, at Philadelphia, Versailles and Paris, at Cadiz and Brussels, at Geneva, Frankfort and Berlin, above nearly all, those of the most enlightened States in the American Union, when they have recast their institutions, are paramount in the literature of politics, and proffer treasures which at home we have never enjoyed.

To historians the later part of their enormous subject is precious because it is inexhaustible. It is the best to know because it is the best known and the most explicit. Earlier scenes stand out from a background of obscurity. We soon reach the sphere of hopeless ignorance and unprofitable doubt. But hundreds and even thousands of the moderns have borne testimony against themselves, and may be studied in their private correspondence and sentenced on their own confession. Their deeds are done in the daylight. Every country opens its archives and invites us to penetrate the mysteries of State. When Hallam wrote his chapter on James II., France was the only Power whose reports were available. Rome followed, and the Hague; and then came the stores of the Italian States, and at last the Prussian and the Austrian papers, and partly those of Spain. Where Hallam and Lingard were dependent on Barillon, their successors consult the diplomacy of ten governments. The topics indeed are few on which the resources have been so employed that we can be content with the work done for us and never wish it to be done over again. Part of the lives of Luther and Frederic, a little of the Thirty Years' War, much of the American Revolution and the French Restoration, the early years of Richelieu and Mazarin, and a few volumes of Mr. Gardiner, show here and there like Pacific islands in the ocean. I should not even venture to claim for Ranke, the real originator of the heroic study of records, and the most prompt and fortunate of European pathfinders, that there is one of his seventy volumes that has not been overtaken and in part surpassed. It is through his accelerating influence mainly that our branch of study has become progressive, so that the best master is quickly distanced by the better pupil.[24] The Vatican archives alone, now made accessible to the world, filled 3239 cases when they were sent to France; and they are not the richest. We are still at the beginning of the documentary age, which will tend to make history independent of historians, to develop learning at the expense of writing, and to accomplish a revolution in other sciences as well.[25]

To men in general I would justify the stress I am

laying on Modern History, neither by urging its varied
wealth, nor the rupture with precedent, nor the perpetuity
of change and increase of pace, nor the growing predominance of opinion over belief, and of knowledge over opinion,
but by the argument that it is a narrative told of ourselves,
the record of a life which is our own, of efforts not yet
abandoned to repose, of problems that still entangle the
feet and vex the hearts of men.   Every part of it is
weighty with inestimable lessons that we must learn by
experience and at a great price, if we know not how to
profit by the example and teaching of those who have gone
before us, in a society largely resembling the one we live
in.[26]   Its study fulfils its purpose even if it only makes
us wiser, without producing books, and gives us the gift
of historical thinking, which is better than historical learning.[27]   It is a most powerful ingredient in the formation
of character and the training of talent, and our historical
judgments have as much to do with hopes of heaven as
public or private conduct.   Convictions that have been
strained through the instances and the comparisons of
modern times differ immeasurably in solidity and force
from those which every new fact perturbs, and which are
often little better than illusions or unsifted prejudice.[28]

The first of human concerns is religion, and it is the
salient feature of the modern centuries.   They are signal-
ised as the scene of Protestant developments.   Starting
from a time of extreme indifference, ignorance, and
decline, they were at once occupied with that conflict
which was to rage so long, and of which no man could
imagine the infinite consequences.   Dogmatic conviction
—for I shun to speak of faith in connection with many
characters of those days—dogmatic conviction rose to be
the centre of universal interest, and remained down to
Cromwell the supreme influence and motive of public
policy.   A time came when the intensity of prolonged
conflict, when even the energy of antagonistic assurance
abated somewhat, and the controversial spirit began to
make room for the scientific ; and as the storm subsided,
and the area of settled questions emerged, much of the

dispute was abandoned to the serene and soothing touch
of historians, invested as they are with the prerogative
of redeeming the cause of religion from many unjust
reproaches, and from the graver evil of reproaches that
are just.   Ranke used to say that Church interests
prevailed in politics until the Seven Years' War, and
marked a phase of society that ended when the hosts
of Brandenburg went into action at Leuthen, chaunting
their Lutheran hymns.[29]   That bold proposition would
be disputed even if applied to the present age.   After
Sir Robert Peel had broken up his party, the leaders who
followed him declared that no popery was the only basis
on which it could be reconstructed.[30]   On the other side
may be urged that, in July 1870, at the outbreak of the
French war, the only government that insisted on the
abolition of the temporal power was Austria ; and since
then we have witnessed the fall of Castelar, because he
attempted to reconcile Spain with Rome.

Soon after 1850 several of the most intelligent men
in France, struck by the arrested increase of their own
population and by the telling statistics from Further
Britain, foretold the coming preponderance of the English
race.   They did not foretell, what none could then foresee,
the still more sudden growth of Prussia, or that the three
most important countries of the globe would, by the end
of the century, be those that chiefly belonged to the
conquests of the Reformation.   So that in Religion, as
in so many things, the product of these centuries has
favoured the new elements ; and the centre of gravity,
moving from the Mediterranean nations to the Oceanic,
from the Latin to the Teuton, has also passed from the
Catholic to the Protestant.[31]

Out of these controversies proceeded political as well
as historical science.   It was in the Puritan phase, before
the restoration of the Stuarts, that theology, blending
with politics, effected a fundamental change.   The essentially English reformation of the seventeenth century was
less a struggle between churches than between sects, often
subdivided by questions of discipline and self-regulation

rather than by dogma. The sectaries cherished no purpose or prospect of prevailing over the nations ; and they were concerned with the individual more than with the congregation, with conventicles, not with State churches. Their view was narrowed, but their sight was sharpened It appeared to them that governments and institutions are made to pass away, like things of earth, whilst souls are immortal ; that there is no more proportion between liberty and power than between eternity and time ; that, therefore, the sphere of enforced command ought to be restricted within fixed limits, and that which had been done by authority, and outward discipline, and organised violence, should be attempted by division of power, and committed to the intellect and the conscience of free men.[32] Thus was exchanged the dominion of will over will for the dominion of reason over reason. The true apostles of toleration are not those who sought protection for their own beliefs, or who had none to protect ; but men to whom, irrespective of their cause, it was a political, a moral, and a theological dogma, a question of conscience involving both religion and policy.[33] Such a man was Socinus ; and others arose in the smaller sects,—the Independent founder of the colony of Rhode Island, and the Quaker patriarch of Pennsylvania. Much of the energy and zeal which had laboured for authority of doctrine was employed for liberty of prophesying. The air was filled with the enthusiasm of a new cry ; but the cause was still the same. It became a boast that religion was the mother of freedom, that freedom was the lawful offspring of religion; and this transmutation, this subversion of established forms of political life by the development of religious thought, brings us to the heart of my subject, to the significant and central feature of the historic cycles before us. Beginning with the strongest religious movement and the most refined despotism ever known, it has led to the superiority of politics over divinity in the life of nations, and terminates in the equal claim of every man to be unhindered by man in the fulfilment of duty to God [34]—a doctrine laden with storm and havoc, which is the secret essence of the Rights of Man, and the indestructible soul of Revolution.

When we consider what the adverse forces were, their sustained resistance, their frequent recovery, the critical moments when the struggle seemed for ever desperate, in 1685, in 1772, in 1808, it is no hyperbole to say that the progress of the world towards self-government would have been arrested but for the strength afforded by the religious motive in the seventeenth century. And this constancy of progress, of progress in the direction of organised and assured freedom, is the characteristic fact of Modern History, and its tribute to the theory of Providence.[35] Many persons, I am well assured, would detect that this is a very old story, and a trivial commonplace, and would challenge proof that the world is making progress in aught but intellect, that it is gaining in freedom, or that increase in freedom is either a progress or a gain. Ranke, who was my own master, rejected the view that I have stated; [36] Comte, the master of better men, believed that we drag a lengthening chain under the gathered weight of the dead hand; [37] and many of our recent classics— Carlyle, Newman, Froude—were persuaded that there is no progress justifying the ways of God to man, and that the mere consolidation of liberty is like the motion of creatures whose advance is in the direction of their tails. They deem that anxious precaution against bad government is an obstruction to good, and degrades morality and mind by placing the capable at the mercy of the incapable, dethroning enlightened virtue for the benefit of the average man. They hold that great and salutary things are done for mankind by power concentrated, not by power balanced and cancelled and dispersed, and that the whig theory, sprung from decomposing sects, the theory that authority is legitimate only by virtue of its checks, and that the sovereign is dependent on the subject, is rebellion against the divine will manifested all down the stream of time.

I state the objection not that we may plunge into the crucial controversy of a science that is not identical with ours. but in order to make my drift clear by the defining aid of express contradiction. No political dogma is as serviceable to my purpose here as the historian's maxim to do the best he can for the other side, and to avoid pertinacity or emphasis on his own. Like the economic precept *laissez faire*,[38] which the eighteenth century derived from Colbert, it has been an important, if not a final step in the making of method. The strongest and most impressive personalities, it is true, like Macaulay, Thiers, and the two greatest of living writers, Mommsen and Treitschke, project their own broad shadow upon their pages. This is a practice proper to great men, and a great man may be worth several immaculate historians. Otherwise there is virtue in the saying that a historian is seen at his best when he does not appear.[39] Better for us is the example of the Bishop of Oxford, who never lets us know what he thinks of anything but the matter before him ; and of his illustrious French rival, Fustel de Coulanges, who said to an excited audience : " Do not imagine you are listening to me ; it is history itself that speaks." [40] We can found no philosophy on the observation of four hundred years, excluding three thousand. It would be an imperfect and a fallacious induction. But I hope that even this narrow and disedifying section of history will aid you to see that the action of Christ who is risen on mankind whom he redeemed fails not, but increases ;[41] that the wisdom of divine rule appears not in the perfection but in the improvement of the world ;[42] and that achieved liberty is the one ethical result that rests on the converging and combined conditions of advancing civilisation.[43] Then you will understand what a famous philosopher said, that History is the true demonstration of Religion.[44]

But what do people mean who proclaim that liberty is the palm, and the prize, and the crown, seeing that it is an idea of which there are two hundred definitions, and that this wealth of interpretation has caused more bloodshed than anything, except theology ? Is it Democracy as in France, or Federalism as in America, or the national independence which bounds the Italian view, or

the reign of the fittest, which is the ideal of Germans ?[45]
I know not whether it will ever fall within my sphere of
duty to trace the slow progress of that idea through the
chequered scenes of our history, and to describe how
subtle speculations touching the nature of conscience
promoted a nobler and more spiritual conception of the
liberty that protects it,[46] until the guardian of rights
developed into the guardian of duties which are the cause
of rights,[47] and that which had been prized as the material
safeguard for treasures of earth became sacred as security
for things that are divine.   All that we require is a work-
day key to history, and our present need can be supplied
without pausing to satisfy philosophers.   Without inquir-
ing how far Sarasa or Butler, Kant or Vinet, is right as
to the infallible voice of God in man, we may easily agree
in this, that where absolutism reigned, by irresistible arms,
concentrated possessions, auxiliary churches, and inhuman
laws, it reigns no more ; that commerce having risen
against land, labour against wealth, the State against the
forces dominant in society,[48] the division of power against
the State, the thought of individuals against the practice
of ages, neither authorities, nor minorities, nor majorities
can command implicit obedience ; and, where there has
been long and arduous experience, a rampart of tried conviction and accumulated knowledge,[49] where there is a fair
level of general morality, education, courage, and self-
restraint, there, if there only, a society may be found that
exhibits the condition of life towards which, by elimination
of failures, the world has been moving through the allotted
space.[50]   You will know it by outward signs : Representation, the extinction of slavery, the reign of opinion, and
the like ; better still by less apparent evidences : the
security of the weaker groups [51] and the liberty of conscience, which, effectually secured, secures the rest.

Here we reach a point at which my argument threatens
to abut on a contradiction.   If the supreme conquests of
society are won more often by violence than by lenient
arts, if the trend and drift of things is towards convul-
sions and catastrophes,[52] if the world owes religious liberty

to the Dutch Revolution, constitutional government to the
English, federal republicanism to the American, political
equality to the French and its successors,[53] what is to
become of us, docile and attentive students of the absorb-
ing Past?   The triumph of the Revolutionist annuls
the historian.[54]   By its authentic exponents, Jefferson and
Sieyès, the Revolution of the last century repudiates
history.   Their followers renounced acquaintance with it,
and were ready to destroy its records and to abolish its
inoffensive professors.   But the unexpected truth, stranger
than fiction, is that this was not the ruin but the renova-
tion of history.   Directly and indirectly, by process of
development and by process of reaction, an impulse was
given which made it infinitely more effectual as a factor
of civilisation than ever before, and a movement began
in the world of minds which was deeper and more serious
than the revival of ancient learning.[55]   The dispensation
under which we live and labour consists first in the recoil
from the negative spirit that rejected the law of growth,
and partly in the endeavour to classify and adjust the
Revolution, and to account for it by the natural working of
historic causes.   The Conservative line of writers, under
the name of the Romantic or Historical School, had its
seat in Germany, looked upon the Revolution as an alien
episode, the error of an age, a disease to be treated by the
investigation of its origin, and strove to unite the broken
threads and to restore the normal conditions of organic
evolution.   The Liberal School, whose home was France,
explained and justified the Revolution as a true development, and the ripened fruit of all history.[56]   These are the
two main arguments of the generation to which we owe
the notion and the scientific methods that make history so
unlike what it was to the survivors of the last century.
Severally, the innovators were not superior to the men of
old.   Muratori was as widely read, Tillemont as accurate,
Leibniz as able, Fréret as acute, Gibbon as masterly in
the craft of composite construction.   Nevertheless, in the
second quarter of this century, a new era began for
historians.

I would point to three things in particular, out of
many, which constitute the amended order.   Of the
incessant deluge of new and unsuspected matter I need
say little.   For some years, the secret archives of the
papacy were accessible at Paris ; but the time was not
ripe, and almost the only man whom they availed was
the archivist himself.[57]   Towards 1830 the documentary
studies began on a large scale, Austria leading the way.
Michelet, who claims, towards 1836, to have been the
pioneer,[58] was preceded by such rivals as Mackintosh,
Bucholtz, and Mignet.   A new and more productive
period began thirty years later, when the war of 1859
laid open the spoils of Italy.   Every country in succession
has now allowed the exploration of its records, and there
is more fear of drowning than of drought.   The result
has been that a lifetime spent in the largest collection
of printed books would not suffice to train a real master of
modern history.   After he had turned from literature to
sources, from Burnet to Pocock, from Macaulay to Madame
Campana, from Thiers to the interminable correspondence
of the Bonapartes, he would still feel instant need of
inquiry at Venice or Naples, in the Ossuna library or at
the Hermitage.[59]

These matters do not now concern us.   For our
purpose, the main thing to learn is not the art of accumu-
lating material, but the sublimer art of investigating it, of
discerning truth from falsehood and certainty from doubt.
It is by solidity of criticism more than by the plenitude
of erudition, that the study of history strengthens, and
straightens, and extends the mind.[60]   And the accession
of the critic in the place of the indefatigable compiler, of
the artist in coloured narrative, the skilled limner of
character, the persuasive advocate of good, or other,
causes, amounts to a transfer of government, to a change
of dynasty, in the historic realm.   For the critic is one
who, when he lights on an interesting statement, begins
by suspecting it.   He remains in suspense until he has
subjected his authority to three operations.   First, he asks
whether he has read the passage as the author wrote it

For the transcriber, and the editor, and the official or officious censor on the top of the editor, have played strange tricks, and have much to answer for. And if they are not to blame, it may turn out that the author wrote his book twice over, that you can discover the first jet, the progressive variations, things added, and things struck out. Next is the question where the writer got his information. If from a previous writer, it can be ascertained, and the inquiry has to be repeated. If from unpublished papers, they must be traced, and when the fountain-head is reached, or the track disappears, the question of veracity arises. The responsible writer's character, his position, antecedents, and probable motives have to be examined into ; and this is what, in a different and adapted sense of the word, may be called the higher criticism, in comparison with the servile and often mechanical work of pursuing statements to their root. For a historian has to be treated as a witness, and not believed unless his sincerity is established.[61] The maxim that a man must be presumed to be innocent until his guilt is proved, was not made for him.

For us, then, the estimate of authorities, the weighing of testimony, is more meritorious than the potential discovery of new matter.[62] And modern history, which is the widest field of application, is not the best to learn our business in ; for it is too wide, and the harvest has not been winnowed as in antiquity, and further on to the Crusades. It is better to examine what has been done for questions that are compact and circumscribed, such as the sources of Plutarch's *Pericles*, the two tracts on Athenian government, the origin of the epistle to Diognetus, the date of the life of St. Antony; and to learn from Schwegler how this analytical work began. More satisfying because more decisive has been the critical treatment of the medieval writers, parallel with the new editions, on which incredible labour has been lavished, and of which we have no better examples than the prefaces of Bishop Stubbs. An important event in this series was the attack on Dino Compagni, which, for the sake of

Dante, roused the best Italian scholars to a not unequal contest. When we are told that England is behind the Continent in critical faculty, we must admit that this is true as to quantity, not as to quality of work. As they are no longer living, I will say of two Cambridge professors, Lightfoot and Hort, that they were critical scholars whom neither Frenchman nor German has surpassed.

The third distinctive note of the generation of writers who dug so deep a trench between history as known to our grandfathers and as it appears to us, is their dogma of impartiality. To an ordinary man the word means no more than justice. He considers that he may proclaim the merits of his own religion, of his prosperous and enlightened country, of his political persuasion, whether democracy, or liberal monarchy, or historic conservatism, without transgression or offence, so long as he is fair to the relative, though inferior, merits of others, and never treats men as saints or as rogues for the side they take. There is no impartiality, he would say, like that of a hanging judge. The men who, with the compass of criticism in their hands, sailed the uncharted sea of original research proposed a different view. History, to be above evasion or dispute, must stand on documents, not on opinions. They had their own notion of truthfulness, based on the exceeding difficulty of finding truth, and the still greater difficulty of impressing it when found. They thought it possible to write, with so much scruple, and simplicity, and insight, as to carry along with them every man of good will, and, whatever his feelings, to compel his assent. Ideas which, in religion and in politics, are truths, in history are forces. They must be respected ; they must not be affirmed. By dint of a supreme reserve, by much self-control, by a timely and discreet indifference, by secrecy in the matter of the black cap, history might be lifted above contention, and made an accepted tribunal, and the same for all.[63] If men were truly sincere, and delivered judgment by no canons but those of evident morality, then Julian would be described in the same terms by Christian and pagan, Luther by Catholic and Protestant, Washington by Whig and Tory, Napoleon by patriotic Frenchman and patriotic German.[64]

I speak of this school with reverence, for the good it has done, by the assertion of historic truth and of its legitimate authority over the minds of men. It provides a discipline which every one of us does well to undergo, and perhaps also well to relinquish. For it is not the whole truth. Lanfrey's essay on Carnot, Chuquet's wars of the Revolution, Ropes's military histories, Roget's Geneva in the time of Calvin, will supply you with examples of a more robust impartiality than I have described. Renan calls it the luxury of an opulent and aristocratic society, doomed to vanish in an age of fierce and sordid striving. In our universities it has a magnificent and appointed refuge ; and to serve its cause, which is sacred, because it is the cause of truth and honour, we may import a profitable lesson from the highly unscientific region of public life. There a man does not take long to find out that he is opposed by some who are abler and better than himself. And, in order to understand the cosmic force and the true connection of ideas, it is a source of power, and an excellent school of principle, not to rest until, by excluding the fallacies, the prejudices, the exaggerations which perpetual contention and the consequent precautions breed, we have made out for our opponents a stronger and more impressive case than they present themselves.[65] Excepting one to which we are coming before I release you, there is no precept less faithfully observed by historians.

Ranke is the representative of the age which instituted the modern study of History. He taught it to be critical, to be colourless, and to be new. We meet him at every step, and he has done more for us than any other man. There are stronger books than any one of his, and some may have surpassed him in political, religious, philosophic insight, in vividness of the creative imagination, in originality, elevation, and depth of thought ; but by the extent of important work well executed, by his influence on able men, and by the amount of knowledge which mankind receives and employs with the stamp of his mind upon it, he stands without a rival. I saw him last in 1877, when he was feeble, sunken, and almost blind, and scarcely able to read or write. He uttered his farewell with kindly emotion, and I feared that the next I should hear of him would be the news of his death. Two years later he began a Universal History, which is not without traces of weakness, but which, composed after the age of eighty-three, and carried, in seventeen volumes, far into the Middle Ages, brings to a close the most astonishing career in literature.

His course had been determined, in early life, by *Quentin Durward*. The shock of the discovery that Scott's Lewis the Eleventh was inconsistent with the original in Commynes made him resolve that his object thenceforth should be above all things to follow, without swerving, and in stern subordination and surrender, the lead of his authorities. He decided effectually to repress the poet, the patriot, the religious or political partisan, to sustain no cause, to banish himself from his books, and to write nothing that would gratify his own feelings or disclose his private convictions.[66] When a strenuous divine, who, like him, had written on the Reformation, hailed him as a comrade, Ranke repelled his advances. "You," he said, "are in the first place a Christian : I am in the first place a historian. There is a gulf between us."[67] He was the first eminent writer who exhibited what Michelet calls *le désintéressement des morts*. It was a moral triumph for him when he could refrain from judging, show that much might be said on both sides, and leave the rest to Providence.[68] He would have felt sympathy with the two famous London physicians of our day, of whom it is told that they could not make up their minds on a case and reported dubiously. The head of the family insisted on a positive opinion. They answered that they were unable to give one, but he might easily find fifty doctors who could.

Niebuhr had pointed out that chroniclers who wrote

before the invention of printing generally copied one predecessor at a time, and knew little about sifting or combining authorities. The suggestion became luminous in Ranke's hands, and with his light and dexterous touch he scrutinised and dissected the principal historians, from Machiavelli to the *Mémoires d'un Homme d'État*, with a rigour never before applied to moderns. But whilst Niebuhr dismissed the traditional story, replacing it with a construction of his own, it was Ranke's mission to preserve, not to undermine, and to set up masters whom, in their proper sphere, he could obey. The many excellent dissertations in which he displayed this art, though his successors in the next generation matched his skill and did still more thorough work, are the best introduction from which we can learn the technical process by which within living memory the study of modern history has been renewed. Ranke's contemporaries, weary of his neutrality and suspense, and of the useful but subordinate work that was done by beginners who borrowed his wand, thought that too much was made of these obscure preliminaries which a man may accomplish for himself, in the silence of his chamber, with less demand on the attention of the public.[69] That may be reasonable in men who are practised in these fundamental technicalities. We who have to learn them, must immerse ourselves in the study of the great examples.

Apart from what is technical, method is only the reduplication of common sense, and is best acquired by observing its use by the ablest men in every variety of intellectual employment.[70] Bentham acknowledged that he learned less from his own profession than from writers like Linnæus and Cullen ; and Brougham advised the student of Law to begin with Dante. Liebig described his *Organic Chemistry* as an application of ideas found in Mill's *Logic*, and a distinguished physician, not to be named lest he should overhear me, read three books to enlarge his medical mind ; and they were Gibbon, Grote, and Mill. He goes on to say, " An educated man cannot become so on one study alone, but must be brought under the influ-

ence of natural, civil, and moral modes of thought." [71]   I
quote my colleague's golden words in order to reciprocate
them.   If men of science owe anything to us, we may
learn much from them that is essential.[72]   For they can
show how to test proof, how to secure fulness and
soundness in induction, how to restrain and to employ
with safety hypothesis and analogy.   It is they who
hold the secret of the mysterious property of the mind
by which error ministers to truth, and truth slowly
but irrevocably prevails.[73]   Theirs is the logic of discovery,[74] the demonstration of the advance of knowledge
and the development of ideas, which as the earthly
wants and passions of men remain almost unchanged,
are the charter of progress and the vital spark in
history.   And they often give us invaluable counsel
when they attend to their own subjects and address
their own people.   Remember Darwin taking note only
of those passages that raised difficulties in his way ;
the French philosopher complaining that his work stood
still, because he found no more contradicting facts ;
Baer, who thinks error treated thoroughly nearly as
remunerative as truth, by the discovery of new objections;
for, as Sir Robert Ball warns us, it is by considering
objections that we often learn.[75]   Faraday declares that
" in knowledge, that man only is to be condemned and
despised who is not in a state of transition."   And John
Hunter spoke for all of us when he said : " Never ask
me what I have said or what I have written ; but if you
will ask me what my present opinions are, I will tell
you."

From the first years of the century we have been
quickened and enriched by contributors from every
quarter.   The jurists brought us that law of continuous
growth which has transformed history from a chronicle
of casual occurrences into the likeness of something
organic.[76]   Towards 1820 divines began to recast their
doctrines on the lines of development, of which Newman
said, long after, that evolution had come to confirm it.[77]
Even the Economists, who were practical men, dissolved

their science into liquid history, affirming that it is not
an auxiliary, but the actual subject-matter of their
inquiry.[78] Philosophers claim that, as early as 1804,
they began to bow the metaphysical neck beneath the
historical yoke.   They taught that philosophy is only the
amended sum of all philosophies, that systems pass with
the age whose impress they bear,[79] that the problem is to
focus the rays of wandering but extant truth, and that
history is the source of philosophy, if not quite a
substitute for it.[80]   Comte begins a volume with the
words that the preponderance of history over philosophy
was the characteristic of the time he lived in.[81]   Since
Cuvier first recognised the conjunction between the course
of inductive discovery and the course of civilisation,[82]
science had its share in saturating the age with historic
ways of thought, and subjecting all things to that influence
for which the depressing names historicism and historical-
mindedness have been devised.

There are certain faults which are corrigible mental
defects on which I ought to say a few denouncing words,
because they are common to us all.   First: the want of
an energetic understanding of the sequence and real
significance of events, which would be fatal to a practical
politician, is ruin to a student of history, who is the
politician with his face turned backwards.[83]   It is playing
at study, to see nothing but the unmeaning and un-
suggestive surface, as we generally do.   Then we have a
curious proclivity to neglect, and by degrees to forget,
what has been certainly known.   An instance or two will
explain my idea.   The most popular English writer
relates how it happened in his presence that the title of
Tory was conferred upon the Conservative party.   For
it was an opprobrious name at the time, applied to men
for whom the Irish Government offered head-money; so
that if I have made too sure of progress, I may at least
complacently point to this instance of our mended manners.
One day, Titus Oates lost his temper with the men who
refused to believe him, and, after looking about for a
scorching imprecation, he began to call them Tories.[84]

The name remained ; but its origin, attested by Defoe, dropped out of common memory, as if one party were ashamed of their godfather, and the other did not care to be identified with his cause and character. You all know, I am sure, the story of the news of Trafalgar, and how, two days after it had arrived, Mr. Pitt, drawn by an enthusiastic crowd, went to dine in the city. When they drank the health of the minister who had saved his country, he declined the praise. "England," he said, "has saved herself by her own energy ; and I hope that after having saved herself by her energy, she will save Europe by her example." In 1814, when this hope had been realised, the last speech of the great orator was remembered, and a medal was struck upon which the whole sentence was engraved, in four words of compressed Latin : *Seipsam virtute, Europam exemplo.* Now it was just at the time of his last appearance in public that Mr. Pitt heard of the overwhelming success of the French in Germany, and of the Austrian surrender at Ulm. His friends concluded that the contest on land was hopeless, and that it was time to abandon the Continent to the conqueror, and to fall back upon our new empire of the sea. Pitt did not agree with them. He said that Napoleon would meet with a check whenever he encountered a national resistance ; and he declared that Spain was the place for it, and that then England would intervene.[85] General Wellesley, fresh from India, was present. Ten years later, when he had accomplished that which Pitt had seen in the lucid prescience of his last days, he related at Paris what I scarcely hesitate to call the most astounding and profound prediction in all political history, where such things have not been rare.

I shall never again enjoy the opportunity of speaking my thoughts to such an audience as this, and on so privileged an occasion a lecturer may well be tempted to bethink himself whether he knows of any neglected truth, any cardinal proposition, that might serve as his selected epigraph, as a last signal, perhaps even as a target. I am not thinking of those shining precepts which are the registered property of every school; that is to say— Learn as much by writing as by reading; be not content with the best book; seek sidelights from the others; have no favourites; keep men and things apart; guard against the prestige of great names;[86] see that your judgments are your own, and do not shrink from disagreement; no trusting without testing; be more severe to ideas than to actions;[87] do not overlook the strength of the bad cause or the weakness of the good;[88] never be surprised by the crumbling of an idol or the disclosure of a skeleton; judge talent at its best and character at its worst; suspect power more than vice,[89] and study problems in preference to periods; for instance: the derivation of Luther, the scientific influence of Bacon, the predecessors of Adam Smith, the medieval masters of Rousseau, the consistency of Burke, the identity of the first Whig. Most of this, I suppose, is undisputed, and calls for no enlargement. But the weight of opinion is against me when I exhort you never to debase the moral currency or to lower the standard of rectitude, but to try others by the final maxim that governs your own lives, and to suffer no man and no cause to escape the undying penalty which history has the power to inflict on wrong.[90] The plea in extenuation of guilt and mitigation of punishment is perpetual. At every step we are met by arguments which go to excuse, to palliate, to confound right and wrong, and reduce the just man to the level of the reprobate. The men who plot to baffle and resist us are, first of all, those who made history what it has become. They set up the principle that only a foolish Conservative judges the present time with the ideas of the past; that only a foolish Liberal judges the past with the ideas of the present.[91]

The mission of that school was to make distant times, and especially the Middle Ages, then most distant of all, intelligible and acceptable to a society issuing from the eighteenth century. There were difficulties in the way; and among others this, that, in the first fervour of the Crusades, the men who took the Cross, after receiving

communion, heartily devoted the day to the extermination
of Jews. To judge them by a fixed standard, to call
them sacrilegious fanatics or furious hypocrites, was to
yield a gratuitous victory to Voltaire. It became a rule
of policy to praise the spirit when you could not defend
the deed. So that we have no common code ; our moral
notions are always fluid ; and you must consider the
times, the class from which men sprang, the surrounding influences, the masters in their schools, the preachers
in their pulpits, the movement they obscurely obeyed,
and so on, until responsibility is merged in numbers, and
not a culprit is left for execution.[92] A murderer was
no criminal if he followed local custom, if neighbours
approved, if he was encouraged by official advisers or
prompted by just authority, if he acted for the reason of
state or the pure love of religion, or if he sheltered himself
behind the complicity of the Law. The depression of
morality was flagrant ; but the motives were those
which have enabled us to contemplate with distressing
complacency the secret of unhallowed lives. The code
that is greatly modified by time and place, will vary
according to the cause. The amnesty is an artifice that
enables us to make exceptions, to tamper with weights
and measures, to deal unequal justice to friends and
enemies.

It is associated with that philosophy which Cato
attributes to the gods. For we have a theory which
justifies Providence by the event, and holds nothing so
deserving as success, to which there can be no victory in
a bad cause ; prescription and duration legitimate ; [93] and
whatever exists is right and reasonable ; and as God
manifests His will by that which He tolerates, we must
conform to the divine decree by living to shape the
future after the ratified image of the past.[94] Another
theory, less confidently urged, regards History as our
guide, as much by showing errors to evade as examples
to pursue. It is suspicious of illusions in success, and,
though there may be hope of ultimate triumph for what
is true, if not by its own attraction, by the gradual

exhaustion of error, it admits no corresponding promise for what is ethically right. It deems the canonisation of the historic past more perilous than ignorance or denial, because it would perpetuate the reign of sin and acknowledge the sovereignty of wrong, and conceives it the part of real greatness to know how to stand and fall alone, stemming, for a lifetime, the contemporary flood.[95]

Ranke relates, without adornment, that William III. ordered the extirpation of a Catholic clan, and scouts the faltering excuse of his defenders. But when he comes to the death and character of the international deliverer, Glencoe is forgotten, the imputation of murder drops, like a thing unworthy of notice.[96] Johannes Mueller, a great Swiss celebrity, writes that the British Constitution occurred to somebody, perhaps to Halifax. This artless statement might not be approved by rigid lawyers as a faithful and felicitous indication of the manner of that mysterious growth of ages, from occult beginnings, that was never profaned by the invading wit of man ;[97] but it is less grotesque than it appears. Lord Halifax was the most original writer of political tracts in the pamphleteering crowd between Harrington and Bolingbroke ; and in the Exclusion struggle he produced a scheme of limitations which, in substance, if not in form, foreshadowed the position of the monarchy in the later Hanoverian reigns. Although Halifax did not believe in the plot,[98] he insisted that innocent victims should be sacrificed to content the multitude. Sir William Temple writes : " We only disagreed in one point, which was the leaving some priests to the law upon the accusation of being priests only, as the House of Commons had desired ; which I thought wholly unjust. Upon this point Lord Halifax and I had so sharp a debate at Lord Sunderland's lodgings, that he told me, if I would not concur in points which were so necessary for the people's satisfaction, he would tell everybody I was a Papist. And upon his affirming that the plot must be handled as if it were true, whether it were so or no, in those points that were so generally believed." In spite of this

accusing passage, Macaulay, who prefers Halifax to all
the statesmen of his age, praises him for his mercy : " His
dislike of extremes, and a forgiving and compassionate
temper which seems to have been natural to him,
preserved him from all participation in the worst crimes
of his time."

If, in our uncertainty, we must often err, it may be
sometimes better to risk excess in rigour than in indulgence, for then at least we do no injury by loss of principle.
As Bayle has said, it is more probable that the secret
motives of an indifferent action are bad than good ; [99] and
this discouraging conclusion does not depend upon
theology, for James Mozley supports the sceptic from the
other flank, with all the artillery of Tractarian Oxford.
" A Christian," he says, " is bound by his very creed to
suspect evil, and cannot release himself. . . . He sees it
where others do not ; his instinct is divinely strengthened ;
his eye is supernaturally keen ; he has a spiritual insight,
and senses exercised to discern. . . . He owns the doctrine
of original sin ; that doctrine puts him necessarily on his
guard against appearances, sustains his apprehension under
perplexity, and prepares him for recognising anywhere
what he knows to be everywhere." [100]   There is a popular
saying of Madame de Staël, that we forgive whatever we
really understand.   The paradox has been judiciously
pruned by her descendant, the Duke de Broglie, in the
words : " Beware of too much explaining, lest we end by too
much excusing." [101]   History, says Froude, does teach that
right and wrong are real distinctions.   Opinions alter,
manners change, creeds rise and fall, but the moral law is
written on the tablets of eternity.[102]   And if there are
moments when we may resist the teaching of Froude, we
have seldom the chance of resisting when he is supported
by Mr. Goldwin Smith : " A sound historical morality will
sanction strong measures in evil times ; selfish ambition,
treachery, murder, perjury, it will never sanction in the
worst of times, for these are the things that make times
evil —Justice has been justice, mercy has been mercy,
honour has been honour, good faith has been good faith,

truthfulness has been truthfulness from the beginning"
The doctrine that, as Sir Thomas Browne says, morality
is not ambulatory,[103] is expressed as follows by Burke,
who, when true to himself, is the most intelligent of our
instructors : " My principles enable me to form my judgment upon men and actions in history, just as they do in
common life ; and are not formed out of events and
characters, either present or past.   History is a preceptor
of prudence, not of principles.   The principles of true
politics are those of morality enlarged ; and I neither
now do, nor ever will admit of any other." [104]

Whatever a man's notions of these later centuries are,
such, in the main, the man himself will be.   Under the
name of History, they cover the articles of his philosophic,
his religious, and his political creed.[105]   They give his
measure ; they denote his character : and, as praise is the
shipwreck of historians, his preferences betray him more
than his aversions.   Modern History touches us so nearly,
it is so deep a question of life and death, that we are
bound to find our own way through it, and to owe our
insight to ourselves.   The historians of former ages,
unapproachable for us in knowledge and in talent, cannot
be our limit.   We have the power to be more rigidly
impersonal, disinterested and just than they ; and to
learn from undisguised and genuine records to look with
remorse upon the past, and to the future with assured
hope of better things ; bearing this in mind, that if we
lower our standard in History, we cannot uphold it in
Church or State.

LECTURES ON MODERN HISTORY

D

I

BEGINNING OF THE MODERN STATE

MODERN History tells how the last four hundred years have modified the medieval conditions of life and thought. In comparison with them, the Middle Ages were the domain of stability, and continuity, and instinctive evolution, seldom interrupted by such originators as Gregory VII. or St. Francis of Assisi. Ignorant of History, they allowed themselves to be governed by the unknown Past; ignorant of Science, they never believed in hidden forces working onwards to a happier future. The sense of decay was upon them; and each generation seemed so inferior to the last, in ancient wisdom and ancestral virtue, that they found comfort in the assurance that the end of the world was at hand.

Yet the most profound and penetrating of the causes that have transformed society is a medieval inheritance. It was late in the thirteenth century that the psychology of Conscience was closely studied for the first time, and men began to speak of it as the audible voice of God, that never misleads or fails, and that ought to be obeyed always, whether enlightened or darkened, right or wrong. The notion was restrained, on its appearance, by the practice of regarding opposition to Church power as equivalent to specific heresy, which depressed the secret monitor below the public and visible authority. With the decline of coercion the claim of Conscience rose, and the ground abandoned by the inquisitor was gained by the individual. There was less reason then for men to be cast of the same type; there was a more vigorous growth of independent character, and a conscious control over its formation. The knowledge of good and evil was not an exclusive and sublime prerogative assigned to states, or nations, or majorities. When it had been defined and recognised as something divine in human nature, its action was to limit power by causing the sovereign voice within to be heard above the expressed will and settled custom of surrounding men. By that hypothesis, the soul became more sacred than the state, because it receives light from above, as well as because its concerns are eternal, and out of all proportion with the common interests of government. That is the root from which liberty of Conscience was developed, and all other liberty needed to confine the sphere of power, in order that it may not challenge the supremacy of that which is highest and best in man.

The securities by which this purpose has been attempted compose the problem of all later history, and centuries were spent in ascertaining and constructing them. If in the main the direction has been upward, the movement has been tardy, the conflict intense, the balance often uncertain. The passion for power over others can never cease to threaten mankind, and is always sure of finding new and unforeseen allies in continuing its martyrology. Therefore, the method of modern progress was revolution. By a series of violent shocks the nations in succession have struggled to shake off the Past, to reverse the action of Time and the verdict of success, and to rescue the world from the reign of the dead. They have been due less to provocation by actual wrong than to the attraction of ideal right, and the claims that inspired them were universal and detached. Progress has imposed increasing sacrifices on society, in behalf of those who can make no return, from whose welfare it derives no equivalent benefit, whose existence is a burden, an evil, eventually a peril to the community. The mean duration of life, the compendious test of improvement, is prolonged by all the chief agents of civilisation, moral and material, religious and scientific, working together, and depends on preserving, at infinite cost, which is infinite loss, the crippled child and the victim of accident, the idiot and the madman, the pauper and the culprit, the old and infirm, curable and incurable. This growing dominion of disinterested motive, this liberality towards the weak, in social life, corresponds to that respect for the minority, in political life, which is the essence of freedom. It is an application of the same principle of self-denial, and of the higher law.

Taking long periods, we perceive the advance of moral over material influence, the triumph of general ideas, the gradual amendment. The line of march will prove, on the whole, to have been from force and cruelty to consent and association, to humanity, rational persuasion, and the persistent appeal to common, simple, and evident maxims. We have dethroned necessity, in the shape both of hunger and of fear, by extending the scene from Western Europe to the whole world, so that all shall contribute to the treasure of civilisation, and by taking into partnership in the enjoyment of its rewards those who are far off as well as those who are below. We shall give our attention to much that has failed and passed away, as well as to the phenomena of progress, which help to build up the world in which we live. For History must be our deliverer not only from the undue influence of other times, but from the undue influence of our own, from the tyranny of environ- ment and the pressure of the air we breathe. It requires all historic forces to produce their record and submit to judgment, and it promotes the faculty of resistance to contemporary surroundings by familiarity with other ages and other orbits of thought.

In these latter days the sum of differences in inter- national character has been appreciably bound down by the constant process of adaptation and adjustment, and by exposure to like influences. The people of various countries are swayed by identical interests, they are absorbed in the same problems, and thrill with the same emotions ; their classics are interchangeable, authorities in science are nearly alike for all, and they readily combine to make experiments and researches in common. Towards 1500, European nations, having been fashioned and composed out of simple elements during the thousand years between the fall of the Roman Empire and that of its successor in the East, had reached full measure of differentiation. They were estranged from each other, and were inclined to treat the foreigner as the foe. Ancient links were loosened, the Pope was no longer an accepted peacemaker ; and the idea of an international code, overriding the will of nations and the authority of sovereigns, had not dawned upon philosophy. Between the old order that was changing and the new that was unborn, Europe had an inorganic interval to go through.

Modern History begins under stress of the Ottoman Conquest. Constantinople fell, after an attempt to negotiate for help, by the union of the Greek and Latin Churches. The agreement come to at Florence was not ratified at home ; the attempt was resented, and led to an explosion of feeling that made even subjugation by the Turk seem for the moment less intolerable, and that hastened the catastrophe by making Western Christians slow to sacrifice themselves for their implacable brethren in the East. Offers of help were made, conditional on acceptance of the Florentine decree, and were rejected with patriotic and theological disdain. A small force of papal and Genoese mercenaries shared the fate of the defenders, and the end could not have been long averted, even by the restoration of religious unity. The Powers that held back were not restrained by dogmatic arguments only. The dread of Latin intolerance was the most favourable circumstance encountered by the Turks in the Eastern Empire, and they at once offered protection and immunities to the patriarch and his prelates. The conquest of the entire peninsula, with the islands, occupied a generation, and it was good policy meanwhile to do nothing that would diminish the advantage or awaken alarm of persecution. Their system required the increase rather than the conversion of Christian subjects, for the tribute of gold as well as the tribute of blood. The Janissaries were selected among the sons of Christian parents, who became renegades, and who, having neither home nor family, no life but in camp, no employment but arms, became not only the best professional soldiers in the world, but a force constantly active to undo the work of pacific statesmen and to find fresh occasion for war. There were occasional outbreaks of blind ferocity, and at all times there was the incapacity of an uncivilised race to understand the character and the interest of alien subjects more cultivated than themselves. But there was not at first the sense of unmitigated tyranny that arose later ; and there was not so great a contrast with life as it was under Italian despots as to make Christians under the Sultan passionately long for deliverance.

From the perjury of Varna, in 1444, when the Christians broke the treaty just concluded at Szegedin, it was understood that they could never be trusted to keep engagements entered into with people of another religion. It seemed a weak-minded exaggeration of hypocrisy to abstain from preying on men so furiously divided, so full of hatred, so incapable of combining in defence of their altars and their homes, so eager in soliciting aid and intervention from the infidel in their own disputes. The several principalities of the circumference, Servia, Bosnia, Wallachia, the Morea, and the islands, varying in nationality and in religion, were attacked separately, and made no joint defence. In Epirus, Scanderbeg, once a renegade, then in communion with Rome, drawing his supplies from the opposite coast of Apulia, which his sentinels on Cape Linguetta could see at sunrise, maintained himself for many years victoriously, knowing that his country would perish with him. John Hunyadi had defended Christendom on the Hungarian frontier so well that the monarchy of his son stemmed the tide of invasion for seventy years. While the Turkish outposts kept watch on the Danube, Mahomet seized Otranto, and all the way upwards to the Alps there was no force capable of resisting him. Just then, he died, Otranto was lost, and the enterprise was not renewed.   His people were a nation of soldiers, not a nation of sailors.   For operations beyond sea they relied on the seamen of the Ægean, generally Christians, as they had required the help of Genoese ships to ferry them over the Hellespont.

Under Bajazet, the successor, there was some rest for Europe.   His brother, who was a dangerous competitor, as the crown went to the one who survived, fled for safety to the Christians, and was detained as a hostage, beyond the possibility of ransom, by the Knights of St. John, and then by the Pope.   The Sultan paid, that he might be kept quiet.

For years the Turks were busy in the East.   Selim conquered Syria and part of Persia.   He conquered Arabia, and was acknowledged by the Sheriff of Mecca caliph and protector of the holy shrine.   He conquered Egypt and assumed the prerogative of the Imaum, which had been a shadow at Cairo, but became, at Constantinople, the supreme authority in Islam.   Gathering up the concentrated resources of the Levant, Solyman the Magnificent turned, at last, against the enemy who guarded the gates of civilised Europe.   Having taken Belgrade, he undertook, in 1526, the crowning campaign of Turkish history. At the battle of Mohacs Hungary lost her independence. The Turks found a Transylvanian magnate who was willing to receive the crown from them ; and the broad valley of the Danube continued to be their battlefield until the days of Sobieski and Eugene.   But the legitimate heir of King Ladislas, who fell at Mohacs, was Ferdinand, only brother of Charles V.; and Hungary, with the vast region then belonging to the Bohemian crown, passing to the same hands as the ancient inheritance of the Habsburgs, constituted the great Austrian monarchy which extended from the Adriatic to the far Sarmatian plain, and Solyman's victory brought him face to face with the first Power able to arrest his progress.   The Turks were repulsed at Vienna in 1529, at Malta in 1564.   This was their limit in Western Europe ; and after Lepanto, in 1571, their only expansion was at the expense of Poland and Muscovy.   They still wielded almost boundless resources; the entire seaboard from Cattaro all round by the Euxine to the Atlantic was Mahomedan, and all but one-fourth of the Mediterranean was a Turkish lake. It was long before they knew that it was not their destiny to be masters of the Western as well as of the Eastern world.

While this heavy cloud overhung the Adriatic and the Danube, and the countries within reach of the Turk were in peril of extinction, the nations farther west were consolidating rapidly into unity and power. By the marriage of Ferdinand and Isabella, by their conquest of Granada and the rise of a new hemisphere at their command, Spain for the first time became a great Power; while France, having expelled the English, having instituted a permanent army, acquired vast frontier provinces, and crushed the centrifugal forces of feudalism, was more directly formidable and more easily aggressive. These newly created Powers portended danger in one direction. Their increase was not so much in comparison with England or with Portugal, as in contrast with Italy. England, through the Tudors, had achieved internal tranquillity; and Portugal was already at the head of Europe in making the ocean tributary to trade. But Italy was divided, unwarlike, poor in the civic virtues that made Switzerland impregnable, rich in the tempting luxuries of civilisation, an inexhaustible treasure-house of much that the neighbours greatly needed and could never find elsewhere. The best writers and scholars and teachers, the most consummate artists, the ablest commanders by land and sea, the deepest explorers of the mystery of State that have been known before or since, all the splendours of the Renaissance, and the fruits of a whole century of progress were there, ready to be appropriated and employed for its own benefit by a paramount Power.

It was obvious that the countries newly strengthened, the countries growing in unity and concentration and superfluous forces, would encroach upon those that were demoralised and weakened. By strict reason of State, this was not the policy of France; for the French frontiers

were assigned by nature everywhere but in the north-
east. There the country was open, the enemy's territory
approached the capital; and the true line of expansion
was towards Antwerp, or Liège, or Strasburg. But the
French were invited into Italy with promise of welcome,
because the Angevin claim to Naples, defeated in 1462,
had passed to the King of France. The Aragonese, who
had been successful in resisting it, was not legitimate, and
had been compelled again to struggle for existence by
the Rising of the Barons. The rising was suppressed;
the discontented Neapolitans went into exile; and they
were now in France, prophesying easy triumphs if Charles
VIII. would extend his hand to take the greatness that
belonged to the heir of the house of Anjou. They were
followed by the most important of the Italian Cardinals,
Della Rovere, nephew of a former Pope, himself afterwards
the most famous pontiff who had appeared for centuries.
Armed with the secrets of the Conclave, the Cardinal
insisted that Alexander VI. should be deposed, on the
ground that he had paid for the papacy in ascertainable
sums of money and money's worth; whereas spiritual
office obtained in that way was *ipso facto* void.

The advent of the French, heralded by the passionate
eloquence of Savonarola, was also hailed by Florence and
its dependencies, in their impatience of the Medicean rule,
now that it had dropped from the hands of the illustrious
Lorenzo into those of his less competent son. Lodovico
Sforza, the Regent of Milan, was also among those who
called in the French, as he had a family quarrel with
Naples. His father, Francesco, the most successful of
the Condottieri, who acquired the Milanese by marriage
with a Visconti, is known by that significant saying:
" May God defend me from my friends. From my enemies
I can defend myself." As the Duke of Orleans also
descended from the Visconti, Lodovico wished to divert
the French to the more alluring prospect of Naples.

In September 1494 Charles VIII. invaded Italy by
the Mont Genèvre, with an army equal to his immediate
purpose. His horsemen still displayed the medieval

armour, wrought by the artistic craftsmen of the Renaissance. They were followed by artillery, the newer arm which, in another generation, swept the steel-clad knight away. French infantry was not thought so well of. But the Swiss had become, in their wars with Burgundy, the most renowned of all foot-soldiers. They were unskilled in manœuvres; but their pikemen, charging in dense masses, proved irresistible on many Italian fields; until it was discovered that they would serve for money on either side, and that when opposed to their countrymen they refused to fight. At Pavia they were cut down by the Spaniards and their fame began to wane. They were Germans, hating Austria, and their fidelity to the golden lilies is one of the constant facts of French history, until the Swiss guard and the white flag vanished together, in July 1830.

Charles reached Naples early in 1495, having had no resistance to overcome, but having accomplished nothing, and having manifested no distinct purpose on his way, when he found himself, for a moment, master of Florence and of Rome. The deliverance of Constantinople was an idea that occurred inevitably to a man of enterprise who was in possession of Southern Italy. It was the advanced post of Europe against the East, of Christendom against Islam; the proper rendezvous of Crusaders; the source of supplies; the refuge of squadrons needing to refit. The Sultan was not an overwhelming warrior, like his father; he had not, like Selim, his successor, control of the entire East, and he was held in check by the existence of his brother, whom Charles took with him, on leaving Rome, with a view to ulterior service, but whom he lost soon after.

Charles VIII. was not a man ripened by experience of great affairs, and he had assumed the title of King of Jerusalem, as a sign of his crusading purpose. But he also called himself King of Sicily, as representing the Anjous, and this was not a disused and neglected derelict. For the island belonged to the King of Aragon, the most politic and capable of European monarchs. Before

starting for Italy, Charles had made terms with him, and
Ferdinand, in consideration of a rectified frontier, had
engaged, by the Treaty of Barcelona, to take no unfriendly
advantage of his neighbour's absence. The basis of this
agreement was shattered by the immediate unexpected
and overwhelming success of the French arms. From
his stronghold in the South it would be easy for Charles
to make himself master of Rome, of Florence, of all Italy,
until he came in sight of the lion of St. Mark. So vast
and sudden a superiority was a serious danger. A latent
jealousy of Spain underlay the whole expedition. The
realm of the Catholic kings was expanding, and an indistinct empire, larger, in reality, than that of Rome, was
rising out of the Atlantic. By a very simple calculation of approaching contingencies, Ferdinand might be
suspected of designs upon Naples. Now that the help-
lessness of the Neapolitans had been revealed, it was
apparent that he had made a false reckoning when he
allowed the French to occupy what he might have taken
more easily himself, by crossing the Straits of Messina.
Ferdinand joined the Italians of the North in declaring
against the invader, and his envoy Fonseca tore up the
Treaty of Barcelona before the face of the French king.

Having been crowned in the Cathedral, and having
garrisoned his fortresses, Charles set out for France, at the
head of a small army. As he came over the Apennines
into Lombardy, at Fornovo he was met by a larger force,
chiefly provided by Venice, and had to fight his way
through. A fortnight after his departure, the Spaniards,
under Gonsalvo of Cordova, landed in Calabria, as auxiliaries of the dethroned king. The throne was once more
occupied by the fallen family, and Charles retained nothing
of his easy and inglorious conquests when he died in
1498.

His successor, Lewis XII., was the Duke of Orleans,
who descended from the Visconti, and he at once prepared
to enforce his claim on Milan. He allied himself against
his rival, Sforza, with Venice, and with Pope Alexander.
That he might marry the widowed queen, and preserve

her duchy of Brittany for the Crown, he required that his own childless marriage should be annulled. Upon the Legate who brought the necessary documents the grateful king bestowed a principality, a bride of almost royal rank, and an army wherewith to reconquer the lost possessions of the Church in Central Italy. For the Legate was the Cardinal of Valencia, who became thenceforward Duke of Valentinois, and is better known as Cæsar Borgia. The rich Lombard plain, the garden of Italy, was conquered as easily as Naples had been in the first expedition. Sforza said to the Venetians : " I have been the dinner; you will be the supper"; and went up into the Alps to look for Swiss levies. At Novara, in 1500, his mercenaries betrayed him and he ended his days in a French prison. On their way home from the scene of their treachery, the Swiss crowned their evil repute by seizing Bellinzona and the valley of the Ticino, which has remained one of their cantons.

Lewis, undisputed master of Milan and Genoa, assured of the Roman and the Venetian alliance, was in a better position than his predecessor to renew the claim on the throne of Naples. But now, behind Frederic of Naples, there was Ferdinand of Aragon and Sicily, who was not likely to allow the king for whom he had fought to be deposed without resistance. Therefore it was a welcome suggestion when Ferdinand proposed that they should combine to expel Frederic and to divide his kingdom. As it was Ferdinand who had just reinstated him, this was an adaptation to the affairs of Christendom of the methods which passed for justice in the treatment of unbelievers, and were applied without scruple by the foremost men of the age, Albuquerque and Cortez. Frederic turned for aid to the Sultan, and this felonious act was put forward as the justification of his aggressors. The Pope sanctioned the Treaty of Partition, and as the Crown of Naples was technically in his gift, he deprived the king on the ground stated by the allies. The exquisite significance of the plea was that the Pope himself had invited Turkish intervention in Italy, and now declared it a cause of forfeiture. In 1501 French and Spaniards occupied their allotted portions, and then quarrelled over the distribution of the spoil. For a time Gonsalvo, "the great Captain," was driven to bay at Barletta on the Adriatic ; but at the end of 1503 he won a decisive victory, and the defeated French, under Bayard, withdrew from the Garigliano to the Po. Naples remained a dependency of Spain, for all purposes, in modern history.

In the midst of foreign armies, and of new combinations disturbing the established balance of Italian Powers, the lesser potentates were exposed to destruction ; and there were forces about sufficient, under capable guidance, to remodel the chaotic centre of Italy, where no strong government had ever been constituted. Cæsar Borgia recognised the opportunity as soon as the French were at Milan ; the Pope was growing old and was clay in his terrible hands. His sister just then became Duchess of Ferrara, on the border of the defenceless region which he coveted ; and the dominions of the King of France, his patron and ally, extended to the Adda and the Po. Never had such advantages been united in such a man. For Cæsar's talents were of the imperial kind. He was fearless of difficulties, of dangers, and of consequences ; and having no preference for right or wrong, he weighed with an equal and dispassionate mind whether it was better to spare a man or to cut his throat. As he did not attempt more than he could perform, his rapid success awakened aspirations for a possible future. He was odious to Venice, but a Venetian, who watched his meteoric course, wonders, in his secret diary, whether this unerring schemer was to be the appointed deliverer. He was a terror to Florence, yet the Florentine secretary, to whom he confided his thoughts in certain critical hours, wrote of him as men have written of Napoleon, and erected a monument to his memory that has secretly fascinated half the politicians in the world.

With his double equipment as a lieutenant of the French king and as a *condottiere* of the Pope, he began by reviving the dormant authority of Rome, where nominal feudatories held vicarious sway.   In the place of many despots struggling not for objects of policy, but for their own existence, there appeared a single state, reaching from sea to sea, from the Campagna to the salt-marshes by the delta of the Po, under a papal prince and *gonfaloniere*, invested with rights and prerogatives to protect the Holy See, and with power to control it.   Rome would have become a dependency of the reigning house of Borgia, as it had been of less capable vassals, and the system might have lasted as long as the brain that devised it.   Lorenzo de' Medici once said that his buildings were the only works that would outlast him ; and it is common in the secular characters of that epoch, unlike the priesthood, not to believe in those things that are abiding, and not to regard organisations that are humble and obscure at first and bloom by slow degrees for the use of another age.

Cæsar's enterprise was not determined or limited by the claims of the Vatican.   He served both Pope and king, and his French alliance carried farther than the recovery of the Romagna.   Florence became tributary by taking him into pay.   Bologna bought him off with a heavy ransom.   Venice inscribed his name in the illustrious record of its nobility.   None could tell where his ambition or his resources would end, how his inventive genius would employ the rivalry of the invaders, what uses he would devise for the Emperor and the Turk. The era of petty tyranny was closed by the apparition of one superior national tyrant, who could be no worse than twenty, for though his crimes would be as theirs, they would not be useless to the nation, but were thoughtfully designed and executed for the sake of power, the accepted object of politics in a country where the right was known by the result.   Cæsar was not an unpopular master, and his subjects were true to him in his falling fortunes.   The death of Alexander and the decline of the French cause in the South cut short his work in the autumn of 1503. Della Rovere, Cardinal Vincula, whose title came from the Church of St. Peter in Chains, the inflexible enemy of

the Borgias, was now Julius II.; and after a brief interval
he was strong enough to drive Cæsar out of the country;
while the Venetians, entering the Romagna under ill
omens for the Republic, occupied the remnant of his
many conquests.

Julius had resisted Alexander, as a man unfit for his
function, and it soon appeared that this was not a private
feud, but a total reversal of ideas and policy. The
change was not felt in religious reform or in patronage
of learning, but first in the notion of territorial politics.
Cæsar had rebuilt the duchy of Romagna in the service
of the papacy; and it was the essence of the schemes of
Julius that it should be secured for the Holy See, together
with all else that could be claimed by right, or acquired
by policy and war. The Borgias had prevailed by arms,
and Julius would not consent to be their inferior and to
condemn his whole career. He must draw the sword;
but, unlike them, he would draw it in the direct interest
of the Church. He had overthrown the conqueror, not
that the conquests might be dissolved, or might go to
Venice, but in order that he himself and his successors
might have power in Italy, and through Italians, over the
world. Upon this foundation he instituted the temporal
power, as it subsisted for three centuries. The jealous
municipal spirit of the Middle Ages had dissolved society
into units, and nothing but force could reverse the tradition and weld the fragments into great communities.
Borgia had shown that this could be done; but also that
no victorious *condottiere*, were he even his own son, could
be trusted by a Pope. Julius undertook to command his
army himself, and to fight at the head of his troops.
Letting his white beard grow, putting on armour, and
proudly riding his war-horse under fire, he exhibited the
most picturesque and romantic figure of his time.

The Venetians, commanding the seaboard with their
galleys, were not easy to dislodge from the towns they
occupied. Essentially a maritime and commercial Power,
their centre of gravity lay so far east that it was once
proposed to move the capital from the Lagoons to the

Bosphorus.   When the advancing Turk damaged their trade and threatened their Colonial empire, they took advantage of Italian disintegration to become a continental state, and the general insecurity and oppression of miniature potentates made it a happy fate to be subject to the serene and politic government, whose three thousand ships still held the sea, flying the Christian flag.   Renouncing non-intervention on the mainland, they set power above prosperity, and the interest of the State above the welfare and safety of a thousand patrician houses.   Wherever there were troubled waters, the fisher was Venice.   All down the Eastern coast, and along the Alpine slopes to the passes which were the trade route to Northern Europe, and still farther, at the expense of Milan and Naples, the patriarch of Aquileia and the Duke of Ferrara, the Emperor and the Pope, the Queen of the Adriatic extended her intelligent sway.   It was under the long administration of the Doge Foscari, Byron's hero, that it dawned upon the Venetians that it might be their mission to supersede the frail and helpless governments of the Peninsula ; and their famous politician and historian, Paruta, believed that it was in their power to do what Rome had done.   Their ambition was evident to their neighbours, and those whom they had despoiled, under every plausible pretext, awaited the opportunity of retribution.

Julius, taking counsel with Machiavelli, found it easy to form a league composed of their enemies.   As it was not the interest of the empire, France and Spain, to spite Venice by strengthening each other, the Venetians imagined they could safely hold their ground, leaving the dependent cities to make their own terms with the enemy.   Padua held out victoriously against Maximilian, but the battle of Agnadello was lost against the French in the same year 1509, in which, fighting under the Crescent in the Indian Ocean, the Venetians were defeated by the Portuguese, and lost their Eastern trade.   They soon obtained their revenge.   Having gained his ends by employing France against Venice in the League of Cambray, Julius now allied himself with the Venetians to expel the French from Milan. He had recovered the papal possessions, he had broken the Venetian power, and in this his third effort to reconstitute Italy, he still succeeded, because he had the support of the Venetians and the Swiss. The French gave battle to the Spaniards at Ravenna and to the Swiss at Novara, and then they evacuated the Milanese.

Lewis XII. swore that he would wreak vengeance on the papacy, and, in conjunction with the Emperor, opened a Council at Pisa, which was attended by a minority of cardinals. Julius met the attack by calling a general Council to meet at the Lateran, which was the first since the great reforming Council, and was still sitting when Julius died in 1513. Like the Council at Pisa, it was regarded at Rome as a move in the great game of Politics, and it made no serious attempt to heal the long-standing and acknowledged wounds of the Church. Its action spread the belief that the reigning diseases were known, but that the remedy was refused, and that reforms that might help religion were not to be expected from Church or State. Julius II. died without having expelled the barbarians, as he had promised. The French were gone, but the Spaniards remained un-shaken, and were still the pivot of the operations of the Holy See. The investiture of Naples was granted to Ferdinand of Aragon, and the fairest region in Europe bound Spain irrevocably to the Popes.

Although the Italian scheme of Julius was left half-way, his Roman scheme was completed ; the intermittent suzerainty of the Middle Ages was straitened out into effective sovereignty over the half of Central Italy, where anarchy used to reign, and the temporal power was fixed on foundations solid enough to bear the coming diminution of spiritual power. The added splendours of modern royalty, round which cardinals of reigning houses—Medici, Este, Farnese, Gonzaga—displayed the pomp and ceremony of semi-regal state,

in palaces built by Bramante and Michael Angelo, with
the ambassadors and protectors of the Powers, and the
heads of princely families that had worn the tiara, made
Rome the magnetic pole of aristocratic society.   As the
capital of an absolute monarchy, as others were, it became
associated with principles which, in the Middle Ages, it
resisted with spiritual and secular weapons ; and the
magnitude of the change was apparent when Leo X.,
by the Concordat of Bologna, conceded to Francis I.
the choice of bishops and the higher patronage of the
Church of France.   For Francis on his accession sent
an army into Italy, the last work of Julius II. was
overthrown at Marignano, and France again was master
of the Milanese.

The final struggle was to come at the vacancy of the
Imperial throne.   Ferdinand of Aragon was dead, and
Naples passed to the King of undivided Spain.   It was
the unswerving policy of Rome that it should not be
united with the Empire, and against that fixed axiom
the strongest dynasty of emperors went to pieces.   The
Reformation had just begun in Germany, and Leo wished
one of the Northern Electors to be chosen as Maximilian's
successor.   In conformity with the political situation, he
would have preferred Frederic of Saxony, the protector
of Luther.   The election of Charles, in 1519, was a
defiance of the Balance of Power, a thing not to the
taste of the Middle Ages, but becoming familiar in
those days.   France, unable formerly to keep Naples
against Spain, had now to defend Lombardy against
Spain, supported by Germany, Naples, and the Netherlands.   Francis maintained the unequal struggle for
four years, although his most powerful vassal, Bourbon,
brought the enemy to the gates of Marseilles.   The
decisive action of the long Italian war was fought at
Pavia in June 1525, where Francis was taken prisoner,
and was compelled to purchase his release by cruel
sacrifices.

The years that followed are only a phase in the
permanent subjugation of Italy, but they are memorable

in another connection.   For the triumph of Pavia brought
the suppression of the Lutherans within the range of
practical politics.   The Peasants' War had damaged their
position ; the Emperor was able now to execute the
Imperial decree of Worms, and there were some in
Germany who desired it.   He made it a condition of
his prisoner's deliverance that he should assist in
destroying them ; and Francis readily offered to do it
by coming in person, and bearing half the charge.
Charles proposed to take him at his word, when he
learnt that the Pope was at the head of a great alliance
against him.   Pope Clement was advised by the best
ecclesiastic in his court, the *Datario* Giberti, to try one
more struggle before the chains were riveted, and before
he became, as they said, a Spanish chaplain.   It is a
war, said Giberti, not for power or dominion, but for the
redemption of Italy from perpetual bondage ; and he
placed his master, for the moment, at the head of the
nation.   Clement concluded a treaty with the Emperor's
enemies at Cognac, released Francis from his oath to
observe the Treaty of Madrid, and endeavoured to make
Pescara, the victor of Pavia, turn traitor by the prospect
of the throne of Naples.

In this way Charles was compelled to turn his arms
against Rome.   He protested that he would risk all his
crowns for the sake of revenge, and appealed to Germany,
with its Lutherans, for support.   Tell them, he wrote, that
they are wanted against the Turk.   They will know what
Turk we mean.   They knew it so well that the lands-
knechts came provided with silken nooses for the necks
of cardinals, besides a gold-thread one for the Pope.
He issued a detailed manifesto against him, the work
of Valdes, one of the rare Lutherans of Spain ; and
those who were in the secret expected that the shrift
would be short.   Francis had intended from the first
moment to break his word, and to execute no conditions
injurious to France, but he came too late.   A large body
of Germans poured over the Alps and joined the Spaniards
in Lombardy.   It was observed afterwards that the

Spaniards were the most vindictive, but it was the
Germans who made the push for Rome ; and Bourbon,
on the plea of economy, as he could not pay them, led
them through the passes of the Apennines, overthrowing
the Medici at Florence on the way. Rome was taken
almost without resistance, and Clement shut himself up
in St. Angelo, while the city was given over to un-
merciful pillage, the prelates were held to ransom, and
all the secret treasure was got at by torture. That
month of May 1527, with its awful experience, was an
end to the pride and the hope and the gladness of the
pagan revival ; a severe and penitential spirit came over
society, preparing to meet the Reformation by reform,
and to avert change in doctrine by a change in morality.
The sack of Rome, said Cardinal Cajetan, was a just
judgment on the sufferers. The city was now the
Emperor's, by right of conquest, to bestow as he chose,
and the Romans were not unwilling that it should be
his capital. Some said that the abolition of the temporal
power would secure peace among the Powers, whilst others
thought that the consequence would be a patriarch in
France, if not in England as well. The last effort of the
French being spent, and Doria having gone over to the
Emperor, taking with him Genoa, the key of French
influence, the chain of transactions which began with the
Neapolitan expedition of 1494, concluded in 1530 with
the siege of Florence. Charles made peace with France
at Cambray, and with the Pope at Barcelona, and received
the Imperial crown at Bologna.

This was the consummation of the Italian wars, by
which the main conditions of modern politics were determined. The conflicts which had lasted for a generation,
and the disorder and violence which were older still, were
at an end ; Italy obtained repose from her master, and
spent for centuries her intellect in his service. Pescara,
Ferrante, Gonzaga, Philibert Emanuel, Spinola, were the
men who made Spain the first of military powers. And
Parma's invincible legions, which created Belgium, wrested
Antwerp from the Dutch, delivered Paris from Henry

IV., and watched the signals of the Armada that they might subdue England, were thronged with Italian infantry.   Excepting Venice, strong in her navy and her unapproachable lagoon, Spain dominated thenceforward over Italy, and became, by her ascendency in both Sicilies, a bulwark against the Turks.

Italy passed out of general politics, and was a force in Europe only through Rome.   The Conclave, and the creation of cardinals to compose the Conclave, made it a constant school of negotiation and intrigue for the best diplomacy in the world.   By favour of the Habsburgs, the papacy obtained a fixed dominion, secure against all comers, requiring no military defence, no wasting and profitless expenditure, nothing to dissolve the mirage of an ideal government, under spiritual and converted men. The pontificates became steadily longer, averaging six years in the sixteenth century, eight in the seventeenth, twelve in the eighteenth, sixteen in the nineteenth, and by the original and characteristic institution which is technically known as nepotism, the selection of a Prime Minister, not from the College of the ecclesiastical aristocracy, but from the family of the reigning sovereign, the tonsured statesmen introduced a dynastic infusion into the fluctuations of elective monarchy.

The triumph and coronation of the Emperor Charles V., when he was superior to all that Europe had beheld since Charlemagne, revived the ancient belief in a supreme authority elevated on alliance with the priesthood, at the expense of the independence and the equipoise of nations.   The exploits of Magellan and Cortez, upsetting all habits of perspective, called up vain dreams of the coming immensity of Spain, and roused the phantom of universal empire.   The motive of domination became a reigning force in Europe ; for it was an idea which monarchy would not willingly let fall after it had received a religious and an international consecration.   For centuries it was constantly asserted as a claim of necessity and of right.   It was the supreme manifestation of the modern state according to the image which Machiavelli had set up, the state that suffers neither limit nor equality, and is bound by no duty to nations or to men, that thrives on destruction, and sanctifies whatever things contributed to increase of power.

This law of the modern world, that power tends to expand indefinitely, and will transcend all barriers, abroad and at home, until met by superior forces, produces the rhythmic movement of History. Neither race, nor religion, nor political theory has been in the same degree an incentive to the perpetuation of universal enmity and national strife. The threatened interests were compelled to unite for the self-government of nations, the toleration of religions, and the rights of men. And it is by the combined efforts of the weak, made under compulsion, to resist the reign of force and constant wrong, that, in the rapid change but slow progress of four hundred years, liberty has been preserved, and secured, and extended, and finally understood.

II

THE NEW WORLD

GREATER changes than those which were wrought by governments or armies on the battlefield of Italy were accomplished at the same time, thousands of miles away, by solitary adventurers, with the future of the world in their hands. The Portuguese were the first Europeans to understand that the ocean is not a limit, but the universal waterway that unites mankind. Shut in by Spain, they could not extend on land, and had no opening but the Atlantic. Their arid soil gave little scope to the territorial magnate, who was excluded from politics by the growing absolutism of the dynasty, and the government found it well to employ at a distance forces that might be turbulent at home.

The great national work of exploration did not proceed from the State. The Infante Henry had served in the African wars, and his thoughts were drawn towards distant lands. He was not a navigator himself; but from his home at Sagres, on the Sacred Promontory, he watched the ships that passed between the great maritime centre at the mouth of the Tagus and the regions that were to compose the Portuguese empire. As Grand-master of the Order of Christ he had the means to equip them, and he rapidly occupied the groups of islands that lie between Africa and mid Atlantic, and that were a welcome accession to the narrow territory of Portugal. Then he sent his mariners to explore the coast of the unknown and dreaded continent. When they reached the Senegal and the Gambia, still more, when the coast of Guinea trended to the East, they remembered Prester John, and dreamed of finding a way to his fictitious realm which would afford convenient leverage for Christendom, at the back of the dark world that faced the Mediterranean.

As the trade of the country did not cover the outlay, Henry began in 1442 to capture negroes, who were imported as slaves, or sold with advantage to local chiefs. In five years, 927 blacks from Senegambia reached the Lisbon market ; and, later on, the Guinea coast supplied about a thousand every year. That domestic institution was fast disappearing from Europe when it was thus revived ; and there was some feeling against the Infante, and some temporary sympathy for his victims. On the other side, there were eminent divines who thought that the people of hot countries may properly be enslaved. Henry the Navigator applied to Rome, and Nicholas V. issued Bulls authorising him and his Portuguese to make war on Moors and pagans, seize their possessions, and reduce them to perpetual slavery, and prohibiting all Christian nations, under eternal penalties, from trespassing on the privilege. He applauded the trade in negroes, and hoped that it would end in their conversion. Negro slavery struck no deep root in Europe. But the delusion, says Las Casas, lasted to his own time, when, half a century after the death of its founder, it began to control the destinies of America.

Henry's brother, the Regent Dom Pedro, had visited the courts of Europe, and brought Marco Polo's glowing narrative of his travels in the Far East, still, in Yule's edition, one of the most fascinating books that can be found. Emmanuel the Great, in the Charter rewarding Vasco da Gama, affirms that, from 1433, the Infante pursued his operations with a view to India. After his death, in 1460, they were carried on by the State, and became a secondary purpose, dependent on public affairs. Africa was farmed out for some years, on condition that an hundred leagues of coast were traced annually. There was a moment of depression, when the Guinea coast, having run eastward for a thousand miles and more, turned south, apparently without end. Toscanelli of Florence was a recognised authority on the geography of those days, and he was asked what he thought of the situation. No oracle ever said anything so wise as the answer of the Tuscan sage. For he told them that India was to be found not in the East, but in the West ; and we shall see what came of it twenty years later, when his letter fell into predestined hands. The Portuguese were not diverted from their aim. They knew quite well that Africa. does not stretch away for ever, and that it needed only a few intrepid men to see the end of it, and to reach an open route to Eastern Asia. They went on, marking their advance beyond the Congo, and erected crosses along the coast to signify their claim ; but making no settlements, for Africa was only an obstruction on the way to the Indies.

Each successive voyage was made under a different commander, until 1486, when the squadron of Bartholomew Diaz was blown offshore, out into the Atlantic. When the storm fell he sailed east until he had passed the expected meridian of Africa, and then, turning northward, struck land far beyond Cape Agulhas. He had solved the problem, and India was within his reach. His men soon after refused to go farther, and he was forced to renounce the prize. On his way back he doubled the Cape, which, from his former experience, he called the Cape Tempestuous, until the king, showing that he understood, gave it a name of better omen. Nevertheless, Portugal did no more for ten years, the years that were made memorable by Spain. Then, under a new king, Emmanuel the Fortunate, Vasco da Gama went out to complete the unfinished work of Diaz, lest Columbus, fulfilling the prophecy of Toscanelli, should reach Cathay by a shorter route, and rob them of their reward. The right man had been found. It was all plain sailing ; and he plucked the ripe fruit. Vasco da Gama's voyage to the Cape was the longest ever made till then. At Malindi, on the equatorial east coast of Africa, he found a pilot, and, striking across the Indian Ocean by the feeble monsoon of 1497, sighted the Ghats in May. The first cargo from India covered the expenses many times over. The splendour of the achievement was recognised at once, and men were persuaded that Emmanuel would soon be the wealthiest of European monarchs. So vast a promise of revenue required to be made secure by arms, and a force was sent out under Cabral.

The work thus attempted in the East seemed to many too much for so small a kingdom. They objected that the country would break its back in straining so far ; that the soil ought first to be cultivated at home ; that it would be better to import labour from Germany than to export it to India. Cabral had not been many weeks at sea when these murmurs received a memorable confirmation. Following the advice of Da Gama to avoid the calms of the Gulf of Guinea, he took a westerly course, made the coast of South America, and added, incidentally and without knowing it, a region not much smaller than Europe to the dominions of his sovereign.

The Portuguese came to India as traders, not as conquerors, and desired, not territory, but portable and exchangeable commodities. But the situation they found out there compelled them to wage war in unknown seas, divided from supports, and magazines, and docks by nearly half the globe. They made no attempt on the interior, for the Malabar coast was shut off by a range of lofty mountains. Their main object was the trade of the Far East, which was concentrated at Calicut, and was then carried by the Persian Gulf to Scanderoon and Constantinople, or by Jeddah to Suez and Alexandria. There the Venetians shipped the products of Asia to the markets of Europe. But on the other side of the isthmus the carrying trade, all the way to the Pacific, was in the hands of Moors from Arabia and Egypt. The Chinese had disappeared before them from Indian waters, and the Hindoos were no mariners. They possessed the monopoly of that which the Portuguese had come to take, and they were enemies of the Christian name. The Portuguese

required not their share in the trade, but the monopoly
itself.   A deadly conflict could not be avoided.   By the
natives, they were received at first as friends ; and Vasco
da Gama, who took the figures of the Hindoo Pantheon
for saints of the Catholic Calendar, reported that the
people of India were Christians.   When this illusion was
dispelled, it was a consolation to find the Nestorians settled
at Cochin, which thus became a Portuguese stronghold,
which their best soldier, Duarte Pacheco, held against a
multitude.   Calicut, where they began operations, has
disappeared like Earl Godwin's estate.   Forbes, who was
there in 1772, writes : "At very low water I have
occasionally seen the waves breaking over the tops of
the highest temples and minarets."   It was an international
city, where 1500 vessels cleared in a season, where trade
was open and property secure, and where the propagation
of foreign religion was not resented.

The Zamorin, as they called the Rajah of Calicut,
ended by taking part with the old friends from the
Arabian Seas, who supplied his country with grain, against
the visitors who came in questionable shape.   The Portuguese lacked the diplomatic graces, and disregarded the
art of making friends and acquiring ascendency by the
virtues of humanity and good faith.   When it came to
blows, they acquitted themselves like men conscious that
they were the pioneers of History, that their footsteps
were in the van of the onward march, that they were
moulding the future, and making the world subservient
to civilisation.   They were Crusaders, coming the other
way, and robbing the Moslem of their resources.   The
shipbuilding of the Moors depended on the teak forests
of Calicut ; the Eastern trade enriched both Turk and
Mameluke, and the Sultan of Egypt levied duty amounting to £290,000 a year.   Therefore he combined with
the Venetians to expel the common enemy from Indian
waters.   In 1509 their fleet was defeated by the Viceroy
Almeida near Diu, off the coast of Kattywar, where the
Arabian seaman comes in sight of India.   It was his last
action before he surrendered power to his rival, the great

Albuquerque. Almeida sought the greatness of his country
not in conquest but in commerce. He discouraged expeditions to Africa and to the Moluccas ; for he believed that
the control of Indian traffic could be maintained by sea
power, and that land settlements would drain the resources
of the nation. Once the Moslem traders excluded, Portugal
would possess all it wanted, on land and sea.

Almeida's successor, who had the eye of Alexander the
Great for strategic points and commercial centres, was
convinced that sea-power, at six months from home, rests
on the occupation of seaports, and he carried the forward
policy so far that Portugal possessed fifty-two establish-
ments, commanding 15,000 miles of coast, and held them,
nominally, with 20,000 men. Almeida's victory had
broken the power of the Moors. Albuquerque resolved
to prevent their reappearance by closing the Persian Gulf
and the Red Sea. With Aden, Ormuz, and Malacca, he
said, the Portuguese are masters of the world. He failed
in the Red Sea. When Socotra proved insufficient, he
attacked Aden, and was repulsed. There was a disconcert-
ing rumour that no Christian vessel could live in the Red
Sea, as there was a loadstone that extracted the nails.
Albuquerque succeeded in the Persian Gulf, and erected a
fortress at Ormuz, and at the other end of the Indian
world he seized Malacca, and became master of the
narrow seas, and of all the produce from the vast islands
under the equator. He made Goa the impregnable
capital of his prodigious empire, and the work that he
did was solid. He never perceived the value of Bombay,
which is the best harbour in Asia, and did not see that
the key of India is the Cape of Good Hope. His
language was sometimes visionary. He beheld a cross
shining in the heavens, over the kingdom of Prester John,
and was eager for an alliance with him. He wished to
drain the Nile into the Red Sea. He would attack Mecca
and Medina, carry off the bones of the prophet, and
exchange them for the Holy Sepulchre. The dependency
was too distant and too vast. The dread proconsul in
his palace at Goa, who was the mightiest potentate

between Mozambique and China, was too great a servant
for the least of European kings. Emmanuel was suspicious.
He recalled the victorious Almeida, who perished on the
way home ; and Albuquerque was in disgrace, when he
died on his quarter-deck, in sight of the Christian city
which he had made the capital of the East.

The secret of Portuguese prosperity was the small
bulk and the enormous market value of the particular
products in which they dealt. In those days men had
to do without tea, or coffee, or chocolate, or tobacco,
or quinine, or coca, or vanilla, and sugar was very rare.
But there were the pepper and the ginger of Malabar,
cardamoms in the damp district of Tellicherry ; cinnamon
and pearls in Ceylon. Beyond the Bay of Bengal, near
the equator, there was opium, the only conqueror of pain
then known ; there were frankincense and indigo ; camphor
in Borneo ; nutmeg and mace in Amboyna ; and in two
small islands, only a few miles square, Ternate and Tidor,
there was the clove tree, surpassing all plants in value.
These were the real spice islands, the enchanted region
which was the object of such passionate desire ; and their
produce was so cheap on the spot, so dear in the markets
of Antwerp and London, as to constitute the most lucrative
trade in the world. From these exotics, grown on
volcanic soil, in the most generous of the tropical climates,
the profit was such that they could be paid for in precious
metals. When Drake was at Ternate in 1579, he found
the Sultan hung with chains of bullion, and clad in a robe
of gold brocade rich enough to stand upright. The
Moluccas were of greater benefit to the Crown than to
the Portuguese workman. About twenty ships, of 100 to
550 tons, sailed for Lisbon in the year. A voyage sometimes lasted two years, out and home, and cost, including
the ship, over £4000. But the freight might amount to
£150,000. Between 1497 and 1612 the number of vessels
engaged in the India trade was 806. Of these, ninety-
six were lost. After the annexation by Philip II., Lisbon
was closed to countries at war with Spain. Dutch and
English had to make their own bargains in the East, and

treated Portugal as an enemy. Their empire declined rapidly, and the Dutch acquired the islands long before the English succeeded on the mainland of India.

The Portuguese acknowledged no obligations of international law towards Asiatics. Even now, many people know of no law of nations but that which consists in contracts and conventions ; and with the people of the East there were none. They were regarded as outlaws and outcasts, nearly as Bacon regarded the Spaniards and Edmund Burke the Turks. Solemn instruments had declared it lawful to expropriate and enslave Saracens and other enemies of Christ. What was right in Africa could not be wrong in Asia. Cabral had orders to treat with fire and sword any town that refused to admit either missionary or merchant. Barros, the classic historian of Portuguese Asia, says that Christians have no duties towards pagans ; and their best writers affirm to this day that such calculated barbarities as they inflicted on women and children were justified by the necessity of striking terror. In the Commentaries of the great Albuquerque, his son relates with complacency how his father caused the Zamorin to be poisoned. These theories demoralised the entire government. S. Francis Xavier, who came out in 1542, found an organised system of dishonesty and plunder, and wrote home that no official in India could save his soul. By him and his brethren many converts were made, and as intermarriages were frequent, the estrangement grew less between the races. Just then, the Inquisition was introduced into Portugal, and sent a branch to Goa. One of the governors afterwards reported that it had helped to alienate the natives, whose temples were closed. But the solid structure of Almeida and Albuquerque was strong enough to defeat a second expedition from Egypt, after Egypt had become a province of Turkey, and an Indian war and insurrection. It declined with the decline of Portugal under Sebastian, in the latter part of the sixteenth century, but it perished through its association with Spain, at the hands of enemies not its own, and not from internal causes.

While the Asiatic empire was built up by the sustained and patient effort of a nation, during seventy years, the discovery of the West was due to one eager and original intellect, propelled by medieval dreams. Columbus had sailed both North and South ; but the idea which changed the axis of the globe came to him from books.   He failed to draw an inference favourable to his design from the driftwood which a tropical current carries to Iceland, and proceeded on the assurance of Pierre d'Ailly and of Toscanelli, that Asia reaches so far east as to leave but a moderate interval between Portugal and Japan. Although he rested his case on arguments from the classics and the prophets, his main authority was Toscanelli ; but it is uncertain whether, as he affirmed, they had been in direct correspondence, or whether Columbus obtained the letter and the Chart of 1474 by means which were the cause of his disgrace.

Rejected by Portugal, he made his way into Spain. He was found, starving, at the gate of a Franciscan convent ; and the place where he sank down is marked by a monument, because it is there that our modern world began.   The friar who took him in and listened to his story soon perceived that this ragged mendicant was the most extraordinary person he had known, and he found him patrons at the court of Castile.   The argument which Columbus now laid before the learned men of Spain was this : The eastern route, even if the Portuguese succeed in finding it, would be of no use to them, as the voyage to Cipango, to Cathay, even to the spice islands, would be too long for profit.   It was better to sail out into the West, for that route would be scarcely 3000 miles to the extremity of Asia ; the other would be 15,000, apart from the tremendous circuit of Africa, the extent of which was ascertained by Diaz while Columbus was pursuing his uphill struggle.   The basis of the entire calculation was that the circumference of the earth is 18,000 miles at the equator, and that Asia begins, as is shown in Toscanelli's chart, somewhere about California.   Misled by his belief in cosmographers, he blotted out the Pacific, and estimated the extent of water to be traversed at one-third of the reality. The Spaniards, who were consulted, pointed out the flaw, for the true dimensions were known ; but they were unable to demonstrate the truths against the great authorities cited on the other side. The sophisms of Columbus were worth more than all the science of Salamanca. The objectors who called him a visionary were in the right, and he was obstinately wrong. To his auspicious persistency in error Americans owe, among other things, their existence.

A majority reported favourably—a majority composed, it would appear, of ignorant men. Years were spent in these preliminaries, and then the war with Granada absorbed the resources and the energies of the Crown. Columbus was present when the last Moorish king kissed the hand of Isabella, and he saw the cross raised over the Alhambra. This victory of Christendom was immediately followed by the expulsion of the Jews, and then the Catholic queen gave audience to the Genoese projector. His scheme belonged to the same order of ideas, and he was eloquent on its religious aspect. He would make so many slaves as to cover all expenses, and would have them baptized. He would bring home gold enough in three years to reconquer Palestine. He had one impressive argument which was not suggested by the situation at Court. Toscanelli had been at Rome when envoys came from the Grand Khan, petitioning for missionaries to instruct his people in the doctrines of Christianity. Two such embassies were sent, but their prayer was not attended to. Here were suppliants calling out of the darkness : Come over and help us. It was suitable that the nation which conquered the Moslem and banished the Jews should go on to convert the heathen. The Spaniards would appear in the East, knowing that their presence was desired. In reality they would come in answer to an invitation, and might look for a welcome. Making up by their zeal for the deficient enterprise of Rome, they might rescue the teeming millions of Farthest Asia, and thus fulfil prophecy, as there were only a hundred and

F

fifty-five years to the end of the world.   The conversion
of Tartary would be the crowning glory of Catholic Spain.

All this was somewhat hypothetical and vague; but
nothing could be more definite than the reward which he
demanded.   For it appeared that what this forlorn adventurer required for himself was to be admiral of the
Atlantic, ranking with the constable of Castile, Viceroy
with power of life and death, in the regions to be occupied,
and a large proportion of the intended spoil.   And he
would accept no less.   None divined what he himself
knew not, that the thing he offered in return was dominion
over half the world.   Therefore, when he found that this
would not do, Columbus saddled his mule and took the
road to France.   In that superb moment he showed what
man he was, and the action was more convincing than
his words had been.   An Aragonese official, Santangel,
found the money, the £1500 required for the expedition,
and the traveller was overtaken by an alguazil a couple
of leagues away, and recalled to Granada.   Santangel
was, by descent, a Jew.   Several of his kindred suffered
under the Inquisition, before and after, and he fortified
himself against the peril of the hour when he financed
the first voyage of Columbus.   Granada fell on the 2nd
of January 1492.   The Jews were expelled on the 20th
of March.   On the 17th of April the contract with
Columbus was signed at Santa Fe.   The same crusading
spirit, the same motive of militant propagandism, appears
in each of the three transactions.   And the explorer, at
this early stage, was generally backed by the clergy.
Juan Perez, the hospitable Franciscan, was his friend ; and
Mendoza, the great cardinal of Toledo, and Deza, afterwards Archbishop of Seville.   Talavera, the Archbishop of
Granada, found him too fanciful to be trusted.

Sailing due west from the Canaries he crossed the
Atlantic in its widest part.   The navigation was prosperous
and uneventful until, changing their course to follow the
flight of birds, they missed the continent and came upon
the islands.   It was the longest voyage that had ever
been attempted in the open sea ; but the passage itself

and the shoals and currents of the West Indies, were mastered with the aid of nautical instruments from Nuremberg, and of the *Ephemerides* of Regiomontanus. These were recent achievements of the Renaissance, and without them the undertaking was impossible. Even with the new appliances, Columbus was habitually wrong in his measurements. He put Cuba 18° too far to the west; he thought San Domingo as large as Spain; and he saw mountains 50,000 feet high in Yucatan. Indeed, he protested that his success was not due to science, but to the study of the prophet Isaiah. Above all things, he insisted that Cuba was part of the Asiatic continent, and obliged his companions to testify to the same belief, although there is evidence that he did not share it.

He had promised Cathay. If he produced an unknown continent instead, a continent many thousands of miles long, prohibiting approach to Cathay, he would undo his own work; the peasants who had exposed his fallacies would triumph in his failure, and the competing Portuguese would appropriate all that he had undertaken to add to the crown of Castile. Without civilisation and gold his discoveries would be valueless; and there was so little gold at first that he at once proposed to make up for it in slaves. His constant endeavour was not to be mistaken for the man who discovered the new world. Somewhere in the near background he still beheld the city with the hundred bridges, the crowded bazaar, the long train of caparisoned elephants, the palace with the pavement of solid gold. Naked savages skulking in the forest, marked down by voracious cannibals along the causeway of the Lesser Antilles, were no distraction from the quest of the Grand Khan. The facts before him were uninteresting and provisional, and were overshadowed by the phantoms that crowded his mind. The contrast between the gorgeous and entrancing vision and the dismal and desperate reality made the position a false one. He went on seeking gold when it was needful to govern, and proved an incapable administrator. Long before his final voyage he had fallen into discredit, and he died in obscurity.

Many miserable years passed after his death before America began, through Cortez, to weigh perceptibly in the scales of Europe. Landing at Lisbon from his first expedition, Columbus, in all his glory, had an audience of the king. It was six years since Diaz proved that the sea route to India was perfectly open, but no European had since set eyes on the place where Table Mountain looks down on the tormented Cape. Portugal apparently had renounced the fruits of his discovery. It was now reported that a Spanish crew had found in the West what the Portuguese had been seeking in the East, and that the Papal privilege had been infringed. The king informed Columbus that the regions he had visited belonged to Portugal. It was evident that some limit must be drawn separating the respective spheres. Rome had forbidden Spain from interfering with the expeditions of Portugal, and the Spaniards accordingly demanded a like protection. On the surface, there was no real difficulty. Three Bulls were issued in 1493, two in May and one in September, admonishing Portuguese mariners to keep to the east of a line drawn about 35° west of Greenwich. That line of demarcation was suggested by Columbus, as corresponding with a point he had reached on 13th September, an hundred leagues beyond the Azores. On that day the needle, which had pointed east of the Pole, shifted suddenly to the west. There, he reckoned, was the line of No Variation. At that moment, the climate changed. There was a smooth sea and a balmy air ; there was a new heaven and a new earth. The fantastic argument did not prevail, and in the following year Spain and Portugal agreed, by the treaty of Tordesillas, to move the dividing meridian farther west, about midway between the most westerly island of the Old World and the most easterly island of the New. By this agreement, superseding the Papal award, Portugal obtained Brazil. When the lines of demarcation were drawn in 1493 and 1494, nobody knew where they would cut the equator on the other side of the globe. There also there was matter for later negotiation.

After the fall of Malacca, Albuquerque sent a squadron to examine the region of islands farther east. One of his officers, Serrano, remained out there, and after as many adventures as Robinson Crusoe, he found his way to the very heart of the Moluccas, to Ternate, the home of the clove. In describing his travels to a friend, he made the most of the distance traversed in his eastward course. Magellan, to whom the letter was addressed, was out of favour with his commander Albuquerque, and on his return home found that he was out of favour with King Emmanuel. For the country which had repelled Columbus repelled the only navigator who was superior to Columbus. Magellan remembered Serrano's letter, and saw what could be made of it. He told the Spaniards that the spice islands were so far east that they were in the Spanish hemisphere, and he undertook to occupy them for Spain. He would sail, not east, but west, in the direction which was legally Spanish. For he knew a course that no man knew, and America, hitherto the limit of Spanish enterprise, would be no obstacle to him.

It seemed an apparition of Columbus, more definite and rational, without enthusiasm or idealism, or quotations from Roger Bacon, and Seneca, and the greater prophets. Cardinal Adrian, the Regent, refused to listen, but Fonseca, the President of the Board of Control, became his protector. Magellan wanted a good deal of protection ; for his adventure was injurious to his countrymen, and was regarded by them as the intrigue of a traitor. Vasconcellos, Bishop of Lamego, afterwards Archbishop of Lisbon, advised that he should be murdered ; and at night he was guarded in the streets of Valladolid by Fonseca's men. Magellan was not the first to believe that America comes to an end somewhere. Vespucci had guessed it ; the extremity is marked on a globe of 1515 ; and a mercantile house that advanced funds is supposed to have been on the track.

Without a chart Magellan made his way through the perilous straits that perpetuate his name in twelve days'

sailing.   Drake, who came next, in 1577, took seventeen
days, and Wallis, one hundred and sixteen.   And then,
at Cape Deseado, the unbroken highway to the fabled
East, which had been closed against Columbus, opened
before him.   The Spaniards discovered Cape Horn five
years later, but it was doubled for the first time in 1616
by the Dutchman who gave his name to it.   From the
coast of Chili, Magellan sailed north-west for three
months, missing all the Pacific Islands until he came to
the Ladrones.   He was killed while annexing the
Philippines to the Crown of Spain, and his lieutenant
Delcano, the first circumnavigator, brought the remnant
of his crew home by the Cape.   On the 9th of September
1522, thirteen wasted pilgrims passed barefoot in pro-
cession through the streets of Seville, not so much in
thanksgiving for that which had not been given to
man since the Creation, as in penance for having
mysteriously lost a day, and kept their feasts and fasts
all wrong.   Magellan's acquisition of the Philippines
lasted to the present year (1899), but his design on
the Moluccas was given up.   Nobody knew, until the
voyage of Dampier, to whom, by the accepted boundary,
they belonged ;   and in 1529 Spain abandoned its
claim for 350,000 ducats.   The Portuguese paid that
price for what was by right their own ;   for Magellan
was entirely wrong both as to the meridian and as to
the South American route, which was much the longest,
and was not followed by sailors.

For more than twenty years Spain struggled vainly
with the West Indian problem.   Four large islands and
forty small ones, peopled by barbarians, were beyond
the range of Spanish experience in the art of government.   Grants of land were made, with the condition
that the holder should exercise a paternal rule over the
thriftless inhabitants.   It was thought to pay better to
keep them underground, digging for gold, than to
employ them on the surface.   The mortality was overwhelming ;   but the victims awakened little sympathy.
Some belonged to that Acadian race that was the first

revealed by the landfall of Columbus, and they were considered incurably indolent and vicious. The remainder came from the mainland and the region of the Orinoco, and had made their way by the Windward Islands as far as San Domingo, devouring the people they found there. Neither the stronger nor the weaker race withstood the exhausting labour to which they were put by taskmasters eager for gold. Entire villages committed suicide together ; and the Spaniards favoured a mode of correction which consisted in burning Indians alive by a slow fire. Las Casas, who makes these statements, and who may be trusted for facts and not for figures, affirms that fifty millions perished in his time, and fifteen millions were put to death.

Without a fresh labour supply, the colony would be ruined. It was the office of the clergy to prove that this treatment of the natives was short-sighted and criminal, and their cause was taken up by the Dominican missionaries. In 1510 the preacher Montesino, taking for his text the words, " I am the voice of one crying in the wilderness," denounced the practice. Their mouthpiece with the Home Government, their immortal mouthpiece with posterity, is Las Casas, whose narrative is our authority. The government was anxious to preserve conquests that began to yield some profit. They appointed Commissions to advise, and followed sometimes one report, sometimes the other, taking generally the line of least resistance. The most important Commission of all, in which Las Casas asserted the duties of Christians and the rights of savages, against Sepulveda, who denied them, never came to a decision.

Failing the native supply, the Spaniards substituted negroes. The slaves forwarded by Columbus had been sent back with tokens of the queen's displeasure, and Ximenes would not permit the importation of Africans. But the traffic went on, and the Indies were saved. Under Charles V. 1000 slaves were allotted to each of the four islands. It did not seem an intolerable wrong to rescue men from the devil-worshippers who mangled their victims on the Niger or the Congo. Las Casas himself was one of those who advised that the negro should be brought to the relief of the Carib, and he would have allowed twelve slaves to each settler. He survived half a century, lived to lament his error, and declared his repentance to the world. He repented from motives of humanity rather than from principle ; his feelings were more sensitive than his conscience, and he resembled the imperious Parliaments of George III. which upheld the slave trade until imaginations were steeped in the horrors of the middle passage.

The supreme moment in the conquest of America is the landing of Cortez at Vera Cruz in 1521. He was an insubordinate officer acting in defiance of orders, and the governor of Cuba, in just indignation, despatched a force under Narvaez to bring him back. Cortez came down from the interior to the coast, deprived Narvaez of his command, and took possession of his men. With this unexpected reinforcement he was able to conquer Mexico, the capital of an illimitable empire. There was plenty of hard fighting, for the dominant race about the king was warlike. They were invaders, who reigned by force, and as they worshipped beings of the nether world who were propitiated with human sacrifice, they took their victims from the subject people, and their tyranny was the most hateful upon earth. The Spaniards, coming as deliverers, easily found auxiliaries against the government that practised unholy rites in the royal city. When Mexico fell Cortez sent a report to Charles V., with the first-fruits of his victory. Then, that no protesting narrative might follow and weaken his own, that his men might have no hope except in his success, he took the most daring resolution of his life, and scuttled his ships. Fonseca had signed the order for his arrest, when the most marvellous tale in that sequence of marvels reached his hands, and the disgraced mutineer was found to have added to the Emperor's dominions a region many times vaster and wealthier than all that he possessed in Europe. In 1522 the accumulated treasure which had been extracted from Mexican mines since the beginning of ages came pouring into the imperial exchequer, and the desire of so many explorers during thirty unprofitable years was fulfilled at last.

Cortez was not only the most heroic of the Conquistadors, for there was no lack of good soldiers, but he was an educated man, careful to import the plants and quadrupeds needed for civilisation, and a statesman capable of ruling mixed races without help from home. From the moment of his appearance the New World ceased to be a perplexing burden to Spain, and began to foreshadow danger and temptation to other nations. And a man immeasurably inferior to him, a man who could not write his name, whose career, in its glory and its shame, was a servile imitation, almost a parody, of his own, succeeded thereby in establishing a South American empire equal to that of Cortez in the North. One of the ships sailing from the islands to the isthmus carried a stowaway hidden in a cask, whose name was Balboa, and who discovered the Pacific.

The third name is Francisco Pizarro. He stood by and listened while a native described a mighty potentate, many days to the south, who reigned over the mountains and the sea, who was rich in gold, and who possessed a four-footed beast of burden, the only one yet encountered, which was taken at first for a camel. He waited many years for his opportunity. Then, with 168 armed men, and with aid from an associate who risked his money in the business, he started for the Andes and the civilised and prosperous monarchy in the clouds, which he had heard of when he was the lieutenant of Balboa. The example of Cortez, the fundamental fact of American history, had shown what could be done by getting hold of the king, and by taking advantage of internal dissension. How much could be accomplished by treachery and unflinching vigour Pizarro knew without a teacher. Whilst he established his power in the highlands under the equator, Almagro occupied the coast in the temperate zone, 1000 miles farther. Together they had con-

quered the Pacific. Then, as no man had the ascendency
of Cortez, the time that succeeded the occupation was
disturbed by internal conflict, in which both the conquerors perished. They had done even more for the
Spanish empire than their greater rival. There were
4,600,000 ducats in the treasury of the Inca, and he filled
his prison with gold as high as he could reach for the
ransom which did not save his life. The mines were
soon in working order ; and, as the expanse of fertile soil
was 3000 miles long, it was clear that Peru, added to
Mexico, constituted an important factor in European
finance.

As time carried away the tumult of conquest, and the
evil generation that achieved it, Spanish America became
the seat of such abundance and profusion as was not
found in any European capital ; and the natives, instructed
and regulated by the missionaries, were the object of an
elaborate protective legislation, which gave reason for
attachment to the mother country. The prodigality of
nature was too much for tropical society, and it accomplished nothing of its own for the mind of man. It
influenced the position of classes in Europe by making
property obtained from afar, in portable shape, predominate
over property at home. Released from the retarding
pressure of accumulated years, it developed towards
revolution ; and all the colonies founded by the Conquistadors on the continent of America became Republics.
These events shifted the centre of political gravity from
land to sea. The resources of the ocean world extended
the physical basis of modern History ; and increase of
wealth involving increase of power, depended thenceforward on the control of distant regions. Vasco da
Gama created a broad channel for the pursuit of Empire
and Columbus remodelled the future of the world. For
History is often made by energetic men, steadfastly following ideas, mostly wrong, that determine events.

III

THE RENAISSANCE

NEXT to the discovery of the New World, the recovery of the ancient world is the second landmark that divides us from the Middle Ages and marks the transition to modern life. The Renaissance signifies the renewed study of Greek, and the consequences that ensued from it, during the century and a half between Petrarca and Erasmus. It had survived, as a living language, among Venetian colonists and Calabrian monks, but exercised no influence on literature.

The movement was preceded by a Roman revival, which originated with Rienzi. Rome had been abandoned by the Papacy, which had moved from the Tiber to the Rhone, where it was governed by Frenchmen from Cahors, and had fallen, like any servile country, into feudal hands. Rienzi restored the Republic, revived the self-government of the city, the memories attached to the Capitol, the inscriptions, the monuments of the men who had ruled the world. The people, no longer great through the Church, fell back on the greatness which they inherited from ancient times. The spell by which the Tribune directed their patriotism was archæology. In front of the Capitoline temple, near the Tarpeian rock and the She-Wolf's cave, he proclaimed their rights over the empire and the nations; and he invited the people of Italy to a national parliament for the restoration of Italian unity and of the ancient glory and power of Rome. Patriotism, national independence, popular liberty, all were founded on antiquarian studies and the rhetorical interpretation of the fragments of the Lex Regia.

The political scheme of Rienzi failed, but it started a movement in the world of thought deeper and more enduring than State transactions. For his ideas were adopted by the greatest writer then living, and were expounded by him in the most eloquent and gracious prose that had been heard for a thousand years. Petrarca called the appearance of the patriotic tribune and rhetorician the dawn of a new world and a golden age. Like him, he desired to purge the soil of Italy from the barbaric taint. It became the constant theme of the Humanists to protest against the foreign intruder, that is, against the feudal noble, the essential type of the medieval policy. It is the link between Rienzi, the dreamer of dreams, and the followers of Petrarca. Boccaccio had already spoken of the acceptable blood of tyrants.

But the political influence of antiquity, visible at first, made way for a purely literary influence. The desire for good Latin became injurious to Italian, and Petrarca censured Dante for his error in composing the *Divine Comedy* in the vulgar tongue. He even regretted that the *Decamerone* was not written in Latin, and refused to read what his friend had written for the level of uneducated men. The classics became, in the first place, the model and the measure of style ; and the root of the Renaissance was the persuasion that a man who could write like Cicero had an important advantage over a man who wrote like Bartolus or William of Ockham ; and that ideas radiant with beauty must conquer ideas clouded over with dialectics. In this, there was an immediate success. Petrarca and his imitators learnt to write excellent Latin. Few of them had merit as original thinkers, and what they did for erudition was done all over again, and incomparably better, by the scholars who appeared after the tempest of the Reformation had gone down. But they were excellent letter writers. In hundreds of volumes, from Petrarca to Sadolet and Pole, we can trace every idea and mark every throb. It was

the first time that the characters of men were exposed
with analytic distinctness ; the first time indeed that character could be examined with accuracy and certitude.

A new type of men began with Petrarca, men
accustomed to introspection, who selected their own ideals,
and moulded their minds to them. The medieval system
could prepare him for death ; but, seeing the vicissitudes
of fortune and the difficulties of life, he depended on the
intellectual treasures of the ancient world, on the whole
mass of accessible wisdom, to develop him all round. To
men ignorant of Greek, like the first generation of the
Renaissance, the fourteenth-century men, much in ancient
philosophy was obscure. But one system, that of the
Stoics, they studied deeply, and understood, for they had
the works of Seneca. For men craving for self-help and
the complete training of the faculties, eager to escape
from the fixed types of medieval manhood, minted by
authority, and taught to distrust conscience, when it was
their own, and to trust it only in others, Seneca was an
oracle. For he is the classic of mental discipline, vigilant
self-study, and the examination of conscience. It is
under these influences that the modern type of individual
man took shape. The action of religion, by reason of
the divided Church, and the hierarchy *in partibus* was at
a low point ; and no age has been so corrupt, so barbarous
in the midst of culture. The finished individual of the
Renaissance, ready for emergencies equal to either fortune,
relying on nothing inherited, but on his own energy and
resource, began badly, little recking rights of others, little
caring for the sanctity of life.

Very early in the first or Latin phase of the revival,
people suspected that familiarity with the classics would
lead to admiration for paganism. Coluccio Salutato,
who had been Florentine Secretary from the time of
Petrarca, and is a classical writer of Latin letters, had to
defend the new learning against the rising reproach of
irreligion ; and the statue of Virgil was ignominiously
removed from the market-place of the town which his
birth has made illustrious, as a scandal to good men.

Petrarca never became a Greek scholar.   He felt the
defect.   To write beautiful Latin was nothing, unless
there was more to say than men already knew.   But the
Latin classics were no new discovery.   The material
increase of knowledge was quite insufficient to complete
the type of an accomplished man.   The great reservoir of
ideas, of forgotten sciences, of neglected truth, remained
behind.   Without that, men would continue to work at a
disadvantage, to fight in the dark, and could never fulfil
the possibilities of existence.   What was impatiently felt
as the medieval eclipse came not from the loss of elegant
Latin, but from the loss of Greek.   All that was implied
in the intended resurrection of antiquity depended on the
revival of Greek studies.   Because Petrarca possessed the
culture of his time beyond all men, he was before them
all in feeling what it needed most.   Knowledge of truth,
not casual and partial, but as complete and certain as the
remaining civilisation admitted, would have to be abandoned, if Latin was still to be the instrument and the
limit.   Then the new learning would not be strong enough
to break down the reliance on approved authors, the
tyranny of great names, the exclusiveness of schools.
Neither rhetoric nor poetry could deprive Aristotle and
Peter Lombard, St. Augustine and St. Thomas, of their
supremacy, give them their position in the incessant
stream of thought, or reduce them beneath the law of
progress in the realm of knowledge.

The movement which Petrarca initiated implied the
revival of a buried world, the enrichment of society by
the mass of things which the western nations had allowed
to drop, and of which medieval civilisation was deprived.
It meant the preference for Grecian models, the supremacy
of the schools of Athens, the inclusion of science in literature, the elevation of Hippocrates and Archimedes to a
level with Terence and Quintilian, the reproduction of
that Hellenic culture which fought the giant fight of the
fourth and fifth century with the Councils and Fathers
of the Church.   That is why the Latin restoration, which
was the direct result of Petrarca's example, was over-

whelmed by the mightier change that followed, when a more perfect instrument reached the hands of men passionately curious and yearning for new things.

At first there was no way of acquiring the unknown tongue. But the second generation of Humanists sat at the feet of Byzantine masters. The first was Chrysoloras, who was sent to Italy on a political mission and settled in 1397 as a teacher of his own language at Florence. When he died, at the Council of Constance, there were Italian scholars who could read Greek MSS. As teachers were scarce, adventurous men, such as Scarparia, Guarino, Aurispa, pursued their studies at Constantinople. Filelfo remained there for seven years, working in great libraries not yet profaned by the Turk. Before the middle of the fifteenth century Italy was peopled with migratory scholars, generally poor, and without fixed appointments, but able to rouse enthusiasm when they offered Plato for Henry of Ghent, and Thucydides for Vincent of Beauvais. By that time the superiority of the new learning, even in its very fragmentary condition, was irresistible.

Just then three events occurred which determined the triumph of the Renaissance. The Emperor came over to the Council of Florence with a number of bishops and divines. In the discussions that followed, Greek scholars were in demand; and one Eastern prelate, Bessarion, remained in Italy, became a cardinal, and did much for the study of Plato and the termination of the long Aristotelian reign. His fine collection of manuscripts was at the service of scholars, and is still at their service, in St. Mark's library at Venice. The fall of Constantinople drove several fugitives to seek a refuge in Italy, and some brought their books with them, which were more scarce and more needful than men. For by that time Greek studies were well established, and suffered only from the extreme scarcity of manuscripts. The third important event was the election of Parentucelli, who became Pope Nicholas V. On that day the new learning took possession of the Holy See, and Rome began to be considered the capital of the Renaissance.

It was not in the nature of things that this should be. For the new men, with their new instrument of intellectual power, invaded territory which was occupied by the clergy. In the Middle Ages the Church, that is to say, first the cloister, then the universities founded under the protectorate of the Church, had the civilising of society, and, apart from law, the monopoly of literature. That came to an end when the clergy lost the superiority of knowledge, and had to share their influence with profane laymen, trained in the classics, and more familiar with pagan than with Christian writers. There was a common presumption in favour of the new point of view, the larger horizon, of opinions that were founded on classical as well as on Christian material. The Humanists had an independent judgment and could contemplate the world they lived in from outside, without quitting it, standing apart from the customary ways. As Pater said : " The human mind wins for itself a new kingdom of feeling and sensation and thought, not opposed to, but only beyond and independent of the spiritual system then actually realised."

This is one of many causes operating at the time to weaken the notion of ecclesiastical control. It was the triumphant return of an exile, with an uproarious popularity and a claim to compensation for arrears. The enthusiasm of those who were the first to read Homer, and Sophocles, and Plato grew into complaint against those by whose neglect such treasures had been lost. Centuries of ignorance and barbarism had been the consequence. There was not only a world of new ideas, but of ideas that were not Christian, which the Christianity of the West had discarded. They began to recover the lost power, and the ages in which they had been unknown became the ages of darkness. As they were also ages in which the Church had exerted supreme authority, antagonism was not to be averted. The endeavour was not only to make the range of men's thought more comprehensive, but to enrich it with the rejected wisdom of paganism. Religion occupied a narrower space in the new views of life than in those of Dante and the preceding

time. The sense of sinfulness was weaker among the
Humanists, the standard of virtue was lower ; and this
was common to the most brilliant of the Italian prelates,
such as Aeneas Sylvius, with the king of the Renaissance,
Erasmus himself.

Lorenzo Valla, the strongest of the Italian Humanists,
is also the one who best exhibits the magnitude of the
change that was going on in the minds of men. He
had learnt to be a critic, and, what was more rare, a
historical critic. He wrote against the belief in the
writings of Dionysius the Areopagite, which was one of
the fixed positions of theology, then and long after.
When the Greeks at the Council of Florence declared
themselves unacquainted with the Apostles' Creed, Valla
warned the Latins not to speak of it as an apostolic
composition. During a war between Rome and Naples,
Valla, in the Neapolitan service, attacked the Donation of
Constantine as the basis of the temporal power, and
exhorted Pope Eugenius to abandon what was a usurpation, and a usurpation founded on fraud. Formidable in
all the armour of the new learning, he did more than any
other man to spread the conviction that the favourite
arguments of the clergy were destined to go down before
the better opinion of profane scholars. Valla is also the
link between Italy and Germany. His critical essay on
the New Testament in the Vulgate influenced Erasmus,
who published it in 1505. His tract against the Donation,
as the title-deed of the temporal sovereignty, was printed
by Ulrich von Hutten, and spread that belief that the
Pope was antichrist, which was afterwards an important
article of the Huguenot Church. He was also a forerunner of the Reformation by his tract on the Freedom
of the Will. This man, who displayed so conspicuously
the resentful and iconoclastic spirit, the religious scepti-
cism, the moral indifference, the aversion for the papal
sovereignty, the contempt for the laws and politics of
feudalism, the hope and expectation of a mighty change,
was an official in the Pope's household.

After the discussion with the Greeks at Florence it

was clear to all men that there was a deeper issue than the revival of classical learning, that there was a Christian as well as a pagan antiquity, and that the knowledge of the early Church depended on Greek writings, and was as essential a part of the Renaissance as the study of Homer or of Pindar.   The inference was drawn by Nicholas V., the first Renaissance pontiff.   He recognised the fact that a divine in full possession of Hellenic literature would be a more competent defender of tradition, a better writer, a stronger disputant, than the long line of scholastic teachers.   He saw that it would be the means of renovating theology and disclosing the authentic and necessary evidences of historical religion.   The most enlightened ecclesiastics of that age understood but vaguely that there was not only benefit and enrichment in a policy that favoured the new learning, but the only possible escape from a serious danger.

Religious knowledge in those days suffered not only from ignorance and the defect of testimony, but from an excess of fiction and falsification.   Whenever a school was lacking in proofs for its opinions, it straightway forged them, and was sure not to be found out.   A vast mass of literature arose, which no man, with medieval implements, could detect, and effectually baffled and deceived the student of tradition.   At every point he was confronted by imaginary canons and constitutions of the apostles, acts of Councils, decretals of early Popes, writings of the Fathers from St. Clement to St. Cyril, all of them composed for the purpose of deceiving.

The example of Lorenzo Valla made it certain that all this was about to be exposed.   The process that began with him lasted for two centuries, to the patriarchs of authentic erudition, Ussher and Pearson, Blondel and Launoy, the Bollandists of Antwerp and the Benedictines of Saint-Maur.   It became apparent that the divines of many ages had been remarkable for their incapacity to find out falsehood, and for their dexterity in propagating it, and it made no little difference whether this tremendous exposure should be made by enemies, and should constitute one series of disasters for religion. This was prevented by the resolve of Pope Nicholas, that the Holy See should sanction and encourage the movement with its influence, its immense patronage, and all its opportunities. Therefore Valla, who had narrowly escaped alive from the Inquisition, became a functionary at the Vatican, and received 500 ducats from the Pope to translate Thucydides. Scholars were attracted by the papal collection of 5000 manuscripts, which were the foundation of the Vatican library, the first in the world after the fall of Constantinople.

The alliance between renovated Hellenism and the Papacy was ratified a few years later, when the most intelligent of the Italian Humanists, Aeneas Sylvius Piccolomini of Siena, was raised to the throne under the name of Pius II., and became the most modern of medieval Popes. He was one of those Churchmen in whom the classical spirit of the time predominated over the ecclesiastical. Twice there was a breach, and a momentary reaction; but on the whole the contract was observed, and the ancient pagans made their way under the shadow of St. Peter's better than the early Christians. Humanists of the type of Valla were domesticated by the prizes held out to them, from the pen of the secretary to the tiara of the pontiff. The apprehended explosion never came; the good and evil that was in the new scholars penetrated the court and modified its tone. Bibbiena's comedies were applauded at the Belvedere; *The Prince* was published by the Pope's printer, with the Pope's permission; a cardinal shrank from reading St. Paul, for fear of spoiling his style; and the scandals in the family of Borgia did not prevent bishops from calling him a god. Calixtus III. said that he feared nothing from any hostile Powers, for he had three thousand men of letters to rely on. His successor, Aeneas Sylvius, considered that the decline of the empire was due to the fact that scholarship had gone over to the Papacy. The main fact in the Italian Renaissance is that an open conflict was averted at the cost of admitting into the hierarchy something of the profane spirit

of the new men, who were innovators but not reformers.
Ficino declares that there was no place where liberty prevailed as it did at Rome.   Poggio, the mocking adversary
of the clergy, was for half a century in the service of the
Popes.   Filelfo was handsomely rewarded by Nicholas for
satires which would now be considered scarcely fit for publication.   Aeneas Sylvius laughed at the Donation of Constantine, and wrote an account of his own Conclave in the
tone of a *fin de siècle* journalist.   He is indeed the founder
of freedom of speech in History.   When his History of
his own time was published, a great number of passages
injurious to his countrymen and to his ecclesiastical
brethren had to be suppressed.   They have been printed
lately, and contain, in fifty pages, the concentrated essence
of the wickedness of Italy.   Platina wrote an angry and
vindictive History of the Popes, and presented it to Sixtus
IV., who made him librarian of the Vatican.   Erasmus,
who had no sort of clerical bias, warmly extols the light
and liberty which he found at Rome in 1515, at the very
eve of the Reformation.

There were branches of classical philology in which
the Renaissance was backward.   The general purpose was
to set up Plato in the place of Aristotle, discredited as
an accomplice of the obscurest schoolmen.   Under the
Medici, a Platonic academy flourished at Florence, with
Ficino and Politian at its head.   But there was a tendency
to merge Plato in Neoplatonism, and to bridge over what
separated him from Christianity.   Neither the knowledge
of Plato, nor the knowledge of the Gospel, profited by the
endeavour.   The only branch of literature in which the
Renaissance gave birth to real classics, equal to the
ancients, was politics.   The medieval theory of politics
restrained the State in the interest of the moral law, of
the Church, and of the individual.   Laws are made for the
public good, and, for the public good, they may be
suspended.   The public good is not to be considered, if
it is purchased at the expense of an individual.   Authorities are legitimate if they govern well.   Whether they do
govern well those whom they govern must decide   The

unwritten law reigns supreme over the municipal law. Modern sentiments such as these could not be sustained in the presence of indifference to religion, uncertainty as to another world, impatience of the past, and familiarity with Hellenistic thought. As the Church declined the ancient State appeared, a State which knew no Church, and was the greatest force on earth, bound by no code, a law to itself. As there is no such thing as right, politics are an affair of might, a mere struggle for power. Such was the doctrine which Venice practised, in the interest of a glorious and beneficent government, and which two illustrious writers, Machiavelli and Guicciardini, made the law of modern societies.

The one thing common to the whole Italian Renaissance was the worship of beauty. It was the æsthetic against the ascetic. In this exclusive study, that is, in art, the Italians speedily attained the highest perfection that has been reached by man. And it was reached almost simultaneously in many parts of Italy, Rome, Florence, Milan, and Venice. First, it was the triumph of classical over medieval models, and the suppression of Gothic. Then it was the outbreak of modern painting, beyond all models, medieval or ancient, in a generation of men remarkable for originality. Rome, which had adopted the new learning under the impulse of Nicholas V., went over also to the new art and became its metropolis. It was the ripest and most brilliant work of the time, and it was employed to give expression to religious ideas, and to decorate and exalt the dignity of the Papacy, with its headquarters at the Vatican. The man who conceived how much might be done by renascent art to give splendour to the Church at the moment when its terrestrial limits were immeasurably extended, and its political power newly established, was Julius II. In 1505 Emmanuel of Portugal, inspired by the prodigies of that epoch of discovery, and by the language of recent canonists, addressed him in these terms: "Receive, at last, the entire globe, thou who art our god."

Julius, who, by the energy of his will and his passion for posthumous fame, was the true son of the Renaissance, asked Michael Angelo to construct a monument worthy of a pontiff who should surpass all his predecessors in glory.   When the design proved too gigantic for any existing Church, he commanded Bramante to pull down the Basilica of Constantine, which for a thousand years had witnessed the dramatic scenes of ecclesiastical history, the coronation of Charlemagne, the enthronement of the dead Formosus, the arrest of Paschal, and to erect in its place a new and glorified St. Peter's, far exceeding all the churches of the universe in its dimensions, in beauty, in power over the imagination of men.   The ruthless destruction indicates the tone of the new era.   Old St. Peter's was not only a monument of history, but a sepulchre of saints.

Julius was not inspired by the Middle Ages.   Under him the Papacy was preparing for a new career, less spiritual than what once had been, more politic and secular and splendid, under new stars.   He had Bramante, Michael Angelo, Rafael, San Gallo, Peruzzi, a concentration of artistic genius such as had never been, not produced by Rome itself, but attracted from every quarter by the master of Rome.   What had been, one hundred years before, a neglected provincial town, became the centre of European civilisation by the action of the Popes, and principally of one ambitious Pope.   The Vatican paintings were largely political, commemorating the sovereign more than the priest, until St. Peter's was designed to exhibit the sublime grandeur and unity of the universal Church, and the authority of its head upon earth.   It was the crowning triumph of the Renaissance. When he was dying, Julius said that the masses are impressed not by what they know, but by what they see.   He transmitted to his successors the conception of a Church to be the radiant centre of religion and of art for mankind ; and we shall see that this was, after all, a disastrous legacy.

The Renaissance, which was at its height in Italy

after the middle of the fifteenth century, was checked
by the wars of Charles V., the siege of Rome, and the
Spanish domination.   Toward 1540 Paolo Giovio says
that scholarship had migrated from the Italians to the
Germans ; and the most learned Italian of the next
generation, Baronius, knew no Greek.   Before its decline
in Italy it had found new homes beyond the Alps,
especially in Germany.   The Germans adopted the new
learning much later, near a century later than the
Italians, when an occasional student, such as Agricola
and Reuchlin, visited Bologna or Rome.   It spread
slowly.   Of the seventeen universities, some, such as
Vienna, Heidelberg, Erfurt, admitted the new studies ;
others, like Cologne, resisted.   There was not the
patriotic sentiment, the national enthusiasm.   It was the
importation of a foreign element, the setting up of an
old enemy, the restoration of a world the Germans,
under Alaric and Theodoric, had overthrown.   They
began with the invention of printing, which exactly
coincided with the fall of Constantinople, as the earliest
specimens of print are indulgences for the Turkish war.
This gave assurance that the work of the Renaissance
would last, that what was written would be accessible
to all, that such an occultation of knowledge and ideas
as had depressed the Middle Ages would never recur,
that not an idea would be lost.   They got their classics
generally from Italy ; but after Aldus had published his
series of ancient writers, still treasured by those whom
Greek contractions do not repel, the New Testament and
the Fathers, edited by Erasmus, were printed at Bâle by
Froben and Amerbach.

The pagan spirit, the impatience of Christianity,
appears only in one or two Germans, such as Mutianus
Rufus, who kept his convictions to himself.   There were
no great theologians, but there was the greatest religious
writer that ever lived, the author of the *Imitation*, and he
was not a solitary thinker, but a member of a congregation
which kept religion alive, especially in North Germany.
The opposition which arose was stronger and more defined

than anything in Italy, but it was against Catholicism, not against Christianity.

The only matter in which German philology surpassed Italian was science. The man who turned the course of the new learning into those channels was Johannes Müller of Königsberg, near Coburg, therefore known as Monteregio; as Regiomontanus Bessarion gave him a MS. of Ptolemy, and he designed a scheme to print the whole body of Greek mathematicians. His *Ephemerides* are the origin of the *Nautical Almanack*, and enabled Columbus and Vasco and Vespucci to sail the high seas; and Nuremberg, where he lived, became the chief seat of the manufacture of nautical instruments. He was made a bishop, and summoned to Rome to reform the calendar. There was one Italian who possessed the scientific spirit, without help from books, by the prerogative of genius; that was Leonardo da Vinci. But he confided his thoughts to diaries and note-books, which are now in process of publication, but which remained unknown and useless in his time.

The conflict between the new learning and the old, which was repressed in Italy by the policy of Rome, broke out in Germany, where it was provoked by the study of Hebrew, not of Greek. At Rome in 1482 a German student translated a passage of Thucydides so well that the lecturer complained that Greece was settling beyond the Alps. It was the first time that the rivalry appeared. That student was Reuchlin. His classical accomplishments alone would not have made his name one of the most conspicuous in literary history; but in 1490 Pico della Mirandola expounded to him the wonders of oriental learning, and Reuchlin, having found a Rabbi at Linz, began to study Hebrew in 1492. His path was beset with difficulties, for there were no books in that language to be found in all Germany. Reuchlin drew his supply from Italy, and was the first German who read the Cabbala. He shared many popular prejudices against the Jews, and read their books to help him with the Old Testament, as he read Greek to help him with the New. He had none of the grace, the dexterity, the passion, of the Humanists, and very little of their enthusiasm for the classics. He preferred Gregory Nazianzen to Homer. Savonarola shocked him by his opposition to Alexander VI. His writings had little scientific value , but he was a pioneer, and he prized the new learning for the sake of religion. Therefore, when he was summoned to give an opinion on the suppression of Jewish books, he opposed it, and insisted on the biblical knowledge and the religious ideas to be found in them. Divines, he said, would not have made so many mistakes if they had attended to the Jewish commentators.

At that time persecution was raging against the Jews in the Peninsula. They had always had enemies in the German towns, and in July 1510, thirty-eight Jews were executed at Berlin. This intolerant spirit began, in 1507, to be directed against their books. None were printed in Germany until 1516; but from 1480 they had Hebrew presses in Italy, at Naples, Mantua, Soncino, and at Constantinople. If their study was encouraged while the printing was permitted, the Jews would become a power such as they never were before printing began, and when none but a few divines could read Hebrew. The movement in favour of destroying them had its home at Cologne, with Hochstraten, the Inquisitor ; Gratius, a good scholar, whose work, known as *Brown's Fasciculus*, is in the hands of every medieval student ; and Pfefferkorn, who had the zeal of a recently converted Jew. In his anxiety to bring over his former brethren he desired to deprive them of their books. He would allow them to retain only the Old Testament, without their commentaries. He would compel them to hear Christian sermons. By degrees he urged that they should be expelled, and at last that they should be exterminated.

Maximilian, the emperor, turned with every wind. Reuchlin, the defender of toleration, was attacked by Pfefferkorn as a sceptic and a traitor, and was accused before the ecclesiastical court. In 1514 the Bishop of Spires, acting for the Pope, acquitted Reuchlin ; the sentence was confirmed at Rome in 1516, and the Dominicans, who were plaintiffs, agreed to pay the costs. Nevertheless they appealed, and in 1520 Rome reversed the previous judgment and condemned Reuchlin. In the midst of greater things the sentence escaped attention, and was only brought to light by a scholar who is still living. But in the meantime the Humanists had taken up the cause of Reuchlin, and the result had been disastrous for the Dominicans. They had not directly assailed the new learning, but their attack on the study of Hebrew had been the most crass exhibition of retrograde spirit. If Jews were not allowed to read Jewish books, such as Maimonides, to whom St. Thomas owes so much, how could Christians be allowed to read pagan classics, with their highly immoral gods and goddesses?

The golden opportunity of making intolerance ridiculous could not be neglected. In the summer of 1515 a volume appeared purporting to contain letters to Ortwin Gratius; and it was followed two years later by another. With some good satire and some amusing caricature, they also contained much personal insult and calumny. The wit is not enough to carry on the joke through 108 letters, carefully composed in Teutonic dog Latin by the best Latinists north of the Brenner. Erasmus, who was diverted at first, afterwards turned away with disgust, and Luther called the authors buffoons. The main writer of the first volume was Crotus Rubianus, and of the other, Hutten. Reuchlin himself disapproved. But he shared in the victory, which was so brilliant that his condemnation by Rome passed without notice, and it was not till our day that the success of the despised Pfefferkorn became known to the world. It was the first effective appeal to opinion against constituted authority, and the most decisive demonstration of the power of the press. And it gave the Humanists occasion so to define the issue that all could understand, in spite of the reserve of Erasmus and of Reuchlin himself.

Erasmus Rogers, the greatest figure in the Renaissance, was born at Rotterdam and brought up in extreme poverty, and he was a valetudinarian and an invalid in consequence of early privation. He lived in France and Belgium, in England and Italy, in Switzerland and Germany, so that each country contributed to his development, and none set its stamp upon him. He was eminently an international character ; and was the first European who lived in intimacy with other ages besides his own, and could appreciate the gradual ripening and enlargement of ideas. He devoted himself on equal terms to classical and to Christian antiquity, and drew from both alike the same lessons of morality and wisdom ; for he valued doctrine chiefly for the sake of a good life and a happy death, and was impatient of subtle dialectics and speculative disputations. With so much of Renaissance studies as did not serve the good estate of souls he showed little sympathy, and was indifferent to art, to metaphysics, to antiquarian pedantry. He endeavoured to make men familiar with the wisdom of the ancients by a collection of 1451 adages selected from their works. His *Colloquies*, the most popular book of his age, sold in 24,000 copies. At first he was more a scholar than a divine ; and though he learnt Greek late, and was never a first-rate Hellenist, published editions of the classics. In later life the affairs of religion absorbed him, and he lived for the idea that the reform of the Church depended on a better knowledge of early Christianity, in other words, on better self-knowledge, which could only result from a slow and prolonged literary process. He started from the beginning by his edition of the Greek Testament, begun here, at Queens', in 1512, published at Bâle by Froben in 1516. It had already been printed from better MSS. by Cardinal Ximenes in the fifth volume of the *Complutensian Polyglot*, which did not appear until 1522. Therefore Erasmus's edition is the first ever published. It was produced at last, in a hurry, to secure the priority, and was not greatly improved afterwards. Part of the Apocalypse was wanting in all his MSS. He restored it by translating it into Greek from the Vulgate, and in six verses made thirty mistakes. His second edition had a letter of approbation from Leo X., and it was the edition which Luther used for his translation. It is a sign of the want of religious interest in the Renaissance, especially in Italy, that printing had been going on for sixty years, and 24,000 works issued from the press, some of them more than a hundred times, before anybody thought of the Greek Testament.

Erasmus occupied his later years with the works of the Fathers, also printed by Froben, the Greeks in Latin translations. " Letters," he said, " had remained Pagan in Italy, until he taught them to speak of Christ." Just as he was entirely destitute of the national fibre, so too he stood apart from the schools or currents of his time. His striving was to replace the scholastics by the Fathers, systematic theology by spiritual religion ; and those Doctors of the Church who inclined to system, such as St. Augustine, repelled him. It may be said that he was not attracted by St. Paul, and preferred the Gospels to the Epistles. He esteemed Seneca more highly than many Christian divines. Although he chose to employ the weapon of irony, and abstained from the high horse and the big word, he was earnest in his desire for the reform of abuses in the Church. He disliked contention, and desired to avoid offence ; but he made enemies in all parts of Europe, and was vehemently denounced by the theologians of Paris and Louvain, by the Spanish friars, by Archbishop Lee, by Zuñiga, the Count of Carpi, and especially by the very learned Steuchus of Gubbio. In later days he was one of the first writers put on the Index. But throughout his career as a divine, that is, for the last quarter of a century that he lived, he was consistently protected, defended, consulted by Popes, until Paul III. offered him a Cardinal's hat and desired that he would settle at Rome. He told Leo X. that he thought it a mistake to censure Luther, with whom he agreed as to many of the matters calling for reform. But whilst Luther attributed the prevailing demoralisation to false dogmas and a faulty constitution, Erasmus sought the cause in ignorance and misgovernment. What came from this division of opinion pertains to the next lecture. Erasmus belonged, intellectually, to a later and more scientific or rational age. The work which he had initiated, and which was interrupted by the Reformation troubles, was resumed at a more acceptable time by the scholarship of the seventeenth century.

IV

LUTHER

DURING the latter part of the Middle Ages, the desire for reform of the Church was constant. It was strongest and most apparent among laymen, for a famous monastic writer of the fourteenth century testified that the laity led better lives than the clergy. To the bulk of ordinary Christians reform meant morality in the priesthood. It became intolerable to them to see the Sacrament administered habitually by sacrilegious hands, or to let their daughters go to confession to an unclean priest. The discontent was deepest where men were best. They felt that the organisation provided for the salvation of souls was serving for their destruction, and that the more people sought the means of grace in the manner provided, the greater risk they incurred of imbibing corruption. In the days when celibacy was imposed under Gregory VII., it was argued that the validity of orders depended on conduct; and that idea of forfeiture by sin, essentially fatal to the whole hierarchical system, was not yet extinct. People learnt to think of virtue apart from the institutions of the Church, and the way was paved for a change which should reduce the part of the clergy in men's lives, and give them families of their own. The hope that a stricter discipline would be enforced by authority from within died away. When Eugenius IV. directed Cesarini to dissolve the Council of Bâle, the Cardinal replied that if he obeyed they would be thought to be mocking God and men, and to have abandoned the notion of reform, and the laity would have some reason to believe that it was a good deed to destroy, or at least to plunder, the clergy.

The religious influence of the Church was brought low by its record of failure. The scheme for governing the world by the hierarchy, pursued for three centuries, had terminated in disaster. For a whole generation no man knew whether the Papacy was in Italy or in France. The attempt to effect improvement through the Councils had been abandoned after many experiments, and the failure to reconcile the Greeks had established the Ottoman Empire in Europe. With the decline of the Church the State rose in power and prerogative, and exercised rights which for centuries had been claimed by the hierarchy. All this did not suggest Lutheranism to Luther, but it prepared the world for it.

Amidst the abuses and excesses of that epoch of lax discipline and indistinct theology, the point of breaking was supplied by a practice of very recent growth. Indulgences had long existed, and after a time they were applied to souls in purgatory. When, at last, plenary indulgences, that is, total remissions of penalty, were transferred to the dead, it meant that they were straightway released from purgatory and received into heaven. Five churches in Rome enjoyed the privilege that a soul was released as often as mass was said at one of the altars, technically known as privileged altars, or as often as certain prayers were said by persons visiting them. There were privileged altars at St. Peter's, at St. Prassede, at Santa Pudentiana, at the Scala Santa. At one, five masses were required; at another, thirty. In the crypt of St. Sebastian one visit was enough. A particular prayer repeated during forty days remitted one-seventh of the punishment, and on the fortieth day the dead man would appear to his benefactor, to thank him. All the benefits available to a pilgrim visiting Rome could be enjoyed at a distance by the purchase of an indulgence from the friars sent round to sell them. Such an indulgence, published by Julius II. for the construction of St. Peter's, was revived by Leo X. in

1517, half the proceeds to go to the Archbishop of
Mentz, that he might pay back a loan to Fugger of
Augsburg. The banker's agent went round with the
appointed preacher and kept the strong box. Tetzel, a
Dominican, preached the indulgence in Saxony, though
not in the territory of the elector, and he employed to the
utmost the arguments authorised by the custom of the
day. Speaking of him and of his colleagues, Benedict
XIV. said that they were the cause of all the trouble that
followed.

Many people thought the indulgences, as then practised,
a mischief, because people took them as equivalent to
absolution ; and the general of the Augustinians spoke of
them as an encouragement to sin. But the extreme
point was the theory that payment of a few pence would
rescue a soul from purgatory. Therefore, when Luther
raised a protest against such propositions, he said no
more than what many other people were saying, and
less than some. And he had no idea that he was not
speaking in thorough harmony with the entire Church, or
that the ground he occupied was new. The Dominicans
stood by Tetzel and made his cause their own. They
were able to say of him that he had only uttered current
doctrine, though it had not the sanction of former ages.
Three hundred of them were present when he received a
degree at Frankfort on the Oder, and the Dominicans at
Rome defended even the most extreme and grotesque of
the sayings attributed to him.

Leo committed the whole business to Silvester Prierias,
Master of the Sacred Palace and official theologian of
the Holy See. Prierias was not a reputable defender of
any religious cause. In one of his books he advises a
judge that he may obtain a confession by a promise of
mercy, meaning mercy to the community, and charges
the notary to put down in what sense the words were
spoken. Accordingly he made the worst possible defence.
St. Thomas, discussing indulgences as they were in his
time, urges that they may be accepted as they are given
by authority. Prierias, an ardent Thomist, regards this

as a valid argument for the practices that were now contested. The problem of right is settled by the evidence of fact. The questors, as they were called, acted as legitimate agents of the Holy See. To deny what authority tacitly approves, is to deny authority; and to appeal from the Pope to the Bible, is to appeal from a higher authority to a lower. This was to ignore the difficulty and to make reforms impossible. The reason for this compendious evasion was that Leo, prior to his election, had taken an oath to revoke the indulgence of Julius II., and to supply otherwise the money required for St. Peter's. The capitulation was in March 1513. The breach of the capitulation, in March 1515. It was not desirable to raise a controversy as to the broken oath, or to let Luther appear as the supporter of the cardinals against the Pope, or of the Pope expecting the tiara against the Pope in possession of it. The effect was to deprive Luther of the hope that he was at issue with a too eager subordinate in Saxony, and to transfer his attack to Rome. It was now officially declared that whatever is is right, and that no improvement or reform is wanted in high places.

A graver personage came upon the scene when it was agreed that Luther should appear before the Legate at Augsburg. Cardinal Cajetan was the weightiest divine of the Court of Rome, and a man of original mind, who was denounced in his order as a dangerous innovator, and whose writings could not be reprinted without large omissions. He is commemorated, in political literature, among the advocates of tyrannicide. He was more dexterous than Prierias, although he also refused a revision of current practices. By putting forward a decree of Clement VI., he drove Luther to declare that no papal decree was a sufficient security for him. So that, having assailed authority in that which it tolerated or ignored, he assailed it now in that which it directly affirmed, and was no longer a mere intruder, proffering unwelcome advice, but a barbarian thundering at the gates of Rome. Cajetan dismissed him ungraciously; and having been warned that a Dominican cardinal might be perilous company in the circumstances, he went off secretly and made his way home. He was already a popular figure in Germany, and the Diet of Augsburg had complained that the drain caused by indulgences left no supplies for the Turkish war.

When Luther returned to Wittenberg he was aware that his ideas extended much farther than he had supposed. Since the refusal to listen to his remonstrance, he knew that he was involved in a conflict in which Rome would be against him. He knew also that many of his countrymen would be on his side. The same discovery was unexpectedly made by the next papal emissary, Miltitz, a Saxon layman, who was sent to convey the Golden Rose to Luther's patron, the elector Frederic. It was well understood at Rome that Cajetan, in pushing Luther one step beyond his original Thesis, by transferring the question from the discretion of Tetzel to the authority under which he acted, had mismanaged the affair. Uncompromising rigour having failed, the opposite treatment was now applied. Miltitz, finding the majority of Germans favourable to Luther, deposited the Golden Rose at Nuremberg, and came into his own country with a resolution to be conciliatory. The friends whom he saw on his way informed Luther, and urged him to meet his countryman in the same spirit. Miltitz saw Tetzel and silenced him ; and the inauspicious preacher did not long survive his disgrace. Having given this proof that he entertained no adverse prejudice, that on the immediate problem they were in sympathy, Miltitz had a conference with Luther at Altenburg.

Luther followed the advice of his friends at Nuremberg. The specific evil he had denounced was now admitted by the authorised representative of the Holy See. He obtained, through him, a reassuring glimpse of Roman opinion, and the certainty that there were men on the spot, unlike Prierias and Cajetan, whose convictions in regard to unreformed abuses were as clear as his own, and whose opportunities were better. They came to an understanding. Luther was to publish an explanation and then the subject was to drop. It did not mean that he was approved; but dubious points were not pressed, for the sake of those on which the force of his case was felt. He wrote to a friend that he would suppress much rather than offend, and the whole thing would die out of itself. The contrast between Miltitz and Cajetan was such that he had reason to be satisfied. Miltitz also considered that he had done well, and had extinguished a conflagration that might have become serious. He advised the Elector not to send the Wittenberg professor out of the country. More eager spirits were impatient of so tame a conclusion; for there were some to whom plenary indulgences for the living or the dead were a drop of water in an ocean of controversy, whilst others thought that authority had been outraged on one side and surrendered on the other. Before the dispute was reopened Luther wrote a letter to Leo X., saying the ecclesiastical authority must be upheld to the utmost. This saying, of little account in his theology, is significant in his entire system of thought. What he meant was that the papal supremacy in the government of the Church had endured so long that the divine sanction was upon it. He did not trace it much farther back than the twelfth century. But that, he considered, constituted a legitimate claim.

Luther, who was a profound conservative and a reluctant innovator, and who felt the fascination that belongs to lapse of time, employed in behalf of the Papacy an argument by which Dante had defended the Empire. Machiavelli derived right from success, and Luther from duration. In reality he held both doctrines, for he thought Zwingli's death in battle an evident judgment on his low sacramental theory. Promoted at the same time by the two most powerful writers in the world, the idea that heaven is responsible for results acquired immense prestige, and long influenced European thinking. The argument by which he justified the Papacy amounted, in fact, to a negation of its claim to divine institution; and at the time when he produced it, early in 1519, he had come to reject not only the excesses of Tetzel, but the entire scheme of indulgences. Although he held to the Papacy only by an ingenious sophism, beyond the Pope there was the Council ; and he might still deem himself a Catholic after the manner of Gerson and the Gallican divines of Constance, who depreciated Rome. That was possible, if nothing in the sequence of his views came into collision with any decree of a General Council.

This was now the question of the day, the question for the summer of 1519. The man who brought it to an issue was John Eck, a theologian of Ingolstadt University, who came to Leipzig to dispute with Luther's colleague Carlstadt, and ended by a disputation with Luther himself. He imagined that Luther did not perceive the consequences. Because he defied the Popes, it did not follow that he would defy the Councils, especially a Council held in Germany, under the protection of a German Emperor a Council zealous for reform and honoured by Germans, as their avenger on the national enemy John Hus. Luther had no special preference for an assembly which burnt an obnoxious professor of theology, and no great interest in reforms which he deemed external, and not making for inward change. He said that there were points on which Hus was right, and the sentence that condemned him wrong. He admitted, in the end, that Councils as well as Popes might be against him, and that the authority by which he stood was the divine revelation. That is how " the Bible, and the Bible only," became the religion of Protestants.

Having succeeded in forcing Luther from his original positions, Eck carried the matter to Rome. A theory so uncertain in its method, so imperfectly tested by the regulated comparison of authorities, might crumble to pieces if all its consequences were made manifest. It was conceivable that a man who had raised such a storm without looking up his books, without weighing the language of Councils or thinking out his thoughts, upon whom the very obvious objections of Cajetan and Eck came as a surprise, who at every step abandoned some

previous proposition, might not feel absolutely and finally
sure that he was right, or might even recognise the force
of the saying that it is well to die for the truth, but not
for every truth. Eck joined with Cajetan in urging the
strongest measures of repression. A different line of
policy suggested itself, in the spirit of Erasmus. It was
to hail Luther as an auxiliary, as the most powerful
leader in the work of eradicating evils which were a
familiar scandal to all religious men, and the constant
theme of ineffective Cardinals on every solemn occasion
Then they might have confronted whatever was to follow
with cleaner hands and a better conscience.

In June 1520, after a year's deliberation, Luther was
condemned as the teacher of forty-one heresies ; and in
January, after he had made a bonfire of the Papal Bull
and of the Canon Law, he was excommunicated. According to imperial constitutions three centuries old, the
next step was that the civil magistrate, as the favourite
phrase was, would send the culprit through the transitory
flames of this world to the everlasting flames of the next.
If that was not done, it might come to pass that the zeal
of Prierias, Cajetan, and Eck would serve to inform the
world that the medieval reign was over, and that the pen
of an angry, rude, and not very learned monk was stronger
than the Papacy and the Empire. It was known from
the first that the Elector of Saxony would defend Luther,
without being a Lutheran. Indeed, he shocked him by
his zeal for indulgences and his collection of 19,000
relics. But he protected Luther as the most famous
teacher of his university. They never met, and when
the Elector on his deathbed sent for him, Luther was
away. Since the Disputation of Leipzig he was the most
conspicuously popular man in Germany. What he had
said about the use and abuse of indulgences had not
inflamed the nation. But the appeal to Scripture was
definite and clear, and it met many objections and many
causes of opposition.

When Luther was discussing the value of indulgences
here and in the other world he meant no more and saw

no farther.   But now he saw the chasm, and possessed a principle on which to found his theology, his ethics, his politics, his theory of Church and State, and he proceeded to expound his ideas thoroughly in three celebrated works, known as his *Reformation Tracts*, which appeared in 1520. Luther's fundamental doctrine had come to him in early life, not from books, but from a friend.   When all the efforts and resources of monastic criticism had led him only to despair, one of the brethren told him that his own works could not bring relief from the sense of unforgiven sin, but only faith in the merits of Christ.   He found such comfort in this idea, which became the doctrine of imputation, and he grasped it with such energy that it has transformed the world.   Predestination seemed to follow logically, and the rejection of free-will ; and, as the office of the ordained priest became superfluous, the universal priesthood, with the denial of Prelacy.   All this was fully worked out in the writings of 1520.

Luther was unconscious at first of the tremendous revolution he was preparing, because he found satisfaction in the strong language of St. Bernard.   Under the shadow of the greatest doctor of the medieval church he felt assured of safety.   And when he spoke of the Bible only, that was not textually more than had been said by Scotus and others, such as Erasmus, and quite lately the Bishop of Isernia at the Lateran Council.   He did not start with a system or an apostolate ; but now that his prodigious power as a writer of German had been revealed, he rejoiced in the conflict.   He obtained his opportunity at the Diet of Worms.   The young Emperor had come over from Spain to receive the crown, and he had accepted the Bull of Leo against Luther.   At that moment he was on friendly terms with Rome, but his chancellor, Gattinara, warned him that the people throughout Germany favoured the reformer ; and Tunstall wrote to Wolsey that 100,000 men would give their lives rather than let him be sacrificed to the Papacy.   Even at Mentz, an episcopal city, the Nuncio Aleander was in danger of being stoned. " The conflicts of Church and State in the Middle Ages," he wrote, " were child's play to this." Therefore, although Luther had been condemned and excommunicated for forty heresies, although he had publicly thrown the Pope's Bull into the fire, and was worthy of death by ecclesiastical and municipal law, the Emperor gave him a free pass to the Diet and back, and sent a herald to arrange the journey.

At Erfurt, on his way, he learnt for the first time how the country was with him. When within sight of the towers and spires of Worms, he was warned by the Saxon minister Spalatin that his life would not be safe ; and he returned the famous answer that he would go on if every tile in the city was a devil. At Oppenheim, almost the last stage, Bucer was waiting his arrival with a strange and unexpected message. A French Franciscan, Glapion, was the Emperor's confessor, and he was staying at Sickingen's castle, a few miles off, in company with Sickingen himself, the dreaded free-lance, with Ulrich von Hutten and with the unfrocked Dominican Bucer, who was to prove the ablest of the German reformers next to Luther. He sent Bucer, with an escort of Sickingen's troopers, to invite Luther to visit him there before he proceeded to Worms. It was clear that the Diet would end with a repulse for authority. The very presence there of a man who had written with such violence, and had been so solemnly condemned, was a defiance. Glapion was a reforming Catholic, and desired the assistance of Luther. He was clever enough to find ground in common with Erasmus, Ulrich von Hutten, and Bucer, and he was ready with far-reaching concessions to secure Luther. Then, he thought, his Emperor would be enabled to purify the Church. Bucer was of opinion that there was nothing to prevent agreement if Luther would interpret his contested writings as Bucer had explained them to Glapion. Gattinara was urgent for a reforming Council ; the union of so many forces would be enough to invigorate the Italian cardinals, and they could carry Rome with them. It was the party of Reform attempting to conciliate the party of Reformation, that they might co-operate in saving the work of the Renaissance and renewing the Church from within. By renouncing " The Babylonish Captivity" alone of his numerous writings, Luther, who had already revoked so many utterances, might obtain acceptance for his main dogma, and bind the united Humanists and the Imperial government to his cause. Those were the terms of the proposed alliance. They were at once rejected.

Luther owed much to Erasmus, but they could never combine. He looked upon the purpose of the other as essentially rationalistic, Pelagian, and pagan. He foresaw that the coming struggle would be not with the old school, but with the new; that the obstacle to the Reformation was the Renaissance, and the enemy's name Erasmus. The Franciscan's profound and dazzling scheme miscarried, and Luther appeared before the Diet. Prompted by Glapion, the Imperial spokesman took no notice of Luther's own specific views, or of the Papal Bull against them. But he invited him to dissociate himself from Wyclif and John Hus on those matters which had been censured at Constance. That Council was the venerated safeguard of Catholic and Imperial reformers, and the strongest weapon of opposition to Rome. A Council which compelled the Emperor to burn a divine alive, after giving him a safe-conduct, was in no good odour just then with Luther, standing by the waves of Rhine, which swept the ashes of John Hus away into oblivion. They then represented to Luther that the Diet was, on his side, against Roman encroachments and the theory of penance; they praised his writings generally, and proposed that unsettled matters should be left to the decision of a future Council. To this he was willing to agree. But he stipulated that there should be no judgment except by the standard of Scripture. They replied that it stood to reason, and could not be made the object of a special condition. They meant different things, and the discussion came to naught. But important concessions had been made, and many opportunities had been offered, for the Diet was drawing up "the grievances of the German nation," and for that policy he was a desirable ally. Luther declined to concede anything, and a month later the Emperor signed the sentence of outlawry. In his Spanish dominions he was a jealous upholder of the Inquisition, even against the Pope, and of all the princes at Worms, secular or ecclesiastical, he was the most hostile and the most impatient.

Meanwhile Luther had gone back to Saxony, had preached on his way to the Benedictines of Hersfeld, and then disappeared in the Thuringian Forest. It was reported that he was dead; that his body had been found with a sword through it. When Charles V. was dying, a baffled and disappointed man, he is said to have lamented that he kept his word to the turbulent friar who had triumphantly defied him. But Leo X. sent orders that the passport should be respected and that the traveller should depart in peace.

Luther at Worms is the most pregnant and momentous fact in our history, and the problem is to know why he so rigidly repelled the advances of the confessor, of the Chancellor of Baden, and the Elector of Treves. Was it simply the compelling logic of Protestantism, or was there some private saltpetre of his own, a programme drawn from his personality and habits of mind? There was no question at issue which had not either been pronounced by him insufficient for separation, or which was not abandoned afterwards, or modified in a Catholic sense by the moderating hand of Melanchthon. That happened to every leading doctrine at Augsburg, at Ratisbon, or at Leipzig. Predestination was dropped. The necessity of good works, the freedom of the will, the hierarchical constitution, the authority of tradition, the seven sacraments, the Latin mass, were admitted. Melanchthon confessed that he held all Roman doctrine, and that there was no difference except as to the celibacy of the clergy and communion under both kinds; the rest was the work of agitators; and he bitterly resented Luther's tyrannical treatment. As Melanchthon had the making of the official statements of doctrine, it would almost appear as if Luther never became a Lutheran. And the truth is that he held one doctrine which he never succeeded in imposing, and which forbade all approach and all endeavours to explain. For he believed that the Pope was anti-Christ. The idea came to him from Lorenzo Valla, whose tract on the Donation was published in 1518 by Hutten. He became convinced almost immediately after writing to Leo that deferential letter which he had agreed upon with Miltitz. It obliged him to force on a breach at Worms. His main objection to the Confession of Augsburg was that this article was excluded from it.

Under the malediction of Church and State, Luther was lost sight of for some months. He was hidden in the Wartburg, the castle of his Elector, above Eisenach, disguised as a country gentleman. He wore a moustache, dined joyously, carried a sword, and shot a buck. Although his abode was unknown, he did not allow things to drift. The Archbishop of Mentz had been a heavy loser by the arrest of his indulgence, and he took advantage of the aggressor's disappearance to issue a new one. He was friendly to Luther, and repressed preaching against him; and the Elector of Saxony ordered that the controversy should not be revived. Luther replied that he would destroy the Elector rather than obey him; the Thesis had been posted in vain, and the spirit of Tetzel was abroad once more; he gave the Archbishop a fortnight, after which he would let the world see the difference between a bishop and a wolf. The prelate gave way, and having arrested one of his priests, who had married, he consented, at the reformer's request, to release him.

The most important result of the stay at the Wartburg was the translation of the New Testament, which was begun towards the end of the year, and was completed in about three months. There were already eighteen German Bibles, and he knew some of them, for a particular blunder is copied from an edition of 1466. All those that I have seen, and I have seen nearly all in Dr.

Ginsburg's collection, are unwieldy folios. Luther's translation was published at a florin and a half, and may now be had for sixty guineas. It was reprinted eighty-five times in eleven years. The text as we know it was revised by his friends twenty years later. It was his appeal to the masses, and removed the controversy from the Church and the school to the market-place. The language had to be modified for the people of the South, and almost rewritten for the North; but it ended by impressing central German as the normal type for the whole country. It was the first translation from the Greek, and it was the work of the greatest master of German.

During the eclipse at the Wartburg Leo X. was succeeded by Adrian of Utrecht, the Regent of Spain, a man of learning and devout life, who proceeded to reverse his predecessor's policy. He addressed a Brief to the Diet at Nuremberg, saying that of all those in authority at Rome none were without reproach, and the evils from which the Church was suffering had been caused and propagated by the papal court. To this memorable exhibition of integrity his envoy added that Luther deserved to be idolised if he had been content with the exposure of abuses, and that the real offender was Leo X. This change of front removed the charge from the outer branch to the centre. Luther had been hitting the wrong man. It was now avowed that the transgressor was not an obscure itinerant, but the sovereign pontiff himself, and that Luther's adversaries were in the wrong. Adrian had been Grand Inquisitor in four kingdoms, and he moderated expectation by inviting the Germans to be worthy of the illustrious example set by their ancestors, who burnt John Hus and Jerome of Prague. Therefore Erasmus, when summoned to Rome to advise with him, declined to come. "If they were going to shed blood," he said, "he would not be wanted."

When, at the end of a year, Luther came out of his retirement, he found that the world had changed. The seed that he had scattered was coming up with variations.

His own Saxon neighbours, led by Carlstadt, were disposed to ride favourite opinions to death, with the exaggeration and exclusiveness of enthusiasts. In Switzerland, Zwingli held doctrines differing widely from his own, with a republican and aggressive spirit that was hateful to him. The Anabaptists started from his impulse, but in their earnest striving after holiness adopted principles which involved a distinct reaction towards medieval religion, and carried the multitude away. Near the Swiss frontier, Zurich encouraged an agitation among the country people, that was fomented by Lutheran and Anabaptist teachers, and broke out soon after into anticipations of 1789. Luther turned from the foe beyond the mountains to the foe within the gates, and employed himself thenceforward in repressing misconceptions of his system to men who were in some sense his disciples. Against Rome the tide was manifestly rising. The danger was on his own side. This is variously called the reversal of original principle, the great surrender, the breach between Reformation and Revolution. Luther was acquiring caution and restraint. The creative period of the Reformation was over. All the ideas by which he so deeply moved the world had been produced in the first five years. Beyond the elementary notions that govern life, he lost interest in the further pursuit of theology. "Abraham," he said, "had faith; therefore Abraham was a good Christian." What else there might be in Christianity mattered less; and nearly all metaphysical inquiry, even on the Trinity, was neglected by the German reformers.

It is the extremity of his Conservatism that has put him wrong, even with those who regard politics as quite distinct from ethics. He defended Passive Obedience; he claimed to be the inventor of Divine Right; and the constitution of the Lutheran Churches contributed even more than the revival of the Civil Law to establish the absolute sovereignty of States. He proclaimed religious liberty, believing that Rome had never persecuted; then he denounced Jews and Anabaptists, and required that there should never be two religions in the same place.

He denounced the ruling classes in his country with extreme violence ; but when the peasants rose, with their just and reasonable demands, and threatened Saxony, he issued a tract insisting that they should be cut to pieces. He valued the royal prerogative so highly that he made it include polygamy. He advised Henry VIII. that the right way out of his perplexity was to marry a second wife without repudiating the first. And when the Landgrave Philip asked for leave to do the same thing, Luther gave it on condition that it was denied. He insisted on what he called a downright lie. The great fact which we have to recognise is that with all the intensity of his passion for authority he did more than any single man to make modern History the development of revolution.

The Humanists had generally supported Luther almost from the beginning, and Melanchthon, the young Professor of Greek, proved his most useful coadjutor. They applauded his attack on abuses, and on the treatment of Germany by Rome ; and it was believed that the Renaissance prepared the Reformation, that Luther had only hatched the Erasmian egg. When the salient points of his system appeared, they began to fall away from him. Nearly all the older men among the leaders died in the Roman communion—Reuchlin, Wimpheling, Mutianus Rufus, Pirkheimer, Zasius, the best jurist in Germany, and Crotus, who wrote the *Epistolæ Obscurorum Virorum*. They were urging the mind of man along all the paths of light open to its effort, and they found the exclusiveness of the new interests an impediment to letters. Younger men remained true to the movement ; but when Erasmus defended, as he had always done, the doctrine of free-will, even Melanchthon was convinced, and imputed to his friend and master the fatalism of the Stoics. Like Fisher and More in England, many of Luther's German opponents, such as Eck and Cochlæus, were men of the Renaissance. The breach with Erasmus, the quarrel with Zwingli and his friends in the south-west, the irruption of the Anabaptists, the dispute with Carlstadt, the sacrifice of Luther's popularity among the masses, by his attack on the peasants, produced a recoil. Many of the regular clergy went over, and many towns ; but the princes and the common people were uncertain. Therefore the Catholic party gained ground at the Diet of Spires in 1529. They carried measures to prevent any further progress of the Lutherans, and it was against this restriction that certain princes and fourteen towns made the protest from which Protestantism has its name.

In the following year Melanchthon drew up the Confession of Faith for the Diet of Augsburg, while Luther remained behind at the castle of Coburg ; his purpose was to explain the essential meaning of Lutheranism, the consecutive order and connection of ideas, so as to exclude the Zwinglians and the Anabaptists, and to reconcile the Catholics. He came to an understanding with the Emperor's secretary, and Stadion, the Bishop of Augsburg, judged that his proposals were acceptable, and thought his own people blind not to coalesce with him. "We are agreed," said the Provost of Coire, "on all the articles of faith." But the divines, interested in the recovery of Church property, would not yield, and their violence had to be restrained by the Emperor. He was a very different personage from the one who had presided at Worms, for he was master now of one-half of Europe, with faculties ripened by a unique experience of affairs. When the Legate Campeggio, the Campeggio of Shakespeare and Blackfriars, exhorted him to punish the heretics with scourges of iron, he replied, "Not iron, but fire." Afterwards he said that they had been represented as worse than devils ; but his confessor had told him to see whether they contradicted the Apostles' Creed, and he found that they were no devils at all, and did not dispute any article of faith. This confessor was Cardinal Loaysa, Archbishop of Seville. We possess the letters which he wrote from Rome at the time, entreating Charles to come to terms with the Protestants, and leave them to their religion, provided they were faithful to him. Loaysa even had

an auxiliary in Pope Clement, who recommended ways
of gentleness, and wished Charles to appear in Germany
without an army. The conclusion was a truce until
a Council was held — a temporary success for the
Protestants, with a prospect of renewed peril, but no
concession of principle.

With the Diet of Augsburg the divines ceased to be
the leaders of the nation. They had played their part
when they produced an accepted statement of their
doctrine in its substance, apart from persons and policy.
They had displayed energy and moderation, but had
shown no power of governing the churches they had
founded. They fell into the background, and made way
for lay politicians. Questions of fundamental principle
disappeared, and questions of management prevailed.
Things became less spontaneous and less tumultuous as
action was guided by statesmen ; and, in defiance of
Luther, the governments assumed the direction of affairs,
and formed the League of Schmalkalden for the defence
of Protestant interests. They were preparing for civil
war, and now by degrees most of the German princes
went over.

V

THE COUNTER-REFORMATION

THE Reformation was extended and established without arousing any strong reaction among Catholics, or inspiring them with a policy. Under the influence of secular interests, profane literature and art, it was a time of slackness in spiritual life. Religious men, like the Cardinals Egidius, Carvajal, and Campeggio, knew, and acknowledged, and deplored, as sincerely as Adrian VI., the growing defects of the ill-governed Church; and at each Conclave the whole of the Sacred College bound itself by capitulations under oath to put an effective check on the excesses of the court of Rome. But at the Lateran Council the same men who had imposed on Leo the obligation to revoke the indulgences suffered them to be renewed; and those who held the language of Erasmus were confronted by a resisting body of officials for whom reform was ruin. Rome flourished on money obtained from the nations in return for ecclesiastical treasures, for promotion and patronage, for indulgences and dispensations. With the loss of Germany the sources of revenue that remained became more necessary; and it was certain that they would be damaged by reform. Chieregato, the bishop who carried to the Diet of Nuremberg that message from Adrian VI. of which I spoke in the last lecture, related in his Memoirs that there was a disposition at one moment to take Luther very seriously, and to avert peril by making the changes he suggested, but that it was decided to repel the attack. There is no other authority for the story, and we only know of it through Father

Paul, whom Macaulay admired as the best modern historian. There is a book attributed to Father Paul in which the use of poison is recommended to the Venetian government. We cannot take our history out of Newgate, and until his authorship is disproved his solitary testimony is insufficient.

While Clement VII. lived, of whom Sadolet said that he did not renounce his good intention of reforming society, but only postponed it, the idealists who aspired after a regenerated Catholicism never found their opportunity. In 1534 he was succeeded by Paul III., Farnese, a stronger if not a better man, and the change was quickly felt. The new pontiff offered a red hat to Erasmus, to Reginald Pole, who was admired by the Italians, and was supposed to have a future before him in England, being sprung from a royal stock ; to Sadolet and Cortese, and to Contarini, the finest character of them all. He appointed a Commission, chiefly consisting of these men, to advise as to things that wanted mending ; and besides their report, he received from Contarini himself private communications on the same engrossing topic. In 1541 Paul sent Contarini as his Legate to Ratisbon, where he held the famous Peace Conference with Melanchthon. The reformers of the Renaissance seemed about to prevail, and to possess the ear of the Pontiff. Their common policy was reduction of prerogative, concession in discipline, conciliation in doctrine ; and it involved the reversal of an established system. As they became powerful, and their purpose clear, another group detached itself from them, under the flag of No Surrender, and the division of opinion which had been already apparent between Cajetan and Miltitz, between the friends of Erasmus and Reuchlin, and their detractors, burst into open conflict. To men trained in the thought of the Middle Ages, with the clergy above the laity and the Pope above the king, the party that aimed at internal improvement by means the exact opposite of those which had preserved the Church in the past, were feckless enthusiasts. They reverted to the old tradition of

I

indefeasible authority wielding irresistible force; and in the person of Caraffa, Bishop of Chieti, afterwards Archbishop of Naples, cardinal, and Pope, under the name of Paul IV., they now came to the front. It was reported from Ratisbon that the Catholic negotiation, with the Legate Contarini at their head, had accepted the Lutheran doctrine of justification. Pole wrote, in his enthusiasm, that it was a truth long suppressed by the Church, now at length brought to light by his friend. Another friend of Pole, Flaminio, helped to write a book in its defence, which appeared in 1542, and of which 60,000 copies were sold immediately—indicating a popularity which no work of Luther or Erasmus had ever attained. This was the famous volume on the Benefit of the Death of Christ, which was supposed to have perished, said Macaulay, as hopelessly as the Second Decade of Livy, until it was discovered in a Cambridge library, and republished in my recollection.

Now it was these men, Pole, Contarini, and their friends Cortese and Sadolet, who dominated in the Sacred College, occupied high places, and helped to govern the policy of Rome. There were nests of Lutherans at Modena, Naples, and elsewhere; but nobody in those days knew the force of multitudes; a few cardinals caused greater alarm than all the readers of the Benefizio, and it soon appeared that the general of the Capuchins, the Bishop of Capo d'Istria, the Bishop of Modena and Nuncio in Germany, inclined the same way as the suspected cardinals. The most eminent men of the Italian clergy were steering for Wittenberg, and taking Rome with them. An uncle of the Duke of Alva, the cardinal of Sant Iago, thereupon suggested to Caraffa that the best way to save the Church was to introduce the Spanish Inquisition; and he was seconded by another Spaniard, a Basque of great note in history, of whom there will be more to tell. Caraffa, who had been Nuncio in Spain, took up the idea, urged it upon the Pope, and succeeded. What he obtained was nothing new; it belonged to the thirteenth century, and it had been the result of two forces, powerful at the time, the Crusades and the belief in witchcraft.

When the first warlike pilgrims started for Palestine at the end of the eleventh century, it occurred to some of them that without toiling so far they could find enemies of Christ, as bad as the Saracens, close at hand. So they fell upon the Jews in the north of France, along the Rhine and the Danube, and murdered them as they passed. This was done at a moment of religious fervour. And when it became known, in the same region, that there were heretics, the same cause produced the same effects, and the clergy were not always able to save them from the wrath of the populace. The many sects known by the name of Albigenses were Gnostics ; but they were better known as Manichees, for the Roman law was severe on Manichees, who were dualists, and by a dualist they meant a worshipper of the devil. Sorcery had not become epidemic and sectarian, but it was suspected occasionally in the twelfth century. We know at the present day to what horrible and loathsome rites Madame de Montespan submitted for the sake of love and hatred. That was done in the most refined and enlightened court in Europe, in the best days of the French intellect, in the home of Bossuet and Racine. It is not difficult to imagine what was believed and what was attempted in ignorant and criminal classes five centuries earlier. Now a witch was, by the hypothesis, a worshipper of the devil, and the dualists fell under the same suspicion of propitiation by sin. It was impossible to exterminate them too quickly, or to devise torments worse than they deserved.

That was the situation towards the middle of the twelfth century. There was a practice which the clergy desired to restrain, and which they attempted to organise. We see by their writings that they believed in many horrible imputations. As time went on, it appeared that much of this was fable. But it also became known that it was not all fabulous, and that the Albigensian creed culminated in what was known as the Endura, which was in reality suicide. It was the object of the Inquisition that such people should not indeed be spared, but should not perish without a trial and without opportunity of resipiscence, so that they might save their souls if not their lives. Its founders could claim to act from motives both of mercy and of justice against members of a Satanic association. And it was not against error or nonconformity simply, but against criminal error erected into a system, that the Inquisitors forged their terrific armoury. In the latter half of the fifteenth century their work was done and their occupation gone. The dread tribunal lapsed into obscurity. Therefore, when the Spaniards demanded to have it for the coercion of the Jews, they asked for what was dormant, but not abolished. It was a revival rather than a creation. And it was for a specifically Spanish purpose. At Rome there were no Moors, and they did not oppress the Jews. Even those who, having passed for Christians, went back to their own faith, were permitted to do so by Clement VII. Against such backsliding the Council of Toledo, under the Gothic kings, had decreed the severest penalties, anticipating Ferdinand and Isabella, or rather Torquemada and Ximenes, by eight hundred years. Founded on the ancient lines, the Spanish Inquisition was modified in the interest of the Crown, and became an important attribute of absolutism.

When the Holy Office for the universal Church was set up in Rome in 1542, it was in many respects distinct both from the first medieval type and from the later Spanish type. In the Middle Ages the headquarters were in the south of France, and the legislation was carried out by Councils at Toulouse, Narbonne, and Béziers. The Popes controlled them through their legates, and issued their own orders to the Dominicans. But it was not one of the institutions of the Court of Rome, and did not always act in harmony with it. It now became part of the Roman machinery and an element of centralisation. A supreme body of cardinals governed it with the Pope at their head. The medieval theory was that the Church condemned, and the State executed, priests having nothing to do with punishment,

and requesting that it might not be excessive. This
distinction fell away, and the clergy had to conquer their
horror of bloodshed. The delinquent was tried by the
Pope as ruler of the Church, and burnt by the Pope as
ruler of the State. Consequently, this is the genuine
and official Inquisition, not that of the Middle Ages,
which was only partly in the hands of Rome ; not that
of Spain, which was founded but not governed by Rome,
and for the developments of which the Papacy is not
directly responsible.

Originally the business of the Inquisitor was to
exterminate. The Albigenses delighted in death, and
they were disappointed when it was put off. But now
it was directed against opinions not very clearly understood or firmly held, that often resembled a reformed
Catholicism more than Protestantism. The number of
victims was smaller. At Venice, where the Holy Office
had a branch, there were 1562 trials in the sixteenth
century, 1469 in the seventeenth, 541 in the eighteenth.
But executions were frequent only in Rome. There, in
many recorded cases, the victim was strangled before
burning. It is doubtful whether death by fire was
adopted as the most cruel ; for boiling had been tried
at Utrecht, and the sight was so awful that the bishop
who was present stopped the proceedings. Roman
experts regard it as a distinctive mark of the new
tribunal that it allowed culprits who could not be
caught and punished in the proper way, to be killed
without ceremony by anybody who met them. This
practice was not unprecedented, but it had fallen into
disuse with the rest during the profane Renaissance, and
its revival was a portentous event, for it prompted the
frequent murders and massacres which stain the story
of the Counter-Reformation with crimes committed for
the love of God. The laws have not been repealed,
but the system continued in its force for no more than a
century ; and before the death of Urban VIII. the fires
of Rome were quenched. At that time persecution unto
death was not extinct in England ; the last instance in

France was in 1762, and in Spain still later.   The immediate objects were obtained in the first thirty years. The Reformation in Italy had by that time come to an end, and the Popes had been supplied with an instrument that enabled them to control the Council of Trent.   Its action did not extend to other countries.

Next to the Inquisition, the second of the several measures by which central organs were created for the Counter-Reformation is the establishment of new orders. The old ones were manifestly ineffective.   The Augustinians produced Luther.   The Dominicans had done still worse, for they produced the adversaries of Luther. The learning of the Benedictines was useless for the purpose of the day, and they were not organised for combat.   A rich and varied growth of new religious orders was the consequence.   The first were the Theatines, then the Capuchins, who were remodelled Franciscans, adapted to the need of the time ; then the Barnabites, the Oratorians, and others.   Caraffa was the most influential of the Theatines, though not their founder ; and he gave them their name, for he was Bishop of Chieti, in Latin Theate.   He did more for another institution than for his own, for it was he who brought forward the extraordinary man in whom the spirit of the Catholic reaction is incorporated.   At Venice he found a group of young men, most of them Spaniards, all of them seekers after perfection, united otherwise in a somewhat vague design of visiting the Holy Land.   Their leader, Ignatius Loyola, at that time an enthusiast, later on a calculator and organiser of the first class, was the same man who helped to transplant to Rome the Inquisition of his own country. As they waited in vain for a passage, Caraffa advised them that their true destination was Rome, where they would be more useful with Protestants than with the heathen ; and thus, by his intervention, the Society was founded which eclipsed his own.

Here at last the Catholics acquired a leader who was a man of original genius, and who grasped the whole, or nearly the whole, situation.   The Papacy had let things go to ruin; he undertook to save the Church through the Papacy. The ship, tossed in a hurricane, could only be rescued by absolute obedience to the word of command. He called his order the Company of Jesus, making it the perpetual militia of the Holy See for the restoration of authority; and he governed it not only with military discipline, but with a system of supervision and counter-checks which are his chief discovery. The worst crime of the Jesuits, says Helvetius, was the excellence of their government. Nothing had done more to aid the Reformation than the decline and insufficiency of the secular clergy. By raising up a body of virtuous, educated, and active priests, the Jesuits met that argument. The theological difference remained, and they dealt with it through the best controversialists. And when their polemics failed, they strove, as pamphleteers, and as the confessors of the great, to resist the Protestants with the arm of the flesh. For the multitudes that had never heard the Catholic case stated, they trained the most eloquent school of modern preachers. For security in the coming generation, they established successful colleges, chiefly for the study of good silver Latin, and they frequented the towns more than the country, and the rich more than the poor. Thus, while they pursued their original purpose as missionaries to the heathen, almost civilising South America, and almost converting China, they kept their forces gathered for the repulse of Protestantism. They so identified their order and the Church itself with the struggle for existence in Europe, that they were full of the same spirit long after the Counter-Reformation was spent and the permanent line of frontier laid down in the Thirty Years' War, and were busy with the same policy down to the Revocation and the suppression of Port Royal in France, and longer still in Poland.

St. Ignatius directed his disciples according to the maxim that more prudence and less piety is better than more piety and less prudence. His main desire was that they should always act together, presenting a united front, without a rift or a variation. He suppressed independence of mind, discouraged original thinking and unrestrained research, recommended commonly accepted opinions, and required all to hold without question the theology of St. Thomas. The training he imposed made ordinary men very much alike. And this is the mistake we have to guard against in considering the Jesuits. The intended unity never was enforced when the order became numerous and was joined by many able men. There arose so great a wealth of talent that it was followed by variety in ideas among them, such as the founder never contemplated. Their general, Aquaviva, forbade every opinion that contradicts St. Thomas. There could be no question whether it was true or false, and no other test of truth than conformity with his teaching. Yet Molina taught, in regard to grace, a doctrine very different from Thomism, and was followed by the bulk of his order. They were expected to think well of their rule and their rulers; but the most perspicacious exposure of what he called the infirmities of the company was composed by Mariana. Jesuits were by profession advocates of submission to authority; but the Jesuit Sarasa preceded Butler in proclaiming the infallibility of conscience. No other Society was so remarkable for internal discipline; but there were glaring exceptions. Caussin, confessor to Lewis XIII., opposed the policy of his superiors, and was dismissed by them. And when the general required works on theology to be revised at Rome, before publication, he was told that Father Gretser of Ingolstadt would never consent. They were all absorbed in the conflict with the Protestants; but when the idea of reunion arose, late in the seventeenth century, there were Jesuits, such as Masenius, one of those who anticipated *Paradise Lost*, who wrote in favour of it.

As trials for witchcraft were promoted by Rome, the Jesuits, especially Del Rio, defended them. But it was another Jesuit, Spee, who broke the back of the custom, though he had to publish his book anonymously and in a Protestant town. They were, of necessity, friends of persecution, though one of them, Faure, said that he knew of 6000 heretics put to death, and doubted if one of them had renounced his belief.   Belief in system, and in an accepted system, was an essential laid down in their constitutions.   But it was Father Petavius who first described the evolution of dogma, and cast every system into the melting-pot of History.   Under the name of probabilism, the majority adopted a theory of morals that made salvation easy, partly as confessors of the great, that they might retain their penitents ; partly as subject to superiors, that they might not scruple to obey in dubious cases ; and partly as defenders of the irrevocable past, that they might be lenient judges.   Nevertheless, the opposition was never silenced, and one general of the order wrote against its most conspicuous and characteristic doctrine.

The order was, from the first, ultramontane, in the old meaning of the term.   But its members in France consented to sign their names to Gallican propositions as the custom of the country, not as truth.   They were ultramontanes in the other sense of the word, as conservatives, advocates of authority and submission, opponents of insubordination and resistance.   Accordingly, they became the habitual confessors of absolute monarchs, in Austria, and in France under the Bourbons, and were intimately associated with the great conservative forces of society.   At the same time they were required to be disciples of St. Thomas Aquinas, and St. Thomas had a very large element of political liberalism.   He believed in the Higher Law, in conditional allegiance, in the illegitimacy of all governments that do not act in the interest of the commonwealth.   This was convenient doctrine in the endeavour to repress the forces of Protestantism, and for a time the Jesuits were revolutionists. The ideas of 1688, of 1776, of 1789 prevail among them from the wars of religion to about 1620.   In some of the medieval writers revolution included tyrannicide. It began to be taught in the twelfth century, and became popular in the sixteenth.   The Jesuits adopted the doctrine at one time, and in such numbers that one of them, Keller, in 1611, says he knows hardly three who were opposed to it. A hundred years later this was deplored as a melancholy deviation by D'Avrigny and other fathers of the Society.

The Society of Jesus is the second in the enumeration of the forces that produced and directed the great historic movement that we call the Counter-Reformation. The third is the Council of Trent. The idea arose very early that the only way to find a remedy for those things of which Protestants complained was to hold a general Council, and it was very earnestly desired by the Emperor. Fifteenth-century divines believed that all things would go well if Councils were constantly held. But the Popes were against it from the first, and at last the Protestants also. It was to be an assembly from which they were excluded, and their interests were to be debated and decided by men whose function it now avowedly was to take their lives. The Duke of Würtemberg marvelled at the unhindered presence of Cardinal Farnese in Germany, as a man of blood. The original purpose, therefore, was lost beforehand. The Council did not tend to reconcile, but to confirm, separation. It met in 1545, and ended in 1563, having been interrupted by two long intervals. Questions of doctrine were considered at the beginning, questions of reform chiefly at the end. Pole, who was one of the presiding legates, proposed that they should open the proceedings with a full confession of failings and of repentance on the part of Rome. Then the others would follow. The policy of his colleagues, on the contrary, was to postpone all inquiry into internal defects, and to repel the Protestant aggression. Therefore, the doctrines at issue were defined. Many things were settled which had remained open, and no attempt was made to meet the Protestant demand. Pole, who had hailed the compromise of Ratisbon, spoke with the grace and moderation that were in his character. At the next Conclave he was so near obtaining a majority of votes that the cardinals bowed to him as they passed before his place, and Pole, ignorant of the force at work against him,

put on paper what he meant to say by way of thanks.
But Caraffa reminded them that he had spoken as a
Lutheran during the Council, and he replied that he had
put the argument for the sake of discussion only, that
Protestants might not say that they had been condemned
undefended. The feud continued, and when Pole was
legate in England, Caraffa, who was then Pope, recalled
him in disgrace, appointing Peto as his successor ; and he
sent his friend, Cardinal Morone, to the prison of the
Inquisition. The effect of these rigours was that Pole,
whose friends in Italy were men afterwards burnt by the
Holy Office, sent poor people to the flames at Canterbury
when he knew that the reign of Mary was nearing its
end ; and Morone, the colleague of Contarini at Ratisbon,
and an admirer of the " Benefizio," having been rescued
from prison by the mob, who tore it down at the death of
Caraffa, wound up the Council, obedient to orders from
Rome, under his successor.

A more persuasive means of expressing opposition
was money. When a divine appeared at Trent, the
legates, or Visconti, the agent of the Cardinal nephew,
decided whether he was to receive payment for his pro-
spective services. Even the Cardinal of Lorraine, the
head of the Gallican party, and one of the first men in
Europe, gave way for a considerable sum. Father Paul,
in a very famous work, describes the Council as a scene
of intrigue in which the good intentions of virtuous prelates
were thwarted by the artifices of Rome. If the bulk of
virtuous prelates resembled Pole and Lorraine, we cannot
say much for the strength of their good intentions. Some
remedies were, however, applied, and the state of the
clergy was improved. On the whole, the reforms were
regarded by the government as a disappointing result of
so much promise and so much effort.

The Council instituted the index of prohibited books,
which is the fourth article in the machinery of resistance.
At first, the new power of the press was treated with large
indulgence. This was changed by the Reformation, and
far more by the organised reaction against it. Books

were suppressed by the State, by the clergy, and by the universities. In 1531 the Bishop of London prohibited thirty books at St. Paul's Cross, as well as all other suspect works existing, and to be hereafter written. Vienna, Paris, Venice, followed the example. In 1551, certain books enumerated by the university of Louvain were forbidden by Charles V. under pain of death. A German divine warned the Pope that if the fathers of Trent were allowed to read Lutheran books they would become Lutherans themselves, and such writings were accordingly forbidden even to cardinals and archbishops. The idea of drawing up a comprehensive list of all that no man should read commended itself to the zeal of Caraffa, having been suggested to him by Della Casa, who had published such a list at Venice. He issued the first Roman index, which, under his successor, who was not his friend, was denounced at the Council of Trent as a bad piece of work, and became so rare that I have never seen a copy. It was proposed that a revised edition should be prepared, and in spite of protests from those who had assisted the late Pontiff, and of the Spaniards, who saw the province of their Inquisition invaded, the thing was done, and what was called the Tridentine Index appeared at Rome in 1564. It alludes only in one place to the work which it superseded. A congregation was appointed to examine new publications, to issue decrees against them as required, and to make out catalogues from time to time of works so condemned. Besides this, censures were also pronounced by the Pope himself, the Inquisition, the Master of the Sacred Palace, and the Secretary of the Index, separately. In this way an attempt was made to control what people read, committing to oblivion the works of Protestant scholars, and of such men as Machiavelli, and correcting offensive texts, especially historians. Several such corrected editions were published at the time, and many things were reprinted with large omissions. But no Index Expurgatorius, no notification of what called for modification, was ever published by Rome, officially ; and when we use the term, we are thinking of Spain, where it grew into a custom. The best way to suppress a book is to burn it, and there were, accordingly, frequent bonfires of peccant literature. One man, Konias, is said to have thus destroyed 60,000 books, principally Bohemian. Freedom of speech and sincerity of history were abolished for many years.

In connection with this repressive policy, and as its counterpart, a scheme ripened to place Rome, with its libraries, its archives, its incomparable opportunities of gathering contributory aid from every quarter of the Church, at the head of ecclesiastical literature. The Calendar was reformed. The text of the Canon Law was corrected. The Latin Vulgate was revised by Pope Sixtus himself, and every further attempt to improve it was energetically put down. Collections of councils and editions of Fathers were projected, and Baronius, of the Oratory, began the greatest history of the Church ever written, and carried it down to the eleventh folio volume.

In this manner the foundations were laid of that later scholarship, that matured and completed Renaissance, by which the Catholics recovered much of the intellectual influence that had passed to other hands, and learning assisted policy in undoing the work of the reformers.

The natural and inevitable centre of the movement which is known as the Catholic Reformation, but which, for reasons already indicated, is better called the Counter-Reformation, was Rome. It was an enterprise requiring consistency in the objects aimed at, variety in the means, combination with the Powers and avoidance of rivalry, an authority superior to national obstacles and political limitations. At first the initiative did not reside with the Papacy. Farnese, in whose pontificate the transition occurred from the religion of Erasmus to the religion of Loyola, allowed men to act for him whose spirit differed from his own. He long put off the Portuguese demand for a tribunal like the Inquisition of Castile, on the ground that it was a mere scheme of spoliation. With the elevation of Cervini in 1555, reforming or Tridentine Catholicism

ascended the papal throne ; but he died before his virtues
or his talents could avail.   Caraffa himself followed.   He
let the Council drop, saying that no such thing was needed,
if governments did their duty.   By his lack of control, he
pushed things to a breach with the moderate party at
home, and with the Habsburgs abroad, and the Roman
people threw his statue into the Tiber, in their rejoicings
when he died, and released seventy prisoners that he
kept in the Inquisition.   His nephews, who compromised
him and had incurred disgrace in his lifetime, were put
to death by his successor.   They were the last papal
nephews of the old type, angling for principalities and
using the Papacy for their own ends.   Pius IV., when he
closed the Council, strove to do its work by reforms at
home.   Three modern saints dominated in his time, and
effected a conspicuous change in the aspect of Rome.
His nephew was Charles Borromeo.   St. Philip Neri was
the best-known and the best-loved figure in the streets of
the city, and Alexandrino governed the Inquisition as an
almost independent power.   He succeeded, as Pius V.,
and then the Counter-Reformation was master.   Pius was
the most austere, the most ardent, the most vehement of
men.   He incited France to civil war, applauded the
methods of Alva, deposed Elizabeth, and by incessant
executions strove to maintain public decency and orthodox
religion.   Protestantism disappeared from Italy in his
day, as it had already done in Spain.   The Counter-
Reformation touched high-water mark with the massacre
of St. Bartholomew, a few months after his death.

The quarter of a century from 1564 to the death of
Sixtus V. in 1590 is the active period of the movement.
It begins when the Council, having determined doctrine,
dispersed ; and it declines when, by the death of Mary
Stuart and the flight of the Armada, the Protestant
succession was secured in England and Scotland, and the
churches acquired their permanent limit.

It may be doubted whether Italian Protestants ever
gave promise of vitality.   The leaders who escaped were
men of original and eccentric thought, who did not

combine well with others ; and it was they who established the Socinian church in Poland, in defiance of both Lutheran and Calvinist. The Italian movement was crushed by violence. The scene of the authentic Counter-Reformation was central Europe, and especially those countries which were the scene of the Reformation itself, Germany and Austria. There the tide, which with little interruption had flowed for fifty years, was effectually turned back, and regions which were Protestant became Catholic again. There too the means employed were not those prevailing under the crown of Spain. They were weapons supplied and suggested by the Peace of Religion, harmoniously forged by the Lutherans themselves at the Diet of 1555. There was to be no mutual persecution, taking persecution to imply the penalty of death, and a persecutor to mean homicide, in the sense to which Europe was accustomed. No subject, on either side, could be deprived of life or property, could be tortured or imprisoned, or even banished, if there were numbers, for that would be ruinous to the State. Governments were forced to oppress him wisely, depriving him of Church and school, of preacher and schoolmaster ; and by those nameless arts with which the rich used to coerce the poor in the good old days, and which, under the name of influence, were not considered altogether infamous by Englishmen in the last generation. When the people had been deprived of their pastors, the children were sent to Catholic schools. Fervent preachers came among them, Jesuits, or it might be Capuchins, widely different in morality, earnestness, education, and eloquence from the parish clergy, whose deficiencies gave such succour to Luther. Most of those who, having no turn for controversy, had been repelled by scandals were easily reconciled. Others, who were conscious of disagreement with the theology of the last thousand years, and were uninfluenced by the secondary and auxiliary motives, had now to face disputants of a more serious type than the adversaries of Luther, and to face them unsupported by experts of their own. Where there had been indifference, ignorance, disorder, in the easy-going days of the Renaissance, there was now the closest concentration of efforts, strict discipline and regularity of life, a better though narrower education, and the most strenuous and effective oratory. Therefore it was by honest conviction as well as by calculated but not illegal coercion that the Reformation was driven back, and Protestants who had been almost the nation became no more than a bare majority. The original spring ran dry, and the expansive force had departed from Lutheranism.

In Austria conditions were of another kind. The country was largely Protestant, and the Emperor, Maximilian II., was not only a friend to toleration, but to Lutheran ideas. Under his auspices a conciliatory, neutral, and unconventional Catholicism came into existence, accepting the doctrinal compromise which had been tendered more than once, discouraging pilgrimages, relics, indulgences, celibacy, and much that had been the occasion of scoffing, an approach to Erasmus, if not to Luther. The outward sign was the restoration of the cup. When his restraining hand was removed, the process of reaction which had done well on the Rhine was extended to the Danube and the Illyrian Alps, with like success. And it was the steady pursuit of this policy in Austria that provoked the Thirty Years' War. In Poland, too, where toleration had been conceded in the avowed expectation that the sects would devour each other, it was exchanged for acts like those I have described. The result of the struggle was that the boundary receded, that a time came of recovery for the Catholics and of decline for the Lutherans in central Europe, and that the distribution has remained practically unchanged. The only example of a country becoming Protestant since then occurred when the principles of the Counter-Reformation, applied by Alva, drove the Netherlands into revolt, and changed the Reformation into revolution. The great and rapid victories of the sixteenth century were gained over the unreformed and disorganised Catholicism of the Renaissance, not over the Church which had been renovated at Trent. Rome, with a contested authority and a contracted sphere, developed greater energy, resource, and power than when it exercised undivided sway over Christendom in the West. The recovery was accomplished by violence, and was due to the advent of men who did not shrink from blood in place of the gracious idealists for whom Luther and Calvin were too strong.

VI

CALVIN AND HENRY VIII.

FOR nearly thirty years Charles V. suffered the Reformation to run its course in Germany, against his will, and
without admitting the principle of toleration. He did
not resign the hope that unity would be restored by a
Council which should effectually reform the Church and
reconcile Protestants ; and there was no prospect of such
a consummation unless by the necessity which they
created. Therefore, without ceasing to be intolerant in
his other dominions, he was content to wait. At length,
in 1545, the Council assembled at Trent and dealt with
the chief dogmas at issue. Then, when the decrees did
not satisfy the Lutherans, the Emperor combined with the
Pope to coerce them. A large contingent of papal troops
crossed the Alps in 1547, and were met by the Lutheran
forces on the Danube. The Protestant League was
divided ; some of its members, true to the doctrine of
non-resistance, remained away ; and one of the Saxon
princes, Maurice, invaded Saxony, on a promise that he
should succeed to the electorate. The Elector hurried
back to his own country, the muster on the Danube was
broken up, and the Italians gained a decisive victory over
the Germans at Mühlberg on the Elbe. Maurice obtained
the stipulated reward, and being then, by virtue of his
new dignity, the chief of the Protestants, turned against
the law by which the Emperor, after his victory, attempted
to regulate the affairs of religion. He secured the help
of France by the surrender of a part of Lorraine, which
Moltke did not entirely recover, and, attacking the

Emperor when he was not prepared, brought him to terms.

At Augsburg, in 1555, peace was concluded between the religions, and continued until the Thirty Years' War. It abolished the fagot and the stake. The Catholics gained nothing by this, for no Lutherans had thought that it could be lawful to put the people of the old religion to death. The Lutherans obtained security that they should not be persecuted. On the other hand, it was agreed that if any territorial prelate seceded, he should forfeit the temporal power which he enjoyed by right of his ecclesiastical dignity. So that the ecclesiastical territories, which composed a large part of Germany, from Salzburg to the Black Forest, and then all down the valley of the Rhine to Liège and Münster, were to be preserved intact. No security whatever was obtained for Protestants outside the Confession of Augsburg. The Lutherans negotiated only for themselves. And no real security was given to the subject. He was not to be punished for his nonconformity, but he might be banished and compelled to pass to the nearest territory of his own persuasion. As these were very near, generally, the suffering was less than it would have been in other countries. Under that condition, the civil power could, if it chose, enforce the unity of religion.

These enactments were an immense advance, practically, but they did not involve the liberty of conscience. The absolute right of the State to determine the religion it professed was not disputed, but it was tempered by the right of emigration. No man could be compelled to change, but he might be compelled to go. State absolutism was unlimited over all who chose to keep their home within the precincts. There was no progress in point of principle. The Christian might have to depart, while the Jew remained. No Protestant could complain if he was expelled from Cologne; no Catholic if he could not have his domicile at Leipzig. The intolerance and fierceness of the Germans found relief in the wholesale burning of witches.

Charles V. would have nothing to do with these innovations. He left it all to his brother Ferdinand, King of Bohemia and Hungary, who was more elastic and pliable than himself. With the Turk over the border, he could not exist without the good-will of both parties ; and he desired the vote of Lutheran electors to make him emperor. He had no Inquisition in one part of his dominions contradicting and condemning toleration in the rest. He was an earnest promoter of reform in the shape of concession. The embers of Hussitism were not extinct in the region of which Bohemia was the centre. Ferdinand had that as well as Lutheranism to contend with, and he desired to avert peril by allowing priests to marry and laymen to receive the cup. That is to say, he desired to surrender the two points for which the Church had struggled successfully against the State in the eleventh century, against the Bohemians in the fifteenth. His conciliatory policy was assisted by the moderation of the Archbishop of Mentz. At Rome they said that the empire was divided equally between Christ and the devil. But the Pope, advised by Jesuits, made no protest.

Ferdinand had so regulated things in his brother's interest, that the measure did not include the Netherlands. The laws which afterwards produced the revolt were not invalid by the Peace of Religion, and the victims of Alva had no right to appeal to it. Charles V. did not choose to surrender that which alone gave unity to his complicated empire. The German princes were allowed to have subjects of one religion only. That prerogative was denied to the Emperor. The imperial dignity, in its ideal character as the appointed aefender and advocate of the universal Church, existed no longer. A monarch reigning over Catholic and Protestant alike was an inferior representative of unity and authority, and a poor copy of Charlemagne. There was no obvious reason for his existence. It was an intolerable hypocrisy to be the friend of Protestants where they were strong, and to burn them where they were weak. The work of his life was undone. In more than thirty years of effort he had neither reconciled the Protestants nor reformed the Church. The settlement of the Reformation was an acknowledgment of defeat, and the result of his career was that religious division had become the law of his empire. Therefore, when the Peace of Religion was concluded, Charles V. laid down the sceptre. The new empire, based on religious equality, he gave to his brother. It was only by detaching it from his hereditary dominions that he could reconstruct what had crumbled to pieces in his hands. Then he rebuilt the great conservative and Catholic monarchy for his son, assigning to him Spain, Naples, Milan, the Netherlands, the Indies, England, and the supreme protectorate of Rome. The mixed possessions went to Ferdinand. The boundless empire, based on the principle of unity, and the championship of the Catholic Church all the world over, was for Philip II. All that was his, to keep or to resign. All that he chose to resign. For with his prodigious good fortune, his inheritance of greatness, his unexampled experience of complex affairs, his opportunities for having at his elbow the best talent in the world, his admirably prudent and moderate temper, Charles V. broke down over the problem of the Reformation, as we shall see that the Counter-Reformation was fatal to his son. And it was in this way that Philip found the lines of his policy laid down for him, before he assumed the crown of Spain, by the conditions under which his father abdicated. The ancient function of the empire passed to him, and the purpose of his vast dominion, the intelligible reason of its apparition among the nations, was to accomplish that in which, under his more gifted father, imperial Germany had failed.

At the date we have reached, soon after the middle of the century, Luther was dead, and the churches of the Confession of Augsburg had reached their full measure of expansion. They predominated in Germany, and still more in Scandinavia ; but Luther had not endowed them with institutions, or imparted to them the gift of self-government. In religious ideas, he was inexhaustible ; but he was deficient in constructive capacity. The local

governments, which were effective, had defended the
Reformation and assured its success against the hostility
of the central government, which was intermittent and
inoperative, and as they afforded the necessary protection,
they assumed the uncontested control.   Lutheranism is
governed not by the spiritual, but by the temporal power,
in agreement with the high conception of the State which
Luther derived from the long conflict of the Middle
Ages.   It is the most conservative form of religion, and
less liable than any other to collision with the civil
authority on which it rests.   By its lack of independence
and flexibility it was unfitted to succeed where governments were hostile, or to make its way by voluntary effort
through the world.   Moreover, Luther's vigorous personality has so much in it of the character of his nation, that
they are attracted even by his defects—a thing which you
can hardly expect to occur elsewhere.   Therefore it was
in other forms, and under other names, that the Protestant
religion spread over Europe.   They differed from the
original less in their theology, which Luther had completed, than in questions of Church government, which he
abandoned to others.

Apart from the sects, which are of the first importance,
but whose story belongs to the Puritan Revolution and
to the following century, two other systems arose at the
time, one in Switzerland, the other in England.   The
general result of what happened when the Reformation,
ceasing to be national, became European, was that it
prevailed in the north, that it miscarried in the south, that
it divided and agitated the centre.   Switzerland was
divided, the towns becoming Protestant on the Zwinglian
type, the country people remaining Catholic, especially in
the central cantons.   The chief towns, Berne and Bâle,
imitated the example of Zürich, where Zwingli committed
the government of the Church to the authorities that
governed the State, differing from the Lutherans in this,
that Zwinglianism was republican and revolutionary.
In Germany, where the organisation was defective, there
was little discipline or control.   In Switzerland there was

a more perfect order, at the price of subjection to the secular authority. Those were the rocks ahead; that was the condition of the Protestant churches, when a man arose amongst them with a genius for organisation, a strong sense of social discipline, and a profound belief in ecclesiastical authority.

At the time when persecution suddenly began to rage in France John Calvin escaped to Strasburg, and there composed his *Institute*, the finest work of Reformation literature. He wrote with a view to show that there was nothing in the Protestant religion to alarm the government, and that the change it demanded was in the Church, not in the State. He dealt more largely with theology than with practical religion, and did not disclose those ideas on the government of religious society that have made him the equal of Luther in History. Geneva, when he came there in 1536, was a small walled town of less than 20,000 inhabitants, with so narrow a territory that France was within cannon range on one side and Savoy on the other. It was secure in the alliance and protection of Berne, which came almost to the gates; for what is now the canton of Vaud was, until the French Revolution, a Bernese dependency. It had been an episcopal city, but the bishop had retired to Annecy, and the Genevese Reformation had been at the same time a Genevese Revolution. Power over Church and State passed to the commonwealth, to the municipality. The new masters, rejoicing in their independence, did not at once settle down; the place was disturbed by factions, and was not a scene of edification.

Calvin set to work to reform the community, to introduce public order and domestic virtue. He was a foreigner by birth, and not conciliatory in disposition; and after a brief experiment, the offended Genevese cast him out. He was not yet thirty. He returned to Strasburg and rewrote his *Institute*, expounding his theocratic theory of the government of the Church by the Church, and of the State by the union of Church and State. He was present at the Diet of Ratisbon, and saw the

Lutherans in a yielding mood, when Melanchthon and Contarini, with the urgent mediator Gropper of Cologne, were very near understanding each other.   That event, as everybody knows, did not come off ; but everybody does not know the consequences, for we shall see that the Counter-Reformation sprang from those conferences at Ratisbon.   Calvin had no part in Irenics.   He was persuaded that the work before them was to create not a new church, but a new world, to remodel not doctrine only, but society; that the chasm could never be bridged, but must grow wider with time.   That conviction was not yet strongly held by the German Lutherans, and they do not all hold it at the present day.   During his absence Cardinal Sadolet wrote to the Genevese, intreating them not to break up the unity of Latin Christendom ; for Geneva was the first town beyond the Teutonic range that went over.   Sadolet was not only reputed the finest Latinist of the age, but he was the most gracious of the Roman prelates, a friend of Erasmus, an admirer of Contarini, and the author of a commentary on St. Paul in which Lutheran Justification was suspected.   The Genevese were not then so rich in literature as they afterwards became, and they were not prepared to answer the challenge, when Calvin did it for them.   In 1541, after a change of government, he was recalled.   He came back on condition that his plans for the Church were accepted, and his position remained unshaken until his death.

The Strasburg clergy, in losing him, wrote that he was unsurpassed among men, and the Genevese felt his superiority and put him on the commission which revised the Constitution.   It was not changed in any important way, and the influence of the Geneva Constitution upon Calvin was greater than his influence on the government of Geneva.   The city was governed by a Lesser or Inner Council of twenty-five, composed of the four syndics, the four of last year, and as many more as made up the twenty-five.   These belonged to the ruling families, and were seldom renewed.   Whilst the Lesser Council ad-

ministered, through the syndics, the Great Council of two
hundred was the legislature. Its members were appointed,
not by popular election, but by the Lesser Council.
Between the twenty-five and the two hundred were the
sixty, who only appeared when the Lesser Council
wanted to prepare a majority in the Greater Council. Its
function was to mediate between the executive and the
legislature. It was a system of concentric circles; for
the twenty-five became the sixty by adding the necessary
number of thirty-five, and the sixty became the two
hundred by the addition of one hundred and forty
members. Beyond this was the assembly of citizens,
who only met twice a year to elect the syndics and the
judge, from names presented by the Lesser Council. The
popular element was excluded. Beyond the citizens were
the burghers, who did not enjoy the franchise. Between
the two there was material for friction and a constitutional
struggle, the struggle from which Rousseau proceeded, and
which had some share in preparing the French Revolution.

Upon this background Calvin designed his scheme of
Church government and discipline. His purpose was to
reform society as well as doctrine. He did not desire
orthodoxy apart from virtue, but would have the faith of
the community manifested in its moral condition. And
as the mere repression of scandals would promote hypocrisy, it was necessary that private life should be investigated by the same authority that was obeyed in public.
Teaching and preaching belong to the clergy alone.
But jurisdiction is exercised by the pastors in conjunction
with the elders. And the elders were the choice of the
civil power, two representing the Lesser Council, four the
sixty, and six the two hundred. That was all that he could
obtain. His success was incomplete, because the government worked with him. A hostile government would be
more adapted to his purpose, for then the elders would be
elected, not by the State, but by the congregation. With
a weak clergy the civil magistrate would predominate over
the Church, having a majority in the consistory. While
Calvin lived no such thing was likely to happen. The

Church co-operated with the State to put down sin, the one with spiritual weapons, the other with the material sword. The moral force assisted the State, the physical force assisted the Church. A scheme substantially the same was introduced by Capito at Frankfort in 1535.

But the secret of Calvin's later influence is that he claimed for the Church more independence than he obtained. The surging theory of State omnipotence did not affect his belief in the principle of self-government. Through him an idea of mutual check was introduced which became effective at a later time, though nothing more unlike liberty could be found than the state of Geneva when he was the most important man there. Every ascertainable breach of divine law was punished with rigour. Political error was visited with the sword, and religious error with the stake. In this spirit Calvin carried out his scheme of a Christian society and crushed opposition. Already, before he came, the Council had punished vice with imprisonment and exile, and the idea was traceable back to the Middle Ages. It had never found so energetic an advocate.

The crown was set upon the system by the trial and execution of Servetus. The Germans, in their aversion for metaphysics, had avoided the discussion of questions regarding the Trinity, which in the south of Europe excited more attention. As early as 1531, long before the rise of the Socinians, the Spaniard Servetus taught anti-Trinitarianism, and continued to do it for more than twenty years. He remained isolated, and it was not until after his death that his opinions attracted followers. Calvin, who thought him dangerous, both by his doctrines and his talent, declared that if ever he came to Geneva he would never leave it alive. He caused him to be denounced to the Inquisition, and he was imprisoned at Vienne on the Rhone, tried, and condemned to be burnt at a slow fire, on evidence supplied by Calvin in seventeen letters. Servetus escaped, and on his way to Italy stopped at Geneva, under a false name, for he knew who it was that had set the machinery of the Holy Office in motion against him, and who had said that he deserved to be burnt wherever he could be found. He was recognised, and Calvin caused him to be arrested and tried without a defender. The authorities at Vienne demanded his extradition, and the Governor of Dauphiny requested that any money Servetus had about him might be sent back to him, as he was to have had it if the execution had occurred in his territory. Calvin disputed with his prisoner, convicted him of heresy, and claimed to have convicted him of Pantheism, and he threatened to leave Geneva if Servetus was not condemned. The Council did not think that the errors of a Spanish scholar who was on his way to Italy were any business of theirs, and they consulted the Swiss churches, hoping to be relieved of a very unpleasant responsibility. The Swiss divines pronounced against Servetus, and he was sentenced to die by fire, although Calvin wished to mitigate the penalty, but refused, at a last interview, the Spaniard's appeal for mercy. The volume which cost Servetus his life was burnt with him, but falling from his neck into the flames, it was snatched from the burning, and may still be seen in its singed condition, a ghastly memorial of Reformation ethics, in the National Library at Paris.

The event at Geneva received the sanction of many leading divines, both of Switzerland and Germany ; and things had moved so far since Luther was condemned for his toleration, that Melanchthon could not imagine the possibility of a doubt. Hundreds of humble Anabaptists had suffered a like fate and nobody minded. But the story of the execution at Champel left an indelible and unforgotten scar. For those who consistently admired persecution, it left the estimate of Calvin unchanged. Not so with others, when they learnt how Calvin had denounced Servetus long before to the Catholic Inquisitors in France ; how he had done so under the disguise of an intermediary, in a prolonged correspondence ; how he had then denied the fact, and had done a man to death who was guilty of no wrong to Geneva, and over whom he had no jurisdiction. It weakened the right of Protestants to complain when they were in the hands of the executioner, and it deprived the terrors of the Inquisition of their validity as an argument in the controversy with Rome. Therefore, with the posting of the Thesis at Wittenberg; with Worms, and Augsburg, and Ratisbon; with the flight of Charles V. before Maurice, and with the Peace of Religion, it marks one of the great days in the Church history of the century. But it obtained still greater significance in the times that were to come. On the whole, though not without exceptions, the patriarchs approved. Their conclusions were challenged by younger and obscurer men, and a controversy began which has not ceased to cause the widest division among men.

The party of Liberty—Castellio, Socinus, Coornhert in the sixteenth century, like Williams and Penn, Locke and Bayle in the seventeenth—were not Protestants on the original foundation. They were Sectaries; and the charge of human freedom was transferred from the churches to the sects, from the men in authority to the men in opposition, to Socinians and Arminians and Independents, and the Society of Friends. By the thoroughness and definiteness of system, and its practical adaptability, Calvinism was the form in which Protestant religion could be best transplanted; and it struck root and flourished in awkward places where Lutheranism could obtain no foothold, in the absence of a sufficient prop. Calvinism spread not only abroad but at home, and robbed Luther of part of Germany, of the Palatinate, of Anhalt, of the House of Brandenburg, and in great part of Hungary. This internal division was a fact of importance later on. It assisted the work of the Counter-Reformation, and became the key to the Thirty Years' War. The same thing that strengthened the Protestant cause abroad weakened it on its own soil. Apart, then, from points of doctrine, the distinctive marks of Calvin's influence are that it promoted expansion, and that it checked the reigning idea that nothing limits the power of the State.

Exactly the reverse of this distinguishes the movement which took place at the same time in England, proceeding from the government before the wave of Reformation struck the shores. Here there were local reminiscences of Lollardry, and a tradition, as old as the Conquest, of resistance to the medieval claims of Rome; but the first impulse did not arise on the domain of religion. From the beginning there was a body of opinion hostile to the king's marriage. The practice was new, it was discountenanced by earlier authorities, and it belonged to the same series of innovations as the recent system of indulgences which roused the resistance of Germany. Precedents were hard to find. Alexander VI. had granted the same dispensation to Emmanuel of Portugal, but with misgivings; and had refused it until the king undertook to make war in person against the Moors of Africa. Julius II., coming immediately after, had exacted no such condition from Henry VII., so that he had done what was never done before him. Sixtus V. afterwards declared that Clement had deserved the calamities that befel him, because he had not dissolved so unholy a union. Others thought so at the time. No protest could well be heard before 1523, when Adrian censured his predecessors for exceeding their powers. After that it could be no offence to say that Julius was one of those whose conduct was condemned by his next successor but one. But it was still a dangerous point to raise, because any action taken upon it implied a breach with the queen's nephew Charles V., and the loss of the old alliance with the House of Burgundy.

After the triumph of Pavia, the captivity of Francis I., and his defiance of the treaty by which he obtained his deliverance, Wolsey accepted a pension of 10,000 ducats from France, England renounced friendship with the Habsburgs, and the breach was already accomplished. The position of Catharine became intolerable, and she led the opposition to Wolsey, the author of the change. Therefore, from 1526, both the religious and the political motive for silence ceased to operate, and there were, just

then, evident motives for speech.   There was no hope
that Catharine would have a son, and the secret that a
queen may reign by her own right, that the nation may
be ruled by the distaff, had not been divulged in England.
In foreign policy and in home policy alike, there were
interests which favoured a new marriage, if its legitimacy
could be assured.

Wolsey had an additional inducement to promote
what we call the divorce, though it was nothing of the
kind, in the fact that the queen was his enemy.   He had
reasons to hope for success.   The armies of Charles had
invaded Italy and threatened Rome, and the papal minister,
Giberti, enchanted with the zeal of the great English
cardinal, wished that he had him at the Vatican in the
place of the tremulous and inconstant Clement.   Spain
was the enemy ; England was the ally.   It was probable
that the Pope would do what he could in the interest of
England, to keep up its enmity with Spain.   The case
was a difficult one, not to be decided on evidence.   Something would remain uncertain, and some allowance must
be made for good or ill will at Rome.   If the invading
Imperialists were defeated, the prospects would be good.
If they held their ground and made the Pope their
dependent, it would be all over with the divorce.   Wolsey
admitted afterwards that he prompted the attempt, and
persuaded the king that he could carry it through.   But
at first he shifted the responsibility on to the French
envoy, Grammont, afterwards a cardinal, who came over
to arrange a marriage with Mary Tudor.   He said that
when he raised some preliminary objection, Grammont
lost his temper, and told him that they might be glad of
such an offer for a princess who was not legitimate.
Another story put into circulation was that Henry had
married under protest, and by compulsion, having been
warned that if he refused he would be dethroned.   Erasmus,
who admired Henry, took care to explain that a king of
England who lost his throne was likely to lose his life.
Wolsey intended to cement the French alliance by
a marriage with Renée, daughter of Lewis XII., not

believing that Anne Boleyn would be an obstacle. But the friends of Anne, the cluster of English nobles who were weary of being excluded from affairs by the son of the butcher of Ipswich, soon made it clear that she was only to be won by the promise of a crown.

From that moment Wolsey, with all his astuteness, was digging his own pit. If he succeeded, he would fall to make way for the Boleyn faction. If he failed, he involved the Catholic cause in his downfall. The first step in the business was the demand for permission to marry a lady not named, notwithstanding any impediment arising from an intrigue with her sister. With that the secret was out, and they knew at Rome what the king's scruples were worth. This was done behind the cardinal's back. When he took the matter in hand, he asked that the Pope should dissolve the first marriage, on the ground that Julius II. had issued a dispensation in terms which could not be justified. That this might not be taken as denying the plenitude of the prerogative, he further asked for a dispensation to marry a second wife without repudiating the first. And he desired that the cause might be judged in this country and not at Rome.

When these negotiations commenced, in the spring and summer of 1527, Rome had been sacked by the Imperialists, and Clement was a prisoner in St. Angelo, or a fugitive at Orvieto, with the strongest motive for resentment against the author of his humiliation. By the summer of 1528, when Lautrec was in Italy at the head of a French army, Clement had conceded virtually the whole of the English demands. He removed every impediment to the marriage with Anne other than the fact that Henry was married already. He authorised the trial of the case in England by Wolsey and Warham ; or again, by Wolsey and Campeggio, Archbishop of Bologna, the best jurist of the sacred college. He pronounced on the question of law, leaving questions of fact to the legates, and he pronounced against the terms of the dispensation, intimating that Julius had done what no Pope has a right to do. He promised that judgment as given in England

would be final, and that he would not remove the cause
to Rome.   He was willing that Richmond, the king's son,
should marry the king's daughter, Mary Tudor.   He did
not turn a deaf ear even to the proposal of bigamy.   For
several years he continued to suggest that Henry should
marry Anne Boleyn and renounce the quest of a divorce.
In 1530, somebody informed him that this would not do,
and that brought him to the last of his resources.   He
proposed to the Imperialists, in order to prevent a schism,
that Henry should live with Anne without marriage and
without divorce.   That he might not be hopelessly wrong
with the Emperor, he required that the most compromising
of these documents should be kept secret.   His friendli-
ness rose with the French advance and fell with the
French disasters.   If Lautrec would approach the vicinity
of Rome, he said, he would do more, because the Emperor
would excuse him on the ground of compulsion.   When
Campeggio reached England, Lautrec was dead and his
army defeated.   The papal secretary wrote, "Decide
nothing, for the Emperor is victorious, and we cannot
afford to provoke him."   There was nothing more to
be done.

While the Court was sitting in London, the Pope
made his peace with Charles; Catharine appealed to him
from his legates in England, and he was obliged to call
the case before him.   The queen's friends demanded the
strongest measures, and Aleander wrote that if you resisted
Henry VIII. he became as gentle as a lamb.   Such
persuasions did not influence the Pope, who put off action
as long as he could, knowing that a breach would inevitably follow.   The French Chancellor warned him that
he would be known to be acting under pressure of the
Emperor, that the censure of Henry would be resented as
the victory of Charles.   The French defeat in Italy was
the ruin of Wolsey, who had caused the breach with
Spain without any advantage.   A year later, when
Campeggio prorogued the Legatine Court, and the divorce
had to be given up, he was dismissed.

One further step had to be taken before settling the

matter in England.   By advice of a Cambridge Don the
universities were consulted.   They gave various replies,
but those that helped the king were not convincing, for they
cost him more than £100,000, and he obliged the clergy to
give him that sum.   As it was obvious for what purpose
Henry was arming himself with these opinions, Charles V.
conceived serious scruples, and thought for a moment that
to give way might be the lesser evil.   At the same time
he sent 450,000 ducats to Rome to facilitate matters ;
for the divorce was the one pending question which
delayed the conclusion of that treaty of Barcelona which
laid Italy for centuries at the feet of Spain.   The uncertainty in the policy of Rome as the power of the
Emperor rose and fell, the open avowal that so much
depended on political considerations, besides the strange
proposal in respect of two wives, led to a belief in England
that the cause was lost by the pressure of interest and
fear, not by principle.   Therefore, the establishment of
the Spanish dominion over Italy was quickly followed by
the rejection of papal supremacy in favour of the English
state.   The bishops themselves were impressed with the
danger of allowing the spiritual power to be influenced
through the temporal power by an enemy of this country,
so that they made no resistance.   England broke with
the Papacy on these, and not on strictly religious grounds.

Tunstall, coming up to attend Parliament, suffered himself to be stopped by a letter from the king, dispensing
with his presence.   Fisher alone offered opposition.   He
caused the royal supremacy to be accepted with the
proviso, " so far as the divine law permits."   And as this
proved only a stepping-stone to the unconditional headship
of the Church, he regarded it as his own fault.   He
refused submission, and put himself in communication
with the Imperialists with a view to effective intervention.
Sir Thomas More, the most modern and original mind
among the men of his time, showed greater caution.   He
admitted the right of Parliament to determine the succession, and made no struggle for Mary Tudor, as he had
made none for her mother.   He did not openly contest

L

the royal supremacy until after sentence. Besides these two, a large number of monks were executed during Cromwell's ministry.

Having given up the Pope, the government had no ground for keeping the religious orders. They did not belong to the primitive Church, and some of them, Grey Friars and Black Friars, were an essential part of the medieval system which was rejected with the papal authority. When Rome was taken in 1527, and Clement a prisoner, Wolsey, with some other cardinals, proposed that he should act as his vicar during captivity, so that the Church should not be receiving orders from the Emperor through the Pope. This proposal is a first glimpse of what was now introduced. The idea of a middle course, between Rome and Wittemberg, occurred easily to every constant reader of Erasmus; and many divines of the fifteenth century suggested something similar. What then prevailed was not a theological view, but a political view. The sovereignty of the modern State, uncontrolled by the opinions of men, commanded the minds both of Cromwell and of Gardiner, rivals though they were. Cromwell is the first public man known to have been a student of Machiavelli's writings; and the first to denounce them was his enemy, Reginald Pole. It is the advent of a new polity. Gardiner believed in it, thinking that nothing else could save Catholicism after the mismanagement of the Church in Germany. And it is the dominant note of the following years, whichever party was prevailing.

That is the broad distinction between the continental Reformation and the contemporary event in England. The one was the strongest religious movement in the history of Christendom; the other was borne onward on the crest of a wave not less overwhelming, the state that admits no division of power. Therefore, when the spirit of foreign Protestantism caught the English people they moved on lines distinct from those fixed by the Tudors; and the reply of the seventeenth century to the sixteenth was not a development, but a reaction. Whereas Henry could exclude, or impose, or change religion at will with various aid from the gibbet, the block, or the stake, there were some among the Puritans who enforced, though they did not discover, the contrary principle, that a man's conscience is his castle, with kings and parliaments at a respectful distance.

VII

PHILIP II., MARY STUART, AND ELIZABETH

THE monarchy of Philip II. was held by no binding idea,
but religious unity.   The dynasty was new, and the king
was not personally imposing or attractive.   The people
of Palermo, Milan, Antwerp, had no motive to make
sacrifices except the fact that their king was the one
upholder of religion in Europe.   Catholics in every country
were his natural allies.

Charles V., who accepted inevitable divisions in Germany, had established the Inquisition in the Netherlands.
Under Philip that policy was consistent, and promised,
in the flood of the Counter-Reformation, to be a source of
power.   He would not fall behind his father.   He drove
the Netherlands into rebellion ; but his intention was
intelligible.   In the sixteenth century the pride of state
does as much for oppression and intolerance as religious
passion.   If he succeeded in repressing heresy, he would
have a very real political advantage over other powers.
In October 1565 he wrote : " As to the Inquisition, my
will is that it be enforced by the Inquisitors as of old, and
as is required by all law, human and divine.   This lies
very near my heart, and I require you to carry out my
orders.   Let all prisoners be put to death, and suffer them
no longer to escape through the neglect, weakness, and
bad faith of the judges.   If any are too timid to execute
the edicts, I will replace them by men who have more
heart and zeal."

By this scheme of violence Philip II. turned the
Reformation into revolution.   He saw that generally

nothing was more striking than the ease with which people changed religious profession ; and he believed that what was done with success in Germany and Austria and England, could be done in the seventeen provinces of the Burgundian crown. The leaders of the popular movement were men of rank, like Egmont and William of Orange, men not likely to go to extremes. And it was an axiom that the masses are always led by few, and cannot act of themselves. But in the Netherlands more than elsewhere the forms, if not the reality, of freedom were preserved, and the sovereign was not absolute. Moreover, he governed from a distance, and, in addition to his constitutional caution and procrastination, correspondence was very slow.

The endeavour of Philip to substitute his will for self-government provoked a Catholic and aristocratic opposition, followed by a democratic and Protestant movement, which proved more difficult to deal with. The nobles were overcome by the strong measures of Alva. The Gueux were defeated repeatedly by Don Juan and Farnese, after the recall of Alva. And it seemed, for many years, that the movement would fail. It is to the statesmanship of William the Silent, who was neither a great soldier nor a strong churchman, that they owed their success. He failed, indeed, to keep Protestants and Catholics together on a wide basis of toleration. In 1579 the southern provinces returned to Spain, and the northern provinces cast off their allegiance. But, by the union of Utrecht, they founded that confederacy which became one of the foremost powers in the world, and the first of revolutionary origin. The southern provinces remained Catholic. The northern were, in great measure, Protestant, but with a large Catholic population. William, the Stadtholder, was killed by an assassin in 1584, before his work was done. He had brought in Alençon, Elizabeth's suitor, that he might secure the help of France. But Alençon proved a traitor ; and during the proconsulate of Farnese, Duke of Parma, the Spaniards gained much ground.

Philip II. stood at the height of his power in the middle of the eighties. He had annexed Portugal, with its immense colonial empire.   By the death of Alençon, the King of Navarre, who was a Huguenot, became the heir to the crown of France, and the Catholic party looked to Spain for their salvation.   Now, after many patient years, he prepared for war with England.   For Drake was ravaging Spanish territory ; and an English army under Leicester, having occupied the Netherlands after the death of William, though they accomplished little, gave just cause for an open quarrel.   Whenever, in the course of the Counter-Reformation, it came to a duel between Spain and England, the fate of Protestantism would be staked on the issue.   That conflict was finally brought about, not by the revolt of the Netherlands, but by the most tragic of all histories, that begins at Holyrood with the murder of Riccio and ends twenty-one years later at Fotheringay.

When Mary Stuart came to Scotland the country had just become Protestant.   She did not interfere with the settlement, but refused to permit the suppression of Catholicism, and became, in opposition to the most violent of the reformers, a champion of religious toleration. John Knox differed from all the Protestant founders in his desire that the Catholics should be exterminated, root and branch, either by the ministry of the State, or by the self-help of all Christian men.   Calvin, in his letter to Somerset, went very far in the same direction, but not so far as this.   The nobles, or rather the heads of clans, in whom the power of society resided, having secured the Church lands, were not so zealous as their preachers, and the queen succeeded in detaching them.   Mary was religious without ferocity, and did not share the passions of her time.   She would have been willing to marry Leicester, and to make herself dependent on English policy, but Elizabeth refused to acknowledge her right of succession, and drove her to seek connection with the Catholic Powers. She wished at one time to marry Don Carlos, that, having been Queen of France, she might become Queen of Spain. This was impossible ; and so she became the wife of Darnley, who united the blood of the Tudors and the

Stuarts. She belonged, on her mother's side, to the house of Guise, whose princes were leaders of the militant Counter-Reformation. The duke, who had slaughtered the Huguenots at Vassy, was now dead. But his brother, the Cardinal, who afterwards claimed the merit of a more signal massacre, was still an important personage in Church and State. Mary, appearing on this background of sanguinary uncles, was believed to be an adherent of their policy, and to take part in all extremes of the Catholic reaction.

Riccio, the Piedmontese secretary, through whom she corresponded with foreign princes, was hated accordingly; and Darnley, who attributed to the Italian's influence his own exclusion from power, consented that he should be made away with. The accomplices who wrought the deed took care that Mary should know that they acted with his approval; and when she found herself the wife of an assassin and a coward, the breach ensued which was sometimes dissembled but never repaired. Three months later their son was born, but Darnley was not present at the christening. His enemies advised the queen to obtain a divorce, but she objected that it would injure the prospects of her son. Maitland then hinted that there might be other ways of getting rid of him. Mary did not yield consent; but the idea once started was followed up, and the king was doomed to death by what was called the Bond of Craigmillar.

At the end of 1566 he fell seriously ill at his father's house at Glasgow. Mary came, spent three days with him, and an explanation took place, amounting apparently to a reconciliation. Darnley was taken to Edinburgh, and lodged about a mile from Holyrood, at the Kirk-o'-Field, where he was repeatedly visited by the queen. On the night of 9th February she went away to attend a ball, and three hours after she had left him his house was blown up, and he was found in the garden, strangled. Nobody doubted at the time, or has ever doubted since, that the crime was committed by the Earl of Bothwell, a rough and resolute soldier, whose ambition taught him to seek fortune as a supporter of the throne. He filled Edinburgh with his troops, stood his trial, and was at once acquitted. Thereupon his friends, and some who were not his friends, acting under pressure, resolved that he should marry the queen. As a widow, she was helpless. Bothwell possessed the energy which Darnley wanted, and, as he was a Protestant, the queen would be less isolated. He had killed her husband ; but then her husband was himself a murderer, who deserved his fate. Bothwell, encouraged by many of the Lords, had only executed justice on a contemptible criminal. There was a debt of gratitude owing to him for what he had done.

Public decorum forbade that the queen should ostensibly accept the offer of a man who made her a widow ten weeks before. Therefore Bothwell waylaid the queen at the Brig of Almond, some miles from Edinburgh, dispersed her attendants, and carried her off to Dunbar. There was a difficulty about the marriage, because he was married already. He now procured a divorce, and, ten days after the outrage at Almond Brig, they reappeared at Edinburgh. The queen publicly forgave Bothwell for what he had done, made him a duke, and, on 15th May, three months after the explosion at Kirk-o'-Field, married him according to the Presbyterian rite. The significant sequence of these events gave an irresistible advantage to her enemies. It was an obvious inference that she had been a party to the murder of the king, when she was so eager to marry the man that slew him. The only answer would be by discarding him. Nobody could think the son safe in the hands of his father's murderer.

Either the Lords must get the queen into their power, or they must dethrone her and govern Scotland during the long minority of her son. The forces met at Carberry Hill. There was no fight. Mary hoped, by a temporary parting from her third husband, to save her crown. She passed into captivity, was shut up at Loch Leven, and compelled to abdicate. The Protestant interest was at last supreme.

Mary escaped from her island prison, gathered an army, gave battle at Langside, and lost it, and then, losing courage before her cause was helpless, fled to England, in the belief that Elizabeth would save her.

From the death of Darnley, still more after her Protestant marriage, she had ceased to be the champion of her own Church. That was again her position when she came to England. There, she was heir to the throne, and the centre of all the hopes and efforts to preserve or to restore Catholicism.

The story of Mary Stuart cannot be told without an understanding in regard to the Casket Letters. They are still the object of an incessant controversy, and the problem, although it has made progress of late, and the interest increases with the increase of daylight, remains unsolved. The view to be taken of the events depends essentially on the question of authenticity. If the letters are what they seem to be, the letters of the queen to Bothwell, then she is implicated in the murder of her husband. If they are not authentic, then there is no evidence of her guilt. Everybody must satisfy himself on this point before he can understand the ruin of the Catholic cause in Scotland and in England, and the consequent arrest of the Counter-Reformation in Europe.

At the same time the issue does not seriously affect the judgment of History on the character of the queen herself. She repeatedly expressed her delight in murder, and her gratitude to those who executed or attempted it, and stands on the same level of morality with the queen her mother-in-law, or with the queen her rival. But the general estimate does not throw light on the particular action, and supplies no help in a hanging matter.

The opinion of historians inclines, on the whole, in her favour. About fifty writers have considered the original evidences sufficiently to form something like an independent conclusion. Eighteen of these condemn Mary, thirty pronounce her not guilty; two cannot make up their minds. Most of the Catholics absolve, and among Protestants there is an equal number for and against.

The greater names are on the hostile side. They do not carry weight with us, because they decided upon evidence less complete than that which we possess. Four of the greatest, Robertson, Ranke, Burton, Froude, were all misled by the same damaging mistake. The equal division of the Protestants shows how little any religious bias has had to do with the inquiry; so that the overwhelming majority on the Catholic side requires explanation.

There have been two reasons for it. Many found it difficult to understand how a woman who died so edifying a death could have been a murderess. It would be easy to find many instances of men in that age who led holy lives and died with serenity, but who, in the matter of homicide, had much in common with the Roman triumvirs, or the heroes of the French Revolution. But persons disposed to admit that difficulty would naturally be impressed by an argument of much greater force. The man who produced the famous letters, the Chancellor Morton, was a notorious villain. He had kept guard at Holyrood while his friends slew Riccio. Further, many have admitted, many more are now ready to admit, that some portion of the letters is forged. In that case, how can we accept evidence which the forgers have supplied? How can we send Mary to the scaffold on the testimony of perjured witnesses? Either we must say that the proofs are genuine throughout, and that Morton did not suffer them to be tampered with, or we must absolve Mary. Nobody, I think, at the present day, will deny that the letters, as we have them, were tampered with. Therefore we must hold Mary to be not guilty. Everybody can see the force of this argument, and the likelihood that it would impress those who expect to find consistency in the lives and characters of men, or even of women.

On 20th June 1567 Morton captured Dalgleish, one of Bothwell's men, who had helped to kill Darnley. In order to escape torture—he did not escape capital punishment—Dalgleish delivered up a silver gilt casket which had belonged to the queen's first husband, and which now contained papers, the property of her third husband

Among them were eight letters, not directed, or dated, or signed, but which were recognised by those who saw them to be in the handwriting of the queen.

Towards the end of July it began to be whispered, by Moray in London, by Throckmorton at Edinburgh, that they proved her complicity in the death of Darnley, and justified the Lords in deposing her. In the following year, when Mary had sought a refuge in England, these papers were produced, and they furnished the argument by which Elizabeth justified the detention of the Scottish queen. The decisive piece is a long document, known as the Glasgow letter, which alludes distinctly to the intended crime. As it contains a conversation with Darnley, which he repeated to Crawford, one of his officers, the confirmation thus supplied caused it to be widely accepted at the time, and by the four writers I named just now.

That is what puts them out of court; for the letter was evidently concocted by men who had Crawford's report before them. The letter is spurious, and it is the only one that connects the queen with the death of Darnley. It does not follow that the others are spurious, for they add nothing to the case. The forgers, having constructed the damning piece, would not be likely to do more. Every additional forgery would increase the risk of detection, without any purpose. What purported to be the originals do not exist. They can be traced down to 1584, and no farther. The handwriting can no longer be tested. Until lately, the French text of the letters was not known, and they could be studied only in translations.

Since 1872, when the Hatfield letters were discovered, and were printed at Brussels, we possess four in their original shape. These cannot be seriously impeached. The comparison of the style and language with that of Mary's undisputed writings shows that they correspond; and they do not resemble in the same degree those of her contemporaries. The ablest of Mary's advocates accept these letters as genuine. But they deny that they were written to Bothwell. The writer speaks of a secret marriage, which she would like to disclose. There certainly was no secret marriage with Bothwell; but it is a possible hypothesis that she may have married Darnley in secret before the ceremonial wedding. Therefore this letter, which is a love letter, is quite legitimate, and is meant for the right address. But the word which the queen uses, marriage, is employed in the sense of a wedding ring, as they say alliance or union, to this day, in the same meaning. She is regretting that she must wear the ring round her neck, and cannot produce it in public, because of Darnley.

Besides the one which is spurious and the four which are genuine, there are three other letters which we do not know in the original French. They cannot be tested in the same manner as those I have just spoken of, and cannot be accepted with the same confidence. If, then, we divide the letters in this way: one evidently forged, four evidently genuine, and three that are best left aside, the result is that there is no evidence of murderous intent. But it would appear that Mary wished to be carried off by Bothwell, and that she meant to marry him. How she proposed to dispose of her living husband, whether by death or by his consent to divorce, we cannot tell. The case is highly suspicious and compromising; but more than that is required for a verdict of guilty in a matter of life and death.

What is known as the Penal Laws begins with Mary's captivity in England. There was the northern rising; the Pope issued a Bull deposing Elizabeth, and Philip undertook to make away with her; for the Queen of Scots, once Queen of France, now fixed her hopes on Spain and the forces of the Counter-Reformation. The era of persecution began which threw England back for generations, while France, Germany, Austria, the Netherlands were striving for religious freedom. It was proposed to extirpate the Catholics. Negotiations were opened with the Scots to give them back their queen, on condition that they would at once put her to death. And when she had been condemned for plotting treason, Elizabeth asked her gaoler to murder her in her prison. The execution at Fotheringay gave Elizabeth that security at home which she could never have enjoyed while Mary lived. But it was the signal of danger from abroad. Philip II. was already preparing for war with England when Mary bequeathed her rights to him. The legal force of the instrument was not great, but it gave him a claim to fight for, constituting the greatest enterprise of the Reformation struggle. Sixtus V., the ablest of the modern Popes, encouraged him. Personally, he much preferred Elizabeth to Philip, and he offered her favourable terms. But he gave his benediction, and even his money, to the Spaniards when there was a chance that they would succeed. And their chances, in the summer of 1588, seemed very good. The Armada was stronger, though not much stronger, than the English fleet ; but the army that was to be landed at the mouth of the Thames was immeasurably superior to the English. This was so evident that Philip was dazzled and listened to no advice. They might have sailed for Cork and made Ireland a Spanish stronghold. They might have supplied Farnese with the land force that he required to complete the conquest of the revolted provinces, putting off to the following year the invasion of England. When they came in sight of Plymouth, Recalde, one of the victors of Lepanto, and Oquendo, whose name lasted as long as the Spanish navy, for the ship of the line that bore it was sunk in Cervera's action, demanded to fight. But the orders were peremptory to sail for Dunkirk and to transport Farnese to Margate. The Armada made the best of its way to Gravelines, where they were attacked before Farnese could embark, and the expedition failed.

An American writer, meditating upon our history at Battle, on the spot where Harold fell, once expressed his thought in these words, " Well, well, it is a small island, and has been often conquered." It was not conquered in August 1588, because Drake held the narrow seas. The credit was not shared by the army. And it may be a happy fortune that the belated levies of Tilbury, commanded by Leicester, never saw the flash of Farnese's guns. For the superiority of Spain was not by sea, nor the greatness of England on land. But England thenceforth was safe, and had Scotland in tow. Elizabeth occupied a position for which her timorous and penurious policy, during so many years, had not prepared the world. She proposed terms to Philip. She would interfere no more in the Low Countries, if he would grant toleration. Farnese entered into the scheme, but Philip refused. The lesson of the Armada was wasted upon him. He did not perceive that he had lost Holland as well as England.

The revolt of the Netherlands created a great maritime power; for it was by water, by the dexterous use of harbours, estuaries, and dykes, that they obtained independence. By their sea power they acquired the trade of the Far East, and conquered the Portuguese possessions. They made their universities the seat of original learning and original thinking, and their towns were the centre of the European press. The later Renaissance, which achieved by monuments of solid work what dilettantism had begun and interrupted in the Medicean age, was due to them and to the refuge they provided for persecuted scholars. Their government, imperfect and awkward in its forms, became the most intelligent of the European governments. It gave the right of citizenship to revolutionary principles, and handed on the torch when the turn of England came. There the sects were reared which made this country free; and there the expedition was fitted out, and the king provided, by which the Whigs acquired their predominance. England, America, France have been the most powerful agents of political progress; but they were preceded by the Dutch. For it was by them that the great transition was made, that religious change became political change, that the Revolution was evolved from the Reformation.

VIII

THE HUGUENOTS AND THE LEAGUE

WHEN the religious frontiers were fixed in the rest of Europe, in France, the most important state of all, they were still unsettled. There the struggle was obstinate and sanguinary, and lasted more than thirty years, ending, towards the close of the century, with the triumph of the Crown over the nation, and the State over the Church.

Although the French had had at least one reformer before the Reformation, and were prepared by the Gallican system for much divergence from prevailing forms of medieval Catholicism, they received the new ideas as an importation from Germany. In that shape, as Lutheranism, they never became an important force in the country, though there was a time of comparative toleration, followed, after 1535, by the severities which at that time became usual in Europe. The number of victims in the last years of Francis I. is supposed to have been eighty-five or a little more. Luther, in his life and thought, presented so many characteristics of the exclusively German type as to repel the French, who, during many years of that generation, were at war with Germany. After his death, the first man among the reformers was a Frenchman, and the system as he recast it was more congenial. Calvinism possessed the important faculty of self-government, whilst Lutheranism required to be sustained by the civil power. For these reasons the Calvinistic doctrines obtained a far more favourable hearing, and it is in that shape only that the Reformation struck root in France.

King Henry II., who had been educated in Spain, where he was detained as a hostage, was resolutely intolerant, and when the general peace was concluded he turned his thoughts to the state of religion. He made an attempt to introduce the Inquisition, but was killed in a tourney before he had achieved his purpose. The Protestants at that time were estimated by Calvin at about 300,000, and in certain districts they were increasing rapidly. They had two translations of the Bible, and a celebrated book of hymns ; and they now began to combine and organise. They were strongest in Dauphiny, which was near Geneva, and at Lyons, which was a centre of trade. Then they spread to Normandy, and in the west, and as time went by it became difficult to say which part of the country or which class of the population was most deeply influenced by their doctrine. No province ever became Protestant, and hardly any town. There never was any prospect that the Reformation would prevail ; but at first, in the tide of early expansion, this was not quite evident, and they dreamt, not of liberty only, but of predominance. They did not profess the liberal principle, and never repudiated the maxim of their chief at Geneva regarding the repression of other sects. They thought it a life and death struggle, persuaded that the Catholics were irreconcilable, and impossible fellow-subjects and neighbours. By image-breaking, assaults on processions, and general violence, they made the part of tolerant Catholics difficult to play. As a religious body, guided by the counsels of Calvin, they should have professed passive obedience. But they were associated with vast political interests, and with men less eager about points of doctrine than about affairs of state, who brought them into action against the government. As there were princes of the blood among them, and even crowned heads, resistance to the authority of the day was not felt to be seditious. In this way it came to pass that while Calvin at Geneva was preaching non-resistance, Calvinists in France formed an armed opposition and became involved in plots.

As the new king was too young to govern, Queen Catharine, his mother, became nominal Regent ; but as he was married to Mary Stuart, her uncles governed the kingdom. One of them was the Duke of Guise, the conqueror of Calais, and the most popular soldier in France. His brother, the Cardinal of Lorraine, one of the most conspicuous ecclesiastics of the age, was a Gallican prelate, obnoxious to Rome, and willing to concede much in favour of the Confession of Augsburg as an arm against Geneva, maintaining his power by every means, and an avowed and unshrinking advocate of assassination. Against the administration of these men, princes and Protestants combined. Their plans were detected ; many accomplices were put to death at Amboise, and the Prince of Condé was arrested, tried, and in imminent danger of execution, when Francis II. died, and the reign of the Guise was at an end.

Catharine, whose effective regency now began in the name of Charles IX., her second son, rested on the moderates. There was so little passion in her religion that people doubted whether there was much conviction. When Pius V. proffered advice as to the king's marriage, she replied that he was old enough to act for himself, without foreign interference. She assured Elizabeth that she would have no objection if she treated her Catholics as Protestants were treated in France on St. Bartholomew's day. Once, on the report of a Protestant victory, she declared that she was quite ready to say her prayers in French. In Italy, her want of zeal made people suppose that she was at heart a Huguenot. She encouraged the liberal and conciliatory legislation of L'Hôpital ; for the most striking feature of the time is the sudden outbreak of tolerant opinion.

To arrest this surrender of Counter-Reformation policy, and the ruin which it portended to the Church in France, Guise fell upon a congregation of Protestants, and mingled their blood with their sacrifices. This is the massacre of Vassy, which provoked the wars of religion. They lasted, with intervals, sometimes of several years, for a whole

M

generation, and effaced the country as a European Power. This long obliteration protracted the struggle in the Netherlands, led to the fall of Mary Stuart, and assisted the triumphant rise and growth of England in the middle years of Elizabeth. During the sixties Coligny advanced steadily to the highest place in his party and in the State, and he repeatedly secured terms which satisfied the Protestant leaders, though at the expense of their followers.

The third war of religion, the war of 1569, in which the Huguenots were defeated in the historic battles of Jarnac and Moncontour, had been so devastating that the government lost the disposition to go on fighting, and counsels of moderation prevailed. Coligny, summoned to advise, was listened to with attention, and a marriage was decided on between the king's sister, Margaret of Valois, and Henry of Bourbon, the young King of Navarre, whose birthright made him the head of the Protestant interest. Before the wedding was celebrated a change occurred in the European situation which profoundly affected the policy of France. The revolt broke out in the Netherlands, the real revolt, which was not the work of Belgian nobles, but of the Water Beggars, who took advantage of the maritime configuration, and accomplished the deliverance of the northern provinces.

This was Coligny's opportunity. It was the manifest policy of France to intervene, now that the conflict was a serious one, and to rectify the frontier along the line of peril, by which the capital was exposed to attack. What could not have been attempted while Alva held the provinces in subjection, was possible now that his power was shaken to its foundation. England was an obstacle, because England preferred Spanish masters in the Low Countries to French; but it was possible to negotiate compensation with Elizabeth; and Charles IX., under pressure from Coligny, concluded a treaty with her. He also decided that a Protestant force should join the Flemish insurgents in their operations against the Duke of Alva. If they succeeded, their success was to be followed up, and the merit of the expected conquest would be theirs. Conciliation and peace at home would be purchased by victories over the Spaniard. If they failed, they would be disavowed. Accordingly, in July 1572, an expedition under Genlis went to the relief of Mons, and was betrayed and defeated. The Huguenots had had their opportunity and had made nothing of it. The perfidy of the French government was detected, and the king, in his embarrassment, denounced the invaders, and urged Alva to make short work with prisoners. At the same time, he did not give up the scheme that had begun so badly, the scheme for the conquest of Flanders by a forlorn hope of Huguenots.

Coligny was to have another chance of securing liberty by the splendour of his services to the country, and the wedding of the Princess Margaret of Valois with Navarre, in defiance of the Pope's refusal of the requisite dispensation, proclaimed that the court had gone over to the Protestants. France was on the brink of a war with Spain, in which the admiral would have the command of her armies. It was to be a war for Protestant predominance, with France at the head of the Protestant interest in Europe, and Protestants in high offices at home. Queen Catharine was resolved not to submit to their ascendency, and she knew a short way out of it. There was a blood-feud of nine years' standing between the House of Guise and the admiral who had never succeeded in vindicating himself from the suspicion that he was cognisant of the murder of the former Duke of Guise at the siege of Orleans. They were glad to obtain their revenge; and one of their bravos, after two days' watching, shot Coligny, wounding him severely but not mortally. His friends, who were collected at Paris in large numbers, insisted on satisfaction. Catharine then informed her son that there could be no punishment and no inquiry, that the real culprit was herself, and that if anything was done, by way of justice, Guise would cast upon her all the ignominy of the attempt, all the ignominy of its failure. Nothing could save her but the immediate destruction of Coligny and his chief adherents, all conveniently within reach. The king hesitated. Not from any scruple; for when the Parliament had offered a reward for the capture of the admiral, he had obliged them to add the words—alive or dead. But he hesitated to surrender the hope of annexing Flanders, the constant and necessary object of national policy.

Late in the day after that on which Coligny received his wound, the civic authorities were warned to hold their men in readiness, when the bell of the church near the Louvre, St. Germain of Auxerre, rang the tocsin. This was the beginning of that alliance between the rural aristocracy of Catholic France and the furious democracy of the capital which laid the inauspicious foundation of the League. Their objects were not entirely the same. The Parisian populace were indiscriminately murderous and cruel, killing every Huguenot they knew. The Spanish envoy wrote: "not a child has been spared. Blessed be God"! Guise had his thoughts fixed on political enemies. Some Protestant officers who lived beyond the Seine, hearing the tumult, took horse and made off before it reached them, and were pursued by Guise for many hours along the north road. When Guise gave up the chase and returned to Paris, his house became a refuge for many obscure persons from whom he had nothing to fear. In his absence, the king had laid the blame upon him, and described the massacre as a result of the old quarrel between Guise and Châtillon. This was not to be borne, and another explanation was speedily devised. It was now stated that a Protestant conspiracy had been discovered, and happily crushed in time by a prompt effort in self-defence. This was suggested by the threatening attitude assumed by Coligny's friends in order to compel punishment for the attempt on his life. Both theories were adopted in dealing with England and the German princes. Whilst orders went forth to the local authorities all over France to imitate the example of the capital, every effort was made to avert a breach with the Protestant Powers.

These efforts were so successful that Elizabeth stood godmother to the daughter of Charles IX., while his brother, Henry of Anjou, was elected King of Poland by a union of parties, although his share in the slaughter was notorious. This idea soon became preponderant; and when provincial governors neglected or refused to obey the sanguinary commands, nothing was done to enforce them. The actual massacre was a momentary resolve: it was not a change of front.

The premeditation of St. Bartholomew has been a favourite controversy, like the Casket Letters; but the problem is entirely solved, although French writers, such as Guizot and Bordier, believe in it; and the Germans, especially Baumgarten and Philippson, deny it. It is perfectly certain that it was not a thing long and carefully prepared, as was believed in Rome, and those who deny premeditation in the common sense of the word are in the right. But for ten years the court had regarded a whole-sale massacre as the last resource of monarchy. Catharine herself said that it had been in contemplation, if opportunity offered, from the year 1562. Initiated observers expected it from that time; and after the conference with Alva at Bayonne, in 1565, it was universally considered probable that some of the leaders, at least, would be betrayed and killed. Two cardinals, Santa Croce and Alessandrina, announced it at Rome, and were not believed. In 1569 Catharine admitted that she had offered 50,000 crowns for the head of Coligny, and corresponding sums for others. The Archbishop of Nazareth reported to the Pope in the autumn of 1570 that the Treaty of St. Germain had been concluded with the intention of slaughtering the Protestants when they were beguiled by the favourable conditions granted them, but that the agents disobeyed. He hoped that the Peace of St. Germain had the same legitimate motive and excuse, and advised that a list of proscription should be drawn up. In short, the idea had been long entertained, and had been more than once near execution. At last, the murder of Coligny was provoked by the imminent war with Spain, and the general slaughter followed. The clergy applauded, but it did not proceed from them.

Excepting Sorbin at Orleans and the Jesuit Auger in the south, few of them were actual accomplices before the fact.   After the energetic approval given by the court of Rome, it was not quite easy for a priest to express dissent.

One dauntless ecclesiastic warned the Pope to prohibit demonstrations which revealed the secret of the priesthood. The man who thus disturbed the unanimity of exultant cardinals was Montalto, afterwards Sixtus V., and he deserves to be recorded, because he outweighs many names.   He thought so ill of his predecessor, Gregory XIII., that he was tempted to revoke the best act of his pontificate, the reformation of the Calendar ; and he was quite perspicacious enough to understand that the massacre was the height of folly as well as the worst of crimes.

We have no reliable statistics of the slain.   The fugitives who escaped to England spoke of one hundred thousand.   At Rome they put the figure for Paris alone at sixty thousand.   For the capital a basis of calculation is supplied by the number of bodies found in the river. The result would be something over two thousand.   In the provinces there are reports from about forty towns. The Protestant martyrology assigns two thousand to Orleans alone.   But Toussaint, one of the ministers, who was there, and had the good fortune to escape, knew only of seven hundred, and that is still the belief in the town itself.   It was said that two hundred perished at Toulouse.   But the president, Duranti, who lost some of his own friends, and whose Memoirs were not written for the public, speaks of thirty-six.   In five towns the victims amounted to between one hundred and seven hundred.   In all the rest they were fewer.   Taking the more authentic figures, and in cases where we cannot decide between statements that conflict, preferring the lower figure, because of the tendency to exaggerate where there is passion or excitement, we arrive at rather more than five thousand for the whole of France.   The editor of Queen Catharine's correspondence, La Ferrière, urged me to make some allowance for persons who lost their lives on the byways in attempting to escape.   That is a probable conjecture, but no evidence takes us as high as eight thousand. I reached that conclusion many years ago, and it is confirmed by what has since appeared, especially by the new *Histoire Générale*, which accepts the limit I have mentioned. The higher estimates commonly given are not based on a critical investigation. The character of the event, and of its authors and admirers, is not affected by numbers. For the massacres of September and the revolutionary tribunal wrought less bloodshed in twenty-three months than the French Catholics had done in about as many days. At a time when papal agents estimated the Huguenots at one-fifth of the entire population, the loss of five thousand, or even of eight thousand, would not seriously weaken them. It checked their increase, and injured mainly the royalist element among them, for Coligny was the leader of the party that desired to support the monarchy.

Lord Clarendon has said that it was a massacre that all pious Catholics, in the time in which it was committed, decried, abominated, and detested. There were, of course, many in France who thought it possible to be a good Christian without being a professional murderer, and who sincerely desired toleration. For such men it was impossible to continue associated with the Catholics of the League, and they were in far closer sympathy with the Protestants. In this way a new party arose, which was called the Politiques, and consisted of those whose solicitude for dogma did not entirely silence the moral sense and the voice of conscience, and who did not wish religious unity or ascendency to be preserved by crime. It was on an ethical issue that the separation took place, but it necessarily involved political consequences of a definite kind.

The Politiques became promoters of the regal authority against the aggression of the clergy, the aristocracy, and the democracy. They had their strength among the jurists and the scholars in an age when France was at the head of all scholarship and jurisprudence. The very reason of their existence was the desire to resist the influence and the spirit of Rome, and to govern France on contrary principles to those professed by ecclesiastical authority and enforced by ecclesiastical law. Therefore they strove to reduce the action of the Papacy within very strictly defined limits, to abolish ultramontanism, and to develop the Gallican theory of Church and State which French divines had produced at the reforming councils of the fifteenth century. As the clergy were subject to a Power which had encouraged extermination, they aimed at the supremacy of the secular order, of the lawyer over the priest, and of the State over the Church. They were the most intelligent advocates of the modern state in relation to society. For them, the representative of the State was the crown, and they did their utmost to raise it above the restraining forces. For the purpose that animated them the sole resource was the monarchy; and it is they who terminated the wars of religion, the League, and the Revolution, and prepared the great period of the Bourbon kings. Their ideas survive, and are familiar to the later world in the classic History of Thuanus.

The survivors closed their ranks and rapidly established a system of self-government, which sought safety in its own organisation, not in the protection of the crown. The intense conservatism of the early Protestants was already giving way in the Netherlands, and it now made way in France for the theory of resistance. A number of books appeared, asserting the inalienable right of men to control the authority by which they are governed, and more especially the right of Frenchmen, just as, in the following century, Puritan writers claimed a special prerogative in favour of Englishmen, as something distinct from the rest of mankind. The most famous is the *Vindiciae contra Tyrannos*, by Junius Brutus, generally attributed to Hubert Languet, but written, as I believe, by Duplessis Mornay, a man eminent as a party leader, who lost ground by entering on religious controversy. As an adherent and even a friend of Henry of Navarre, he was moderate in his language. This is the beginning of the literature of revolution. But the Huguenots quickly restrained themselves, for the same reason which, as we shall see, drove the Catholics of the League to the extremity of violence and tyrannicide. The cause of these dissimilar consequences was the problem of succession to the crown. Henry III. had no children, and the future of the Valois dynasty rested on his only brother, the Duke of Anjou, formerly of Alençon, the favoured and apparent suitor of Elizabeth, who by his perfidy and incompetence lost the government of the Netherlands.

In 1584 Anjou died, and nobody remained between the king and Henry of Navarre, the head of the Bourbons. Therefore, if the king died, the next heir would be the chief of the Protestants, a relapsed heretic, whom the Pope had excommunicated. It would be the ruin of the Catholics as a political party, and the renunciation of Catholicism as a system of law and authority, for a relapsed heretic was a culprit to whom the Church could show no mercy. To make him king was to defy the ecclesiastical code, and to abandon the practice of Rome and Spain for that of Germany under the Peace of Religion. The example of Denmark, of Sweden, and of England showed that a Protestant king would impose his religion on the people. They preferred to fight for the principle that a people should impose its religion on the king. This consideration was the origin of the League, as a great confederation distinct from earlier and less important associations. It was constituted out of three distinct elements : first, Guise and his partisans, who had carried on the civil wars, and were the Catholic portion of the aristocracy ; then the Parisian democracy, who had acted with the others against Coligny and the Huguenots, who cherished a strong municipal spirit, and eventually created a supreme commune, such as had existed in the fourteenth century, and was seen again in 1792 and in 1871 ; lastly, Philip II. of Spain, who gave a million crowns.

Gregory XIII. bestowed a qualified sanction, which was not enough to allay the scruples of some men,

Beyond the suppression of Protestantism and the restored ascendency of the Church, on which all were agreed, there was a design to develop local self-government and provincial institutions. All the liberties, they said, that had come down from Clovis, and more if possible. The League was a movement directed against the crown, even if it surrendered to them. There was an idea, vague at first, afterwards more distinct, that Guise descended from Charlemagne, and had a valid claim to the throne; and this was a rift in his alliance with the King of Spain. For Philip hoped to secure the crown of France for his own daughter Isabella, who became the ruler, and the successful ruler, of Belgium. At the time when the League was formed, in January 1585, Philip had reached the highest point in his career. He had annexed Portugal and its immense dominion. William of Orange was dead, and Farnese had already recovered an important part of the insurgent region. He had succeeded, for a quarter of a century, in avoiding a breach with Elizabeth, in spite of the expulsion of his ambassador and of Drake's victorious piracies. If he had pursued the same cautious policy, and had employed, under Farnese against the Dutch, the resources he wasted against England, he might have ended his reign in triumph. The prudence for which he was renowned deserted him when he joined the League, and then made it subservient to the purposes of the Armada. His object was that France should continue to be divided against itself, and that neither Henry III. nor his own confederate Guise should prevail. While those disorders continued, and made the French powerless abroad, the expedition of the Armada was carried out, without interference, and failed by mismanagement.

Meantime, Henry III. was supported in a half-hearted way by Protestants and Politiques, who did not trust him, and Guise, at the head of the population, made himself master of Paris. Henry retired to Blois. After that outrage, refusing to acknowledge that the breach was irremediable, the duke followed, and trusted himself, undefended, in his enemy's hands. Then followed the only thing by which Henry III. could retain his power. He took six days to make up his mind that it was right, and then ordered Guise to be despatched. His brother, the cardinal, met with the same fate. Catharine of Medici, who was in the castle of Blois when this happened, and also had thirty years' experience in such things, died immediately, after giving her son warning that the merit is not in the way you cut the thread, but in the way you sew it. He thought that he was safe at last, and the applause of Europe followed him on his march against the capital. He had shown so much weakness of will, such want of clearness and resource, that nobody believed he had it in him. In the eyes of Parisians he was guilty of the unpardonable sin, for he had killed the popular leader and the champion of orthodoxy. As he was also an ally of heretics and an accomplice of Navarre, a young Dominican came into his camp and stabbed him. His name was Jacques Clément, and he became a popular hero and martyr, and his example is cited by Mariana as the true type of tyrannicide. The action of the crazy friar produced effects that were not intended, for it made Henry of Navarre King of France. A long struggle awaited him before he prevailed against the League, the armed citizens of Paris, the Pope, and the King of Spain. He succeeded by the support of the Royalists and Legitimists, who detached themselves from the theological conflict, and built up an independent ideal of political right.

IX

HENRY THE FOURTH AND RICHELIEU

THE argument of the following half century, from the civil wars to the death of Richelieu, as in the English parallel from the Armada to the Long Parliament, was the rise of political absolutism. Henry IV., the prince who made it acceptable and national, and even popular in France, was fitted to disarm resistance, not only by brilliant qualities as a soldier and a statesman, but also by a charm and gladness of character in which he has hardly a rival among crowned heads. He succeeded in appeasing a feud which had cost oceans of blood, and in knitting together elements which had been in conflict for thirty years. The longing for rest and safety grew strong, and the general instinct awarded him all the power that was requisite to restore public order and dominate surging factions.

The Catholics held out till 1594 at Paris, and still longer in Rome. But the League began to go to pieces when its invincible protector, Farnese, died in 1592. Then Mayenne, the general of the League, who was a Guise, and his brother's successor as leader of the Catholic nobility, came to a breach with the fierce democracy of Paris. The siege, by intensifying antagonism and passions, had produced new combinations in politics and a wider horizon. The Parisians who, twenty years earlier, had adopted massacre as a judicious expedient, now adopted revolution. The agitators and preachers who managed opinion, taught the right of armed resistance, the supremacy of the masses, the duty of cashiering kings, the lawfulness of tyrannicide. The blending of inquisition with revolution was a novelty.

Since the popes had become temporal sovereigns, like the kings of the Gentiles, the tendency of the Church was towards conservatism and sympathy with authority. But the Parisian clergy, when opposing monarchy associated with Protestantism, endeavoured to employ the utmost violence of popular feeling. And they had the support of Rome. A papal legate was shut up in the capital, encouraging it to resist. He belonged to the ancient and illustrious house of Caetani. The last head of that family, the father of the Duke of Sermoneta, lately minister of foreign affairs, once showed me an inscription, in monumental Latin, setting forth how he had at last paid off the immense debt incurred by the legate in the defence of Paris. With Caetani was Bellarmin, the most famous controversialist of the sixteenth century, who there imbibed the doctrines which made him one of the masters of revolutionary Catholicism, and a forerunner of Algernon Sidney. There, too, Mariana had witnessed the scenes of 1572, and learnt the mingled lesson of conditional authority, revolt, and murder, which he taught publicly, and without incurring censure at Madrid or Rome. For thirty years these views prevailed over a wider circle, and were enforced in many volumes too ponderous to survive.

In France the revival of these sanguinary sentiments served to increase reaction and to strengthen the party of the throne. In preference to such defenders of religion and the public good, people turned to the austere Royalists and Gallicans. The change was not final or complete, and did not carry all men with it. Imitators of Jacques Clément arose among the clergy, and Henry fell at last by the hand of a fanatic. When Mayenne sent the leaders of the populace to the scaffold, the defence became hopeless. Henry foiled his enemies by becoming a Catholic. He was not capable of taking dogmatic issues much to heart, and never ceased to hope for reunion, believing that the breach could be repaired, and that men who took pains to understand each other would find that there was no insurmountable obstacle to reconciliation. Many profited by the change who doubted his sincerity. But Henry was in the hands of Duperron, one of the most expert divines of modern times, who proved more than a match for Duplessis Mornay, and whom Casaubon, a better scholar than Duplessis Mornay, described as a thunderbolt of a man. Nobody supposed that he would have conformed if it had involved the sacrifice of the crown. It is not clear that it did actually involve the sacrifice of his conviction. The Pope, under Spanish influence, hesitated long to acknowledge him. It was a defeat and a humiliation to accept as eldest son of the Church an excommunicated heretic, who, by the law of the Supreme Tribunal, deserved to die, and to submit to him because he was victorious over Catholics of France and Spain. His elevation was a boon to the French, because he restored the prosperity of their Church; but it was none to Rome, because his belief was a compromise between Roman doctrine and ethics the reverse of Roman. The delicate negotiation was carried to a satisfactory end by Cardinal D'Ossat, whose despatches were long received, and perhaps still are, as the best in the language, and the model of all diplomacy. Spain followed Rome, and a conference was held under the presidency of the Pope, which concluded peace in the Treaty of Vervins. Then Philip II. died, a defeated and disappointed man, whose schemes were wrecked by an inflexible intolerance; but with his military power undiminished, still the master of incomparable legions, still the ruler of the greatest empire in History.

Henry IV. closed the era of religious wars by granting liberty to Protestants on terms intended to insure permanence. All offices, civil and military, were thrown open; they retained their cities of refuge, and acquired the machinery of equal justice, by the expedient of mixed tribunals. The Catholics gained even more; for whereas Protestant churches were excluded from Paris, and from certain towns which had capitulated on that condition, the mass was restored everywhere, and particularly in two hundred and fifty towns from which the Huguenots, who predominated in the west and south, had banished it.

The Edict of Nantes forms an epoch in the progress of toleration, that is, in the history of liberty, which is the marrow of all modern History.   It is a more liberal scheme than the Peace of Religion, which satisfied the previous generation of Germans.   It pacified France, and afforded to the minority sufficient strength and safety, not on the basis of religious equality, but in the shape of circumscribed and definite privilege.   Some of the Acts of Pacification which failed had been more ample.   Socinians went much deeper in the sixteenth century, and Independents in the seventeenth.   The edict involved no declaration of new principles, and no surrender of ancient claims.   The government made concessions of a purely practical kind, which might be revoked thereafter, if the Huguenots became less formidable and the crown more powerful.   There was no recognition that they were concessions of the moral order, which it would be usurpation to refuse, or to which the subject had a right under a higher law.   The action of the crown was restricted, without detriment to its authority.   No other religious body was admitted but that which had made its power felt by arms in eight outbreaks of civil war.   Beyond them, persecution was still legitimate.   The power of the Protestants was acknowledged, not the prerogative of conscience.   The Edict of Nantes was not one of those philosophical instruments which breed unending consequences, growing from age to age, and modifying the future more and more.   It was a settlement, not a development.   This was the method chosen in order to evade resentment on the part of Catholics and the weakening of the crown.   To speak in general or abstract terms of the sovereign conscience was to urge the contrast between the Roman Inquisition and the spirit of early Christianity, and to promote a breach with the Catholicism of Southern Europe.   To proclaim that the civil magistrate has no right to regulate belief was to limit monarchy and to repel the Politiques, who were the legislators of the day, and who attributed all power on earth to the State, admitting a wise restraint, but no renunciation of right.

The plan adopted achieved the desired result. The Protestants enjoyed the faculty of self-government, and their great writers and scholars were free to influence opinion by their writings. While the stubborn fixity of German Lutherans and Swiss Calvinists lifted them out of the stream of actual history, French Protestantism, like English, was full of growth and originality. The law of the new government was to raise the Crown above parties, and the State above the nation. It was part of the doctrine which Machiavelli revealed to the men of the Renaissance. The Middle Ages had practised class government. The interests dominant in society dominated the State, and employed it for their own advantage. The territorial aristocracy, or the clergy, legislated for themselves and controlled taxation. Venice, which was a republic not of landowners but of shipowners, was the first to revert to the ancient notion of the State acting for its own purposes, bound to no interest, following the opinion of no majority. Venice turned from the sea to the land, and became an Italian Power, in obedience to no class, on public grounds only, regardless of other influences. The French monarchy, as Henry restored it, was of necessity raised above the contending parties, and was the organ of no inspiration but its own. He dropped the states-general, which had been turbulent and hostile, and carried out his measures in defiance of the parliaments. That of Rouen refused for ten years to register the Edict of Nantes. Feeling safe with the Protestants and with the Politiques, who were the real basis of his administration, he devoted himself to the task of winning over their Catholic opponents. The Jesuits represented Rome, the Counter-Reformation, and the League, and were banished for tyrannicide. Henry recalled them, and made one of them, a divine whose life has been written in four volumes, the keeper of his conscience. He was solicitous of the friendship of Rome, and of influence in the College of Cardinals, where his moderating hand was soon felt.

The king's conciliatory policy triumphed in a quarrel which broke out between Rome and Venice. The Papacy desired to enforce a system of its own in matters of Church and State, and, in other words, to make laws for the nations to obey. The Canon Law did not come down from heaven, but was enacted from time to time in the past, and was to be enacted furthermore in the future. Venice, as a modern state, self-sufficing and concentrating power, legislated for its clergy as well as for its laity, resenting interference outside questions of pure doctrine. The two pretensions clashed under Paul V., a zealous and uncompromising pontiff, the founder of the House of Borghese. He claimed a jurisdiction in Venice which could not have been asserted successfully in France or Spain, because a surrender of authority which may be made to superior force cannot be made voluntarily where there is no compulsion. But the court of Rome was the chief seat of those aspirations after the control of states, which had been so lately renewed.

Since the failure of the schemes against Elizabeth and the victory of Gallicans over the League and the medieval ideal, a new heresy, the political heresy, had been discovered, which Cardinal Baronius, the foremost of the Roman divines, denounced as the most damnable of all heresies. By that was meant the notion of a science of politics limiting the ecclesiastical domain ; an ethical and political system deriving its principles elsewhere than from the Church, and setting up a new and rival authority yet to be defined, ascertainable in no book, and not accepted by the nations. Those amongst us who deny the existence of a political science, and believe that ethics cannot be made to include politics, have ardent supporters in the Roman clergy of three centuries ago. The Venetian theorists who could be caught were burnt at Rome. One, who did not trust himself in Roman hands, was badly wounded near his own door. This was the famous Father Paul, whose *History of the Council of Trent* issued from this controversy. He was a Servite monk and theological adviser to the government, and the emissaries who flocked

N

from England, France, Geneva, and the German states, to see how far the Venetians would move away from Rome, believed that he was at heart a Calvinist. In reality Sarpi had more of the eighteenth century than of the sixteenth in his turn of mind, and stood far aloof from the doctrines over which his contemporaries contended, and the expectations entertained of his countrymen were illusory. The city was placed under an interdict, and the orders that were faithful to Rome departed across the Lagoon, singing hymns. The Pope looked about for means of coercion when Henry mediated. He owed much to Venice, which was the first of the Catholic Powers to recognise him. In action, he called to his men to watch where his white plume waved, and to follow wherever they saw it. In gratitude to the Republic he presented it with his suit of armour, which is still conspicuous at the Arsenal, the helmet still displaying the famous feather, changed to a melancholy yellow. Henry induced both parties to yield something of their extreme attitude, and prevented a collision. No such conflict has ever since occurred in Europe.

The other great event in his foreign policy was his protectorate of the Netherlands. By his influence, pursued through an intricate negotiation, the twelve years' truce was concluded. Spain would not consent to a permanent treaty, and when the Thirty Years' War broke out, again fought with her ancient enemy. It was during this truce that the best-known events of Dutch history occurred— the Synod of Dort, the suppression of the Republicans and Arminians by Maurice of Nassau, when he put Olden Barnevelt to death, and compelled the most illustrious of all Dutchmen, Grotius, to make his escape packed in a box of books.

After some years of prosperous tranquillity, Henry IV. found himself the first personage in Europe. He had done much for the army, something for the finances and the national wealth. He was watching for an opportunity to break the power of the Habsburgs, which surrounded him everywhere, and threatened Amiens, not a hundred miles from Paris. He relied on Protestant alliances, and did not despair of the Pope. From Sully's Memoirs, and also from other sources, we learn the lines upon which he schemed to remodel the map of Europe. The Memoirs are not written by Sully himself, and have been tampered with. The Grand Design was never executed, never even attempted, and need not be discussed. Henry boasted to the Spanish ambassador that he would lose no time over Italy; that he would breakfast at Milan, hear mass at Rome, and dine at Naples. "Then," said the Spaniard, "you will be in time for vespers in Sicily." Before starting for his expedition Henry had his queen crowned, that she might act as regent in his absence. On his way to arrange the ceremony of her entrance into Paris he met his death. Rumours of a plot had reached him and made him nervous. While the conspirators were watching for him to pass, a solitary fanatic, Ravaillac, drove a knife between his ribs, and gave a respite to the House of Austria.

Henry's institutions broke down immediately after his death. His widow, Mary of Medici, was unequal to the task of continuing a policy of independent action, relying on no group of friends and on no established force of opinion. The clergy influenced her as they had never influenced her husband. The princes of the blood, the great nobles, the Protestants, became turbulent; and the states-general, summoned for the last time before Lewis XVI., afforded no assistance. The queen gave her confidence to Concini, a Florentine like herself, whom she created a marshal of France. Her son, Lewis XIII., ordered him to be killed in the courtyard of the palace; and his wife, the queen's foster-sister, was put to death by complaisant judges. The young king's favourite, Luynes, governed for a time, until the queen obtained the first post for an adviser of her own, who was the strongest Frenchman of the old régime.

With Richelieu, as with all great men, we do well to ascertain low-water mark, that praise and admiration may not be carried too far. He was not a good administrator, for he considered the general interest, not that of any number of individual men.   Every Frenchman had felt the benefit of Henry's appeasing wisdom, and a season of prosperity had ensued.   But no individual was the better for Richelieu's eighteen years of supreme office. He wasted the treasure on ambitious enterprises, and sacrificed the happiness of the people to the greatness of the king.   No man was richer in sagacious maxims, or in experience of mankind ; but he was destitute of principle,—I mean of political principles, which are the guide of public life as moral principles are the guide of our private lives.   To serve his deliberate purpose, he shrank from no arbitrary or violent excess, putting innocent men to death without scruple, if he thought them danger-ous.   In such cases, he said, it is better to do too much than too little.   He retained a superstitious belief in magic, and never soared above his age with the vision of great truths and prevision of the things to come.   But he understood and relentlessly pursued the immediate purpose of his time.

The work of Henry IV. had been undone during his son's minority, and had to be begun over again.   The crown was only one among many rival forces.   Richelieu decided that they should all be made subject and sub-servient, that the government alone should govern, not any men or any group behind the government, striving for their own ends.   He meant that there should be no dominant interest but the reason of State, no authority but the sovereign, no will but his own.   He pursued this object with perfect distinctness and resolution, and had succeeded when he died in 1642.

The court was an obstacle.   The queen-mother, who had made his fortune, went against him, and the king's brother became a pivot of conspiracy.   For a moment, they triumphed.   Lewis withdrew his confidence from the too imperious and successful minister, who had made his master so powerful and so helpless ; but in one short interview the cardinal recovered his position.   The queen retired from the council, went out of the country, and died, an exile, in the house of Rubens at Cologne.   When the greatest nobles of France, strong in their feudal traditions, rose against his new, and illegal, and oppressive authority, Richelieu repressed every attempt, and cut off the head of every offender.   For he said that clemency was the bane of France.

The Huguenots, safe, but not satisfied under Henry, had felt that they were in danger after his death, and sought to transform the self-government ceded to them at Nantes into a defensive association against the sovereign. The spectre of federalism threatened the hard-won unity of France, and challenged the very essence of Richelieu's policy.   The decisive struggle took place at La Rochelle. Richelieu directed the siege himself, carrying out works as enormous as those of the siege of Tyre, and infusing his spirit into men who did not see that the political issue was superior to the military.   The English fleet outside was helpless to assist, and the starving town yielded to the clerical warrior.   Many thousands had perished, fighting, as they averred, for toleration, in reality for predominance.

The fall of Rochelle was the end of political Protestantism in France as it issued from the civil war; of the attempt to imitate that which the League had done, and to build up a confederation too strong for the State. But the strictly religious privileges conceded thirty years earlier were immediately renewed, and they were faithfully observed.   What Richelieu resisted implacably was disintegration, not Calvinism.   He had no difficulty in tolerating religious dissent.   He would not tolerate political opposition.   Richelieu was a bishop, a cardinal, a practised writer of theological controversy, a passionately resolved defender of the national unity, and of the French patriotism, which the religious struggle had imperilled, but he was not intolerant.   Under him, and under his successor, the Sicilian Cardinal Mazarin, the religion which had been thought so dangerous was allowed to prosper, and the highest offices were crowded with Huguenots.   The rapid expansion of French power was largely due to this policy. It was then that the French proved superior to the Spaniards in war, and the long supremacy of Spain came to an end on land half a century after it had terminated at sea. Several of the marshals were Protestants, including Turenne, the most illustrious of them all. The tolerant spirit of the ecclesiastical statesmen caused the rise of France, and its decline followed the intolerance of Lewis XIV.

Richelieu, if not deeply religious, was thoroughly a Churchman ; but his attitude towards Protestants separated him, on most fundamental points, from the Spanish and Roman persecutors, and he differed considerably from the great divines of the preceding generation. He had just come to power when a book was published at Rome by Sanctarelli renewing the theories of Bellarmin and Suarez, which had excited the indignant resentment of the university and the Parliament. Richelieu required the Paris Jesuits to renounce the doctrines which their brethren proclaimed essential to orthodoxy. And they did what he required of them, accepting, in France, the sentiments of France, and protesting, at Rome, that they retained the sentiments of Rome. They became the friends of their very arbitrary protector. When Father Caussin, the king's confessor, warned him against the cardinal's wars, and his Protestant alliances, his superiors agreed to remove him.

Richelieu refused allegiance to system or party, and opposed the Jansenist and the Gallican as he did the Jesuit extreme. He desired to be aided, not hampered by the Church, and cultivated as much independence as allowed friendship with Rome. Towards the end of his life it was his object to become patriarch of France. The Pope who reigned in his time had been in France when Cardinal Barberini. He was a pontiff of a modern type, when compared with many of his recent predecessors ; and it was in his pontificate that the Roman Inquisition put out its fires. He did not escape the influence of the Frenchman's more vigorous personality. He shared his dread of the Habsburgs and his interest in Gustavus, but they came to a breach at last.

It was in Richelieu's time, and under his auspices, that the great division occurs between the modern Papacy and the medieval, which the Counter-Reformation had revived. The striking contrast between France under Richelieu and France under Lewis XIV. is the tolerance of the one and the intolerance of the other. But no spirit of independence could be safe under the absolutism which the cardinal inaugurated, and which was a glaring inconsistency as long as consciences were free. The change, which was sure to come, came when, under very peculiar constellations, Lewis XIV. desired to show that he was a better Catholic than the Pope.

The cardinal never abandoned the hope of healing the division of churches, which was a calamity in his eyes, both as a statesman and a divine. He provided for Huguenot ministers who were reconciled, and he made serious plans to prepare for reunion, plans which Bossuet resumed, but which had to be given up when the king resorted to violence. The deepest part of the scheme to exalt the throne was the endeavour to raise France above the nations. The opportunity was afforded by the Thirty Years' War. All Europe was involved, the Protestant Powers uniting against the House of Habsburg, which, by tradition, by pretension, and by its actual position and power, was the one constant obstacle to the desired supremacy of the French king. Richelieu assisted them, and ended by openly joining them. Once he said, " I will prove to the world that the age of Spain is passing away and the age of France has come."

It was the contrast of two different epochs of civilisation, of two worlds succeeding each other, rather than a conflict of rival Powers. Spain was inseparably united with the Church and a declared enemy to the rest of Christendom. France lived at peace with Protestants, and based her policy on their support, having political but not religious enemies to combat, gaining all that Spain lost by exclusiveness. It was the adoption of a new doctrine. The interest of the State above the interest of the Church, of the whole above the aggregate of parts, determined the foreign as well as the domestic policy of the statesmanlike prelate. The formidable increase of State power, in the form of monarchy, was an event of European proportion and significance. General History naturally depends on the action of forces that are not national, but proceed from wider causes. The rise of modern kingship in France is part of a similar movement in England. Bourbons and Stuarts obeyed the same law, though with a different result.

X

THE THIRTY YEARS' WAR

THE last and most important product of the Counter-Reformation was the Thirty Years' War. In Germany the rights of the churches had been defined by the Peace of Religion, and the principles of the settlement were not seriously contested.

When the Archbishop of Cologne married and became a Protestant, he endeavoured to retain his political position as one of the electors; but the Catholics were strong enough to prevent it, as a thing foreseen and clearly provided against by law. There had been a constant propaganda on both sides, each gaining ground in some direction, the Lutherans losing much by the extension of Calvinism at their expense. By operation of the accepted maxim that the civil power shall determine which religion may be practised within its territory, Lutheran governments becoming Calvinist carried their subjects with them, weakening the Protestant cause, and presenting a divided front to opponents. In this matter there was one significant exception. The House of Brandenburg became Calvinist, the country remained Lutheran, while the minister, Schwarzenberg, was a Catholic. To this timely divergence from the ideas and customs of the sixteenth century, to this fundamentally different view of the function and uses of the State, the Hohenzollerns owe no small portion of their greatness in history. The Protestants were in the majority, but the Imperial government was still in Catholic hands.

In the hereditary dominions of the House of Habsburg

the situation was different. Under Maximilian II. Austria
had been the least intolerant of European governments.
Equal toleration prevailed at that time in Poland, and led
to the growth and prosperity of the Socinians ; but the
Austrian policy aimed at a compromise between the
churches, and at a system of concessions which made
them much alike.

Under Maximilian's inefficient son, the country went
asunder. One branch of the family carried out the Counter-
Reformation in Styria ; while, north of the Danube, the
majority of the inhabitants was either Lutheran or Utraquist,
that is, attached to Communion under both kinds, which
had been the germ of Hussitism, and was the residue that
remained after the fervour of the Hussite movement had
burnt itself out. In 1609 Bohemia and Silesia obtained
entire freedom of religious belief ; while in the several
provinces of Alpine Austria unity was as vigorously
enforced as the law permitted—that is, by the use of
patronage, expulsion of ministers, suppression of schools,
confiscation of books, and, generally, by administrative
repression, short of violence.

It was not stipulated in the *Majestätsbrief*, as the
instrument of 1609 was called, which was the charter of
toleration under the Bohemian crown, that Protestants
might build churches on the domains of the Catholic
clergy ; but this they claimed to do, inasmuch as the
right was conceded to them on the crown lands, and in
Bohemia these were technically considered to include
Church lands. Accordingly, one was built at Braunau,
and was stopped by authority ; another at Klostergrab, and
was pulled down. At the same time, the intention to
reverse legislation and repress Protestant religion on both
sides of the Danube alike was openly confessed.

The Styrian archduke, the head of the clerical party,
became King of Bohemia and Emperor-elect, the kinsmen
who were nearer the succession withdrawing in his favour.
The Habsburgs felt strong enough to carry forward the
Counter-Reformation even in Bohemia and the dependent
lands, where nine-tenths of the people were Protestants,

with rights assured by a recent and solemn instrument. They had in their favour the letter of the Peace of Religion, by which no prince could be required to rule over subjects differing from him in religion, and the more probable reading of the rule as to the building of places of worship. Against them was the unquestioned text of the *Majestätsbrief*, not yet nine years old. The new emperor did not meditate a breach of faith. Real violence was unavailing where the opponents were in a large majority. The Counter-Reformation had produced in Central Europe a scheme of mitigated persecution, which stopped short of tragedy, and laboured to accomplish, by infinite art and trouble, what the readier methods of the Holy Office and the Penal Law were expected to do. Ferdinand II. was a slow, laborious, friendly man, with a sense of duty and a certain strictness of private life, but without initiative or imagination.

The Bohemian leaders saw the danger of submitting to a man who, without being a persecutor like Henry VIII. and Philip II., would know how to oppress them wisely. Their crown had once been elective ; and the ceremony of election had been revived ten years before when the last king ascended the throne. They resolved to resist Ferdinand, and to call another in his place. War would inevitably follow ; and in order that the country might be committed to their quarrel, as there was no strong popular movement at first, and no national or political issue, they judged that they must begin by giving proof of their deadly meaning. The conspirators, with Count Thurn at their head, made their way into the Hradschin, the gloomy palace that overlooks Prague, and deliberately threw two hostile members of the government, Slavata and Martinitz, out of window. It seems that there is a contagious charm about that sort of exercise which is not evident to those who have not practised it. For seeing an inoffensive secretary, Fabricius, who was trying to make himself as small as possible in the crowd, they threw him after the others. The victims had a fall of fifty feet. None of the three was much the worse for it, or for the shots that were fired at them ; and it is difficult to account for their escape.

Ferdinand, who possessed no army, and was not safe in his palace at Vienna from the insurgents who sympa- thised with Prague, had no means of coping with the insurrection. He turned for aid to his friends in Germany. There, defensive confederacies had been formed both by Protestants and Catholics. The Catholics, con- sisting chiefly of ecclesiastical princes with the Duke of Bavaria at their head, composed what was known as the League, to protect their interests against more aggressive adversaries. And the aggressive adversaries, chiefly Calvinists, for Lutherans combined more easily with Catholics, constituted what was called the Union. For some time they had expected hostilities, and were preparing recruits. There was no lack of fighting material ; but the nation was poor in organisation, and ill supplied with money, and was therefore insufficiently armed. They looked abroad for auxiliaries,—the Union, to Savoy and Venice, Holland and England ; the League, to Spain. Henry IV. had been on the point of seizing the occasion of this open rivalry, and of a disputed succession, to invade the Empire in the summer of 1610. After his death France dropped for a time out of European complications, and thereby helped to postpone the outbreak of expected war. After the insane and stupid outrage at Prague it became an immediate certainty, and Maximilian of Bavaria, the ablest prince who ever reigned in that country, came to the aid of his cousin the emperor, with his own statesmanship, the forces of the League, and an ever-victorious general. The Bohemians had the support of the Union ; and the chief of the Union, the elector Palatine, was elected to be their king. As his wife was the Princess Elizabeth, king James's only daughter, there was hope of English aid. Without waiting to verify that expectation, the elector quitted his castle at Heidelberg, and assumed the proffered crown. But the coalition between Rhenish Calvinists and the Lutherans of Prague did not work. The new subjects exhibited none of the warlike vigour which, under Ziska, had made the Empire tremble ; and the Scottish father-in-law was too good a conservative and professor of kingcraft to abet revolution.

When the army of the League, under Tilly, appeared before Prague, on the slopes of what is called the White Mountain, there was no real resistance, and the new king became a fugitive and an exile, dependent on friends. As he spent but one winter in his capital, he is remembered as the Winter King. For us, he is the father of Rupert and of the Electress Sophia, from whom the king has his crown. Bohemia was treated as a conquered country. The Protestant religion was gradually suppressed, and the insurgents punished by immense confiscations. The country, which had been civilised and prosperous, was the first portion of the empire ruined by the outbreak of hostilities. Ferdinand made the most of the Catholic triumph. Tilly led his victorious army across Germany, from the Moldau to the Rhine. The Palatinate was conquered. Frederic was outlawed, and Maximilian of Bavaria became an Elector in his stead, so that the Catholic Electors, who had been four to three, were now five to two. The Heidelberg Library was removed from the castle, then the finest in Germany, and was sent as a present to the Pope.

Tilly was a Belgian, born in the town of that name, near Waterloo, to which Blucher retreated after Ligny. He had learnt war under Farnese, and served with the League at Ivry. He fought against the Turks on the Danube, and became a marshal in 1605. He was a soldier of the Spanish school, rigid and severe ; but he was no criminal, like Alva and Farnese, and was the best and most trustworthy servant of the Catholic cause in Germany. For ten years, from the White Mountain, he carried all before him. The Union was dissolved. But German princes and adventurers took arms one after the other, and dashed themselves to pieces against him. When he was master of the valley of the Rhine, foreign Powers, alarmed at his progress, began to intervene. France, England, Holland advanced funds, and Christian

IV. of Denmark led an army into Northern Germany. Tilly defeated him, as he had defeated every other enemy. His incessant success strengthened the Catholics, the League, the Duke of Bavaria, more than the emperor.

Ferdinand's allies served him so well that they threw him into the shade. The losses of the Protestants were not directly his gains. For that, in order that he might reap the full harvest which others had sown, he needed a great army commanded by a general of his own. In due time he acquired both one and the other. He commissioned Wallenstein to raise an Imperial force, independent of the League, and to complete the conquest of Germany.

Wallenstein was a Bohemian noble, a convert and pupil of the Jesuits, better known for his success in finance than in war. When the confiscations were going on, he speculated in land. Having thriven greatly, he lent large sums to the emperor. He gave valuable assistance in debasing the coinage, and became by far the richest man in the country. Watching the moment, he was able to offer Ferdinand an army of 24,000 men, to be raised by himself, paid by himself, commanded by himself, and by officers appointed by him. The object of the armament was not to save the empire from the foe, for the foe was being perpetually defeated ; but to save the emperor from the League, and the oppressive superiority of Bavaria.

It was the beginning of the Austrian army. The regiments that followed Wallenstein to the sea still subsist, and are the same that fought under Eugene and the archduke Charles. They were quickly victorious ; they overran Silesia, and at the bridge of Dessau they gained a victory over Mansfeld.

Mansfeld was one of the mere adventurers who disgrace the war. But he was a born soldier. Repulsed on the Elbe, he made his way through the hereditary provinces, intending to embark at Venice for England. In a Bosnian village his strength gave out. His death was nobler than his life, and is a legendary reminiscence in Germany. For he buckled on his armour, made his companions hold him upright, and met death standing, with his drawn sword.

Wallenstein was rewarded by being made Duke of Mecklenburg and admiral of the Baltic. He governed his principality well; but his fleet and his docks were destroyed by the Danes, and he was forced to raise the siege of Stralsund. He was unable to act in combination with Tilly and the League. They wished to make their religion dominate, without detriment to their position in the empire. Wallenstein meant that the emperor should dominate, at the expense of the princes, whether Catholic or Protestant, between whom he made no distinction. The very existence of the force under his command implied that the purpose and policy of the Habsburgs were not those of their allies, and that, after profiting by their services, he meant to rob them of their results. His imperialism was so dazzling, his success so unbroken, that Ferdinand would not check him, but strove to appease the League with fair assurances, and to induce its efficient leader Maximilian to trust the commander-in-chief.

Ferdinand had now reached a degree of power that Charles V. never enjoyed. He had crushed the revolution at home, the opposition in Germany, and Lutheran loyalty was still unshaken. In his desire to conciliate the League, while he made their conquests serve his power, in March 1629 he published an edict restoring to the clergy all the Church property in Protestant hands. The Lutherans would have to give back two archbishoprics, twelve bishoprics, innumerable abbeys; while the Calvinists were to lose the benefit of the Peace of Religion. The Edict of Restitution gave up the immediate purposes of the empire for those of the Church, and drove all Protestant forces to unite in resistance to it. And it extended the rights of conquest over princes who had taken no part in the war. It was the repudiation of Wallenstein's policy, and of his schemes for regenerating the Empire, and he caused it to be known that he would not execute the new orders. Ferdinand had to choose between Wallenstein and the League. By the advice of France, represented by a Capuchin, who was the ablest diplomatist then living, he dismissed his generalissimo, and accepted the dictation of the Catholic League. He had to face the consequences of his Edict of Restitution at the moment when he disarmed.

Just then, when all the Protestants were roused to anger and alarm, and when Wallenstein had laid down his sword, Gustavus landed in Rügen. He had been fighting in Poland for the Baltic coast, and there he had encountered an imperial force. Richelieu aided him in making peace with the Poles, and he went forth with a trained army, assured that he would unite all the Protestants of Germany against the Habsburgs. He spent many months in securing his base of operations, by onerous alliances imposed on Pomerania, and on his reluctant brother-in-law, the elector of Brandenburg.

When at length the way through Silesia to the heart of Austria lay open before him, Tilly arrested his march by laying siege to Magdeburg, which commanded the Elbe, and was a Protestant stronghold in the North. The King of Sweden made no attempt to relieve the besieged city ; and in May 1631 Pappenheim, the hardest hitter among the German commanders, took the place by storm. The defenders deprived him of the fruits of victory by setting fire to Magdeburg, and burning it to the ground. Tilly, with difficulty, saved the Cathedral, and handed it over to the Catholics. He then took Leipzig without resistance, hoping to coerce Saxony ; but the Elector, in this extremity, abandoned the neutrality he had maintained throughout the war, and went over to the Swedes. At Breitenfeld, a few miles out of Leipzig, Gustavus, feebly aided by the Saxons, defeated the Imperialists in the greatest battle of the war. It was a victory of the musket over the pike, and the beginning of the long struggle between line and column. Tilly's ranks were ten deep, and the Swedes only three, so that every musketeer fired. The world now perceived that the tardy, patient soldier, who had seemed too cautious about his retreat to prepare his advance, was a mighty conqueror, full of invention and resource and untold design.

He struck at once for the heart of the empire, made himself master of Würzburg, and overran the ecclesiastical principalities of the Rhine, which were the basis of Catholic power. At Mentz Gustavus held his court, treating the princes as his inferiors, endeavouring to conciliate the population. He did not live to declare his schemes of policy ; but all men knew that he meant to be the head of a great Protestant Confederation, and to disarm their adversaries by secularising the dominions of the clergy. He had made no settlement for the future when he marched against Bavaria, the other stronghold of the League. Below Augsburg Gustavus forced the passage of the Lech, which Tilly disputed, and where the latter received the wound of which he died soon after, in the impregnable fortress of Ingolstadt. For more than two centuries his remains were so perfectly preserved that I have looked on his austere features. Down to the last months of his life he had been victorious over every foe, and was the most dangerous enemy of the Protestant cause. Legend took possession of him, and down to the last generation he was accused of being the destroyer of Magdeburg, and of having, from mere fanaticism, deprived himself of his prize. All that he had achieved in incessant triumph fell to pieces at his first defeat ; and the armies of the League no longer stood between Gustavus, now at the head of 100,000 men, and the Austrian capital. But his career of success ended with the fall of his great rival.

When Tilly was defeated, the despairing emperor appealed once more to Wallenstein, who was living in great splendour, aloof from affairs, and showing as much capacity in the administration of his domains as he had shown in war. It was not two years since he had been deposed in disgrace, at the instance of the German princes. Therefore when, in their extremity, they turned to him for protection, they placed themselves in the power of an enemy on whom they had inflicted a mortal injury. He had felt it so deeply that he was in actual treaty, at the

o

time, with Gustavus, for an expedition against Vienna. As Duke of Mecklenburg he was an independent potentate, and he regarded himself as released from the allegiance of a subject. Before breaking off his negotiation with the Swede, he beheld his enemies at his feet. Wallenstein was able to dictate his terms, and to make himself secure against a second dismissal. His army was his own. He meant to obey while obedience suited his purpose, and to act for himself when it did not. Unlike Tilly, the aims of his life were political, not ecclesiastical. With so many reasons for distrust on one side and resentment on the other, a catastrophe could hardly be averted. With Saxony and the Saxon general Arnim, who had been one of his colonels, he kept up an understanding; and they evacuated Bohemia, which they had occupied after Breitenfeld.

Wallenstein's new battalions came into line, and he took up a strong fortified position near Nuremberg, with 60,000 men; while Gustavus stood at the foot of the Alps, and his adherents wondered whether he meant to cross them, and to attack Catholicism in its centre. When the king knew that the imperial army had risen again, and threatened his communications on the road through Franconia, he hurried to measure swords with Wallenstein. He was heavily repulsed, and moved once more towards the Danube, expecting to be followed. He was still the dominating force in Germany, supported, if not trusted, by Lutheran and Calvinist alike. At that moment Gustavus committed a fatal mistake. If, as Oxenstiern advised, he had descended the valley of the Danube into the hereditary provinces, the Imperialists must have pursued him at a disadvantage, and could not have reached Vienna before him. But Gustavus turned westward, towards Suabia, and Wallenstein disregarded his movements. Gathering his forces, he threw them upon Saxony, which had refused to give up the Swedish alliance. The King of Sweden hastened to the rescue, while the Saxon army stood apart, waiting the event. Pappenheim had been detached, and the Swedes, in superior force, found a great opportunity before them. But Wallenstein sent an order in good time to his famous *Lieutenant-divisionnaire*, telling him to give up everything and join at once. That paper, which saved the empire, one of the most memorable autographs in the world, can still be seen, darkened with Pappenheim's blood, in the Museum of the Austrian army. He rode into battle at Lützen with eight regiments of horse, seeking Gustavus. They never met, for they were both killed, and as the king's charger flew in terror along the line, the empty saddle told his soldiers of their loss. It was an indecisive day, leaving the balance of forces nearly as they remained, until Moltke, in one pitched battle, succeeding where Gustavus, Turenne, Frederic, and even Napoleon failed, overthrew for ever the military power of Austria.

Neither the Duke of Weimar nor Oxenstiern enjoyed the personal ascendency of Gustavus Adolphus. The minister could not deal as he did with German princes, nor the German prince with German territory. The Swedish cause was very seriously weakened, and as the emperor gave up the idea of restitution, which was hopeless, and which had done so much to intensify animosities, and as Wallenstein commanded and Tilly was dead, it became possible to discuss terms of peace with the Saxons, who dreaded the moderated emperor less than the formidable Swedes. That situation gives the basis of the tragedy that followed. Wallenstein enjoyed undivided command. If the enemy accepted his proposals, he thought himself strong enough to compel their acceptance at Vienna. He opened two negotiations, one with the Saxons, to get rid of the Swedes, the other with the Swedes themselves. The latter was promoted by his friends, the Bohemian exiles ; but Oxenstiern was reluctant, and required that Wallenstein should declare against his master. If he would do that, he should have the crown of Bohemia. Wallenstein refused, and the matter was allowed to drop.

The scheme which he proposed to the Saxons and Brandenburgers was the restoration of peace on the principles of religious liberty ; the control of belief by

Government abolished ; everything rescinded which had been done since 1618 in contradiction with this principle ; the departure of the Swedes to be purchased by an indemnity. These are the main ideas. They were reasonable conditions of a lasting peace, and would have saved many years of useless war, and prevented the ruin of Germany. Wallenstein designed that the emperor should be compelled to submit, if necessary, by a display of force. What Ferdinand wished for beyond this, what he had striven for all along, the Catholic domination, was hopeless. And if not hopeless, it was a thing not to be desired, and not worthy of the cruel sacrifice of continued warfare. It was the interest of Spaniard, Bavarian, and clergy to frustrate Wallenstein's scheme. They represented that he was a traitor, that he was plotting with the enemies of the empire, that he crowded his camp with Protestants, that he wanted to be king, and compassed the death of his master. Some of it was plausibly near the truth ; and their suspicions were confirmed when the Duke of Weimar took Ratisbon. The Elector of Bavaria had sent full warning ; the Aulic Council had sent positive orders. But Wallenstein refused to move.

Fearing that he might be deposed before he could execute what he had long meditated, he summoned his colonels to Pilsen, and threatened to resign. They pledged themselves to stand by him. The clause, saving their duty to the emperor, was struck out of the declaration by him. He still hoped to succeed. But Ferdinand issued orders that he should be no longer obeyed ; and these orders, proclaimed at Prague to sound of drum, were accepted by the army. A successor was appointed ; Piccolomini, the real victor at Lützen, was made field-marshal ; and the officers were drawn away by the prospect of the impending confiscations. They amounted, eventually, to fourteen millions of florins. The Spanish envoy, Oñate, at last sent word in Ferdinand's name that Wallenstein should be mastered, alive or dead. Wallenstein understood that he was in danger, and begged Weimar to come to his assistance with cavalry.

He started from Pilsen, with the remnant of his troops, to meet Weimar at Eger, where two Scotch Presbyterians were in command, who inspired confidence. But on the way he met the Irish regiment of dragoons, with their colonel, Butler, and required them to accompany him. They were going to Prague, to join his enemies, and were the authors of his death. Butler persuaded the two Scotsmen, Lesley and Gordon, and the few officers, known to be Wallenstein's immediate friends, were invited to a banquet in the castle of Eger, and there cut down. When the Countess Kinsky, who was the wife of one of them, learnt her husband's death, she had the presence of mind instantly to destroy his papers, and the secret of Wallenstein's treason was lost in that conflagration. Devereux, one of Butler's captains, went with a handful of men to the general's quarters and despatched him. The deed was approved by the emperor, and the murderers were rewarded. This is the dramatic end of the struggle, so far as it was caused by genuine problems of Church and State.

A war of aggression and desolation ensued, and lasted many years, without higher significance. When the Imperialists had gained another victory at Nördlingen, Lutheran Saxony made its peace, at Prague, in 1635.

Then Richelieu took up the conflict, to carry on his feud with both branches of the House of Habsburg, and the empire sank lower and lower, German princes and generals betraying their country to the national enemy. In 1643, when Richelieu was dead, a chance of peace began. Five years later it was concluded for Germany, at Münster and Osnabrück, not for Spain. The Empire lost much in population and territory, which were taken by France; still more in authority, which fell from the emperor's hands into the hands of the several princes, now virtually sovereign and subject to no control. The peace of Westphalia gave no accession to the Protestant interest.

In extension, the Protestants lost by the Thirty Years' War. They lost one-half of the Palatinate, incorporated in Bavaria ; and they submitted to exclusion from the Austrian dominions, all but Silesia. Calvinists were now admitted to equal rights with the rest. Protestants and Catholics recovered what they had possessed in 1624. Therefore the cause of the insurgent Bohemians was abandoned, and the men who were thrown out of the window triumphed in the end. Concerning liberty of conscience not a word was said. The power of the interfering State was not shorn, but the idea that the division of Christendom might be healed by force passed away from the minds of men. It had taken thirty years of incessant bloodshed to extinguish the Counter-Reformation.

XI

THE PURITAN REVOLUTION

At the death of Elizabeth, England separated from the Continent in politics, and moved thenceforth in a different direction. Long before, political observers like Commynes and Fortescue recognised the distinctive character and the superiority of the insular institutions ; but these were not strong enough to withstand the Tudors, and the work had to be begun over again. It was begun, upon the ancient ways, with tradition and precedent ; and when that was found to be not quite convincing, it was pursued by means of new, general, and revolutionary principles. The combination, or alternation, of these methods of policy is the peculiar note of the times before us.

When King James of Scotland became King James of England, the country obtained the benefit of being an island, protected by the sea. There was no longer a hostile and warlike neighbour, compelling military preparation and the concentration of power, which made foreign governments absolute. An English officer once congratulated Moltke on the splendid army which he had created and led. The marshal shook his head, and replied that the German army was a terrible burden on the country, but that the long Russian frontier made it a necessity.

James, who had been helpless at home against the nobles and the Kirk, conceived high notions of authority, high ideals of what a monarch may legitimately do for his country, acting by his own lights, his own will, his own conscience, not as flotsam on the changing and uncertain wave of opinion. And he came to England expecting that its wealth and civilisation, and its intellectual culture, which reached just then its culminating point, would afford a more favourable field for advanced theories of State. The Stuarts owed something to each of the two strongest and most obvious currents of political thought in their time. From Machiavelli they took the idea of the State ruling itself, for its own ends, through experts, not depending on the forces of society or the wishes of men uninformed upon complex problems of international policy, military administration, economy and law. And they adopted from Luther his new and admired dogma of the divine right of kings. They consistently rejected an opposite theory, well known to James from his teacher Buchanan, derived from Knox and his medieval masters, and wrongly imputed to Calvin, —the theory of revolution. They had the judges with them, that is, the laws of England. They had the Established Church, the keepers of conscience and consecrated expounders of the divine will. They had the successful example of the Tudors, showing that a government may be absolute and at the same time popular, and that liberty was not the supreme desire of English hearts. And they had the general drift and concurrence of Europe, as well as of the intellectual world at home, of Hooker, of Shakespeare, and of Bacon. The best philosophers, the most learned divines, many even of the most consummate jurists in the universe sustained their cause. They were not bound to believe that idle squires or provincial busybodies understood the national interest and the reason of State better than trained administrators, and claimed to be trusted in the executive as they were in the judiciary. Their strength was in the clergy, and the Anglican clergy professed legitimacy and passive obedience, in indignant opposition to the Jesuits and their votaries. The king could not be less monarchical than the divines ; he could not renounce their support ; and the bond between them was therefore a close one. Starting from the position that the sovereign will shall control and not be controlled, there was no certain evidence that the opposition to it would be deep, or formidable, or sincere. The quick increase of the middle class, which was the seat of sectarianism, could not well be discovered from the returns of taxation. The Stuarts might fairly be persuaded that they were not only wiser than their opponents, but more liberal than they, for the Puritans repeatedly demanded that the wages of heresy should be death. The distinction in point of liberality between king and parliament is manifest in the Catholic question.

James I. wished to avoid persecution. In discussion with two very superior men, Andrewes and Casaubon, he developed conciliatory views pointing to eventual reunion. His mother had been the champion and martyr of Catholic monarchy. His wife was a convert of the Jesuits. He regarded the Penal Laws as defensible on the ground of political danger only, not on the ground of religion. He desired to obtain a working arrangement with Rome, which should ensure the loyalty of the Catholics, in return for the inestimable benefit of toleration. Pope Clement VIII., Aldobrandini, was not satisfied, and sent instructions that James should not be acknowledged unless he pledged himself to much larger concessions. He feared, he said, to go too far in favour of a heretic. His briefs were not made public, but they came to the knowledge of Catesby, to whom they were very welcome. A king who might not be acknowledged was a king who might be deposed. When his advances were rejected, James issued a proclamation against the priests, which was the determining provocation of the plot. The violence with which Elizabeth defended her life against a multitude of conspirators was easily understood. But her successor was under no sentence of deprivation, and the legitimacy of his claim was untouched by arguments forged against the daughter of Anne Boleyn. The Catholics had reasonably hoped that the better treatment which they received at the beginning of the new reign, of the new dynasty, would be continued.

Under the shock of disappointment some deemed

themselves absolved from allegiance, and left to their own means of self-defence. They regarded James as their aggressor. We cannot tell how much they knew of the odious filthiness of his private life and conversation, which foreign envoys described in language which nobody has ever had the courage to print. In any group there might be desperate and passionate men capable of devising crimes which they disguised under the gilding of a higher purpose. We have seen some of them at the murder of Riccio and the defenestration of Prague. But here there were deeper waters. Some of the accomplices, such as Digby, were men otherwise of blameless and honourable character, who could not be accused of hypocrisy. Then certain leading Jesuits were implicated. They were so far from encouraging the scheme that they procured from Rome a formal prohibition of violent designs. But they gave no hint of danger, and their silence was defended on the ground that although a general warning might have been given to save a Catholic prince, the seal of confession was absolute as against a Protestant.

A belief arose that these people were incorrigible. The precedent of 1572 established the right of murder. The doctrinaires of the League and their contemporaries added to it the right of revolution, applying to princes the rule followed against less exalted Protestants. How theorists were divided, or by what subtle exceptions the theory was qualified, nobody rightly knew. The generation that had beheld Guy Fawkes remained implacable. Not so King James. He resolved to perpetuate a broad division between the men of blood and their adversaries, and he founded thereon the oath of allegiance, which did no good. The Stuarts could honestly believe that the motives of persecuting parliaments were not inspired by a genuine sense of public duty, and that they themselves were defending the sacred cause against furious oppressors. The issues are not as plain, the edge is not as sharp as we suppose when we look back on the result. The question to be fought out between king and parliament was not monarchy or republic, democracy or aristocracy,

freedom or the proteus that resists or betrays freedom.
At many points the Stuart cause resembles that of constitutional monarchy on the Continent, as it was in France
under Lewis XVIII., and in Prussia under the Emperor
William. If Bismarck had been there he would have
been the strength of the Royalists, and Cromwell might
have met his match.

On almost every occasion, under James I., opposition
made itself felt, and it became practically important, and
anticipated the future in 1621. Then the Commons,
guided by the most famous English lawyer, Coke, struck
down Bacon, and deprived the Stuarts of the ablest
counsellor they ever had. Impeachment and responsibility of ministers remained.

James's reign is also the beginning of colonial empire.
Virginia was a cavalier settlement, proceeding from the
epoch of exploration and the search for gold ; and New
England was a plebeian and sectarian establishment, planted
by men who fled from oppression. They did not carry
with them very clear notions of human right ; but these
ripened under their oppressive rule among those whom
they persecuted. There was local self-government and
federation in Connecticut, and spiritual self-government
and toleration in Rhode Island ; and from there the two
institutions spread to the United States, and when the
time came, the cavaliers of Virginia, who went out
under James I., surpassed the fugitives of the *Mayflower*.
They produced the Declaration of Independence, and
bequeathed to America religious liberty and the political
function of the Supreme Court. Of the first five presi-
dents, four were Virginians. And in our own history, the
ablest of the men who resisted Cromwell had studied
practical politics in Massachusetts Bay.

The third political event by which the reign of the first
Stuart profoundly influenced the modern world is the rise
of those whom we call Congregationalists when we think
of them as a Church, and Independents when we mean a
party. It is on their account that this epoch is more
fitly called the Puritan Reformation than the Puritan

Revolution. For it is by the sects, including the Independents, that the English added to what was done by
Luther and Calvin, and advanced beyond the sixteenth-
century ideas.   Continental Protestantism reacted on the
Anglican settlement, and our exiled sectaries, before crossing the Atlantic, came into touch, in Holland, with the
most original and spiritual remnant of the German Reformation.   There Robinson completed the system of Robert
Browne, a secondary and uninspiring figure, of whom we
read : " Old father Browne, being reproved for beating his
old wife, distinguished that he did not beat her as his
wife, but as a curst old woman."

The power of Independency was not in relation to
theology, but to Church government.   They did not
admit the finality of doctrinal formulas, but awaited the
development of truth to come.   Each congregation
governed itself independently, and every member of the
Church participated in its administration.   There was
consociation, but not subordination.   The Church was
governed, not by the State or by bishops or by the
presbytery, but by the multitude of which it was composed.   It was the ideal of local self-government and of
democracy.   Institutions which are the work of History
were abolished in favour of popular control ; and an
Established Church, a Church connected with the State,
was the supreme abomination, and went by the name of
Babylon.

The political consequences reached far.   The supremacy
of the people, being accepted in Church government, could
not be repudiated in the State.   There was a strong
prejudice in its favour.   " We are not over one another,"
said Robinson, " but one with another."   They inclined
not only to liberty, but to equality, and rejected the
authority of the past and the control of the living by the
dead.   The sovereignty of the yellow parchment fell
before the light of reason.   As there was no State Church,
there could be no right of coercion over consciences.
Persecution was declared to be spiritual murder.   The
age of Luther and the Reformation was an age of dark-

ness. All sects alike were to be free, and Catholics, Jews, and Turks as well. The Independents fought, as they expressed it, not for their religion, but for liberty of conscience, which is the birthright of man. There was no place in their creed for a special prerogative of Englishmen over other nations, or of Independents over other churches. All this was in the stringent logic of the system, the immediate consequence of their dogmas on the constitution of the Church, and this gave to their liberalism the invaluable foundation of religion. Not every one of them saw equally far, or applied principles with equal courage. In the matter of tolerance they were supported by the Baptists, and after the appearance of Penn, by the Quakers, though their historian deplores it as an unheard-of dogma. In 1641 there was only one congregation in London, and it consisted of sixty or seventy members. Ten years earlier Lord Brooke writes that there were not above two hundred Nonconformists in all England. It is clear that the rapid growth of numbers baffled all calculation. The Independents did not bring on the Civil War, but they were strong enough to bring it to a conclusion ; and when all the direct effects of their victory passed away, their ideas survived.

Charles, a better man but a worse king than his father, had none of his insight. When, after the Petition of Right, he governed without a parliament, the problem is whether he did it for the sake of power or for the sake of religion. It resembles the problem of the American Civil War, whether the confederates were fighting for State rights or for slavery. We call him the martyr of Anglicanism. But there is one moment in his career when, at the price of unparliamentary monarchy, he could have saved Episcopacy. He was in the hands of Strafford and of Laud, and they were strong men. When Charles had to think and act for himself, it may be that his thoughts were not always clear. He was attached to the English Church, but the religious controversy puzzled him. There was a very able man among the queen's chaplains who held that the Thirty-nine Articles might be interpreted favourably to Rome. " The religion of Rome and ours," said Laud, " is all one." It is not strange, perhaps, that he should have been suspected, when so many of the king's ministers—Windebanke, Cottington, Weston—became Catholics, and the same thing was whispered of others. After Worcester, when the Earl of Derby was being taken to Newark to be executed, a strange horseman joined the cavalcade, and rode for a time by the prisoner's side. It was said that this was a priest, who received him, and absolved him, in the hour of death. Although the Roman emissaries who negotiated with the archbishop, and offered him the red hat of a cardinal, never quite understood him, and could not explain why he who was so near was yet so far, they had no hopes of bringing him over. There was even a time when they reported more promising things of Ussher.

But for the religious question, the political opposition could not have carried the country with it. The Roman agents and nuncios were part of the religious question, and it is not prelacy alone that was at stake. In considering the old charge of a design to carry over England to Rome, we must remember this, that the art of understanding adversaries is an innovation of the present century, characteristic of the historic age. Formerly, a man was exhausted by the effort of making out his own meaning, with the help of his friends. The definition and comparison of systems which occupies so much of our recent literature, was unknown, and everybody who was wrong was supposed to be very wrong indeed.

We cannot avoid the question whether the three great victims—Strafford, Laud, and Charles—deserved their fate. It is certain that they were put to death illegally, and therefore unjustly. At the same time, the superior enlightenment and wisdom were not always on the side of parliament. But we have no thread through the enormous intricacy and complexity of modern politics except the idea of progress towards more perfect and assured freedom, and the divine right of free men. Judged by that test, the three culprits must be condemned. That is a principle which cuts very deep, and reaches far, and we must be prepared to see how it applies in thousands of other instances, in other countries, and in other times especially the times in which we live.

When war broke out, the country was divided, not unequally.   North and west were for the king ; but north and west were backward in comparison with the south-east, which possessed London and the longer purse. The familiar line from South Devon to the Humber simplifies too much.   For Charles held Oxford and Nottingham, while the parliament had the seaports, though not all the intervening region, from Plymouth to Hull, and reached the Severn at Gloucester, and the Irish Sea about the Mersey.   Parties were not moved to their depths on either side, as men are by the question of existence, and the contending armies were generally small.   Therefore, the struggle was slack and slow, and the Presbyterian sects became masters of the situation, and decided for the parliament.   At first, through want of energy, great opportunities were lost.   In Montrose Scotland produced a soldier of genius ; but in England the Ironsides prevailed by their organisation and discipline. German writers on military history declare Cromwell to have been the best leader of cavalry in modern war, the master and superior of their own Frederic, whose fame is due largely to his skill in that arm.   The end was an overwhelming victory and a crushing defeat.   But as the chief cause was the genius of one extraordinary man, and the sudden growth and spreading of the religious party to which he belonged, the effect lasted no longer than his life.   The fabric he had reared was overthrown without an effort, offering no resistance to the destroyer.   The soldier, therefore, was greater than the statesman. Opinion, of late years, has become very favourable to Cromwell, thanks chiefly to Mr. Gardiner.   But until the *Lives* by Mr. Firth and Mr. Morley are completed, the last word, for our time, will not be spoken.

Those to whom the great Nonconformist is an object of admiration, have certain conspicuous flaws to contemplate. Cromwell, by his approval of Pride's Purge, was an accomplice after the fact. Colonel Pride expelled the majority, in order that the minority might be able to take the life of the king. It was an act of illegality and violence, a flagrant breach of the law, committed with homicidal intent. In ordinary circumstances such a thing would have to bear a very ugly name. Nor was it an act of far-sighted policy, for the outraged Presbyterians restored Charles II. without making terms. Then, the Protector professed to see the hand of God, a special intervention, when he succeeded, and things went well. It was not the arm of the flesh that had done these things. They were remarkable Providences, and the like. There is not a more perilous or immoral habit of mind than the sanctifying of success. Thirdly, he was the constant enemy of free institutions. Scarcely any Englishman has so bad a record in modern history. Having allowed all this, we cannot easily say too much of his capacity in all things where practical success is concerned, and not foresight or institutions. In that respect, and within those limits, he was never surpassed by any man of our race, here or in America.

As political thinkers both Vane and Harrington are more profound. Harrington is the author of what Americans have called the greatest discovery since the printing-press. For he has given the reason why the great Rebellion failed, and was followed by the reaction under Charles II. He says that it failed because it omitted to redistribute the property of the kingdom. The large estates constituted an aristocratic society, on which it was impossible to construct a democratic state. If the great estates had been broken up into small ones, on a definite plan, the nation would have been committed to the new order of things, and would have accepted the law of equality. Poverty would have been diminished on one side, and nobles would have been abolished on the other. A timorous conservatism and legal scruples made this impossible, and government, by a law of nature, took its shape from the forms and forces of society. It is needless to go quite so deep as this to see that the Cromwellian system, which was the work of a minority, led by a man of pre-eminent services and talents, crumbled when the necessary leader was gone.

The Commonwealth is the second stage on the road of revolution, which started from the Netherlands, and went on to America and France, and is the centre of the history of the modern world.   Seen from a distance the value of that epoch is not in that which it created, for it left not creations but ruins, but in the prodigious wealth of ideas which it sent into the world.   It supplied the English Revolution, the one that succeeded, the American, the French, with its material.   And its ideas became efficacious and masterful by denying their origin.   For at first they were religious, not political theories.   When they renounced their theological parentage, and were translated into the scientific terms of politics, they conquered and spread over the nations, as general truths, not as British exports.   For a long time to come we meet with little that goes beyond the conservatism of Hobbes, or the liberalism of Vane, and Harrington, and Milton, and of Lilburne in his saner moments.   That is our inheritance from the Long Parliament, the Civil War, and the Commonwealth.

We have to deal with events which belong essentially to Constitutional History, and must treat them with a light touch, that we may not trespass on appropriated ground.   Our topic is, how absolute monarchy, which just then succeeded so brilliantly over the Channel, was attempted in England, under conditions of no apparent danger, failed and failed at a great cost.   And how, in the course of the struggle, ideas were developed which proved ultimately strong enough, as well as sufficiently lasting, to carry out an entirely new structure of constitutional government.   It is the point where the history of nations turned into its modern bed.   It is the point also where the Englishman became the leader of the world.

XII

THE RISE OF THE WHIGS

THE Liberal ideas bred in sectarian circles, here and in America, did not become the common property of mankind until they were detached from their theological root, and became the creed of a party. That is the transition which occupies the reign of Charles II. It is the era in which parties took the place of churches as a political force.

A gentleman has written to remind me that the Independents did not jointly or corporately renounce the connection between Church and State, or assert religious liberty as a principle of government. They did individually that which they never did collectively, and such individuals were acting conformably to the logic of the system. In the Petition of 1616 they say, "We deny also a national, a provincial, and diocesan church under the Gospel to be a true, visible, political church." John Robinson writes: "It is the Church of England, or State Ecclesiastical, which we account Babylon, and from which we withdraw in spiritual communion." In 1644 we are told: "Godwin is a bitter enemy to presbytery, and is openly for a full liberty of conscience, to all sects, even Turks, Jews, Papists." The author of the tract, *What the Independents would have*, writes that he thinks it a sin either to follow an erring conscience or to go against it; but to oppose it the greater sin, for he that will do the least sin against conscience is prepared in disposition to do the greatest. Therefore he reckons liberty of conscience to be England's chiefest good.

When I said that the English exiles in Holland came in contact with the most spiritual remnant of the Reformers, I meant the German Anabaptists. The English Baptists and the Quakers were as much opposed to the principle of persecution as the Independents I have quoted.

Only two conditions were imposed on Charles II. before he came over. One of these was liberty of conscience. Cromwell had died without leaving behind him an established Constitution, and his lieutenants succeeded no better than his son. The army refused to obey a parliament of their own creating, the remnant which remained when Pride expelled the majority. It was a parliament founded not on law but on violence, on the act of men thirsting for the king's blood. The simplest solution was to restore the Long Parliament, to give power to the Presbyterian majority, which had been excluded, and was not responsible for the miscarriages and the constitutional instability of the last eleven years. The idea was so obvious that it occurred to everybody—to Monk in Scotland, to Fairfax at York, and to the army which Lambert collected to meet Monk at Newcastle, and which dispersed without fighting for its own imperial supremacy.

It is worth while to study, in the second volume of Guizot's *Richard Cromwell*, the consummate policy with which Monk prepared the desired result. For the recall of the excluded members was the restoration to power of men who had persisted in negotiating with Charles I., of men who had been Royalists in season and out of season. They were no friends of arbitrary government; but it was certain that they would restore the monarchy. A premature rising of incautious Royalists was put down ; and the object of Monk was to gain time, until the blindest could perceive what was inevitable. His hand was forced by Fairfax, who was ill with gout, but had himself lifted into the saddle, and raised Yorkshire for a free parliament. Under that flag Monk crossed the Tweed at Coldstream on New Year's Day. He was already the master of England, and met with no resistance on the way to Westminster. The

Republicans, in their extremity, offered him the crown, which Monk refused. He likewise refused the offers of the king, who would have made him chancellor and grand constable, besides making lavish grants of money, which the general was believed to like. He knew that he was sure of his reward when the time came. It came quickly. The Long Parliament made way for a Convention Parliament, which renewed the fundamental laws, and finally abolished the feudal rights of the crown. Whilst these bills were being voted, Charles issued the Declaration of Breda, proposed by Monk, and resumed the crown without a struggle.

The nation was glad to escape from the misgovernment of the Republic, which had weighed heavily on numerous classes, and believed that the crown had received a lesson which could not be forgotten. The new government was not imposed by a victorious monarchy. It was an expression of the national wish. Parliament retained control, and there was no political reaction.

The changes now introduced went to strengthen not the prerogative, but the gentry, who were the governing class. They were relieved from the payment of feudal dues, by means of a tax which fell on other classes ; members were taken from the towns and added to the country districts ; and the militia, which was to protect society from the parliamentary army, was placed in the hands of the gentry. The new order of things was the work not of a party, but of a class. The dominant cavaliers were willing to refuse a share in their power to the old Puritan enemy, and passed every measure for inflicting disabilities on the Nonconformists. They were excluded from all offices, in the Church and in the State, even in the municipalities. In this way, by a religious test, the class that consisted mainly of Churchmen secured all political authority for themselves. They, however, added a political test. They imposed an oath in favour of non-resistance. Nobody could hold office who was not what was afterwards known as a Tory. This was Anglican doctrine ; and the clergy set to work to rule the country in conjunction with the conservative country gentlemen, on a basis of principles laid down by Hobbes, the philosopher of the day, who denied the rights, and even the existence of conscience.

Clarendon was minister ; and it was an ingenious and politic thing in his eyes to suppress the Roundhead by suppressing the Presbyterian. He had reflected more deeply than any man then living on the problem of Church and State ; and he did not believe in the sacred fixity of divisions founded on schemes of Church government only. Archbishop Ussher had made great concessions to the Presbyterians. Baxter had made concessions to Prelacy. The see of Hereford was offered to him, and it was thought he might accept it. Leighton, who was as much the greatest Puritan divine in Scotland as Baxter in England, did accept the offer of a mitre, and became Archbishop of Glasgow. The restored government was intolerant, because, by intolerance, it could exercise political repression. This did not apply to the Catholics. Clarendon had pledged himself that they should profit by the indulgence which was afterwards promised at Breda. When he adopted the policy of coercion against the Puritans, he was unable to keep his promise. The unnatural situation could not last after his fall. The Puritans had made war upon the throne, and the Catholics had defended it. When it was restored, they proclaimed their principles in a series of voluntary declarations which dealt with the customary suspicions and reproaches, and fully satisfied the purpose aimed at by the oath of allegiance. No people could be more remote from the type of Allen and Parsons than the English Benedictines and the Irish Franciscans who hailed the revived monarchy. Against such men the old argument of Elizabethan persecutors was vain.

After the fall of Clarendon a different policy was attempted. The rigid exclusiveness of the Puritans had bequeathed one sinister vice to the English people. They were complacent in their insularity, and had a prejudice against the foreigner. It had been directed against

Spain, for the sake of Plate fleets to seize and coasts to pillage; and now it was strongest against the Dutch, who were dangerous rivals by sea, both in peace and war. It was least, at that time, against France, whose great statesman, Mazarin, had made terms with the Republic, and retained the friendship of the restored king.   A trivial dispute on the Guinea Coast was fanned into a quarrel by the Duke of York, who was a sailor, and who hoped to strengthen his position at home by his professional skill, in which he only partially succeeded.   This is the war that terminated in the memorable change of front of the Triple Alliance, uniting the Dutch, the English, and the Swedes against France.   It was a popular but totally ineffective measure; and in 1669 England abandoned her allies and went over to France.   Lewis XIV. accomplished this important diplomatic success by the Treaty of Dover, the first in the process of events that overthrew the Stuart monarchy, and brought in the modern type of Constitution.

Soon after his return to England, Charles opened negotiations with Rome, which were carried on through one of his sons, born before Monmouth, who became a Jesuit; and he vainly endeavoured to obtain supplies from Alexander VII.   Later on, he sought them in France. It was impossible, he said, to restore the royal authority unless it was done through the restoration of Catholicism. That could be secured, if Lewis would make him independent of the House of Commons.   The scheme was prepared in January 1669, Arlington consenting, for a bribe of £12,000.   It was decided to restore the Catholic Church in England by such a display of force as should be sufficient to raise the crown above the restraints of parliament.   In execution of the design Lewis advanced £80,000, and undertook, in case of resistance, to furnish a force of 6000 men, to be a French garrison in England, for the repression of Protestants.   The sum was much less than Charles demanded, for the object of the French king was not to strengthen, but to weaken him.   The second point in the Treaty was that England engaged to support France in any claims she might have upon Spain. Lastly, England was to help her ally against Holland, in return for further payments and the annexation of Walcheren. But it was agreed to postpone the Dutch war until the year 1672. That is the solid substance of the phantom which is called the Popish Plot.

It was, in reality, a plot, under cover of Catholicism, to introduce absolute monarchy, and to make England a dependency of France, not only by the acceptance of French money, but by submission to a French army. Charles I. and his ministers had gone to the block for less than this.

If the thing should become known, nobody could foretell the consequences. Turenne was told, because he would be wanted if it came to blows ; and Turenne told a lady of his aquaintance, who proved indiscreet. The king, in a fury, asked him how he could be such a fool. The marshal, not unaccustomed to the experience of being under fire, replied that he was not the only man who had been made a fool of by a woman, and King Lewis XIV. did not see his way to pursue the conversation. His political object was secured, even if nothing should be done in England to fulfil the agreement. He had Charles completely in his power. The secret text only needed to be divulged, in order to raise the country against him. He never again could be formidable. If all other devices for dividing him from his people were insufficient, this one could not fail. Many years later Lewis caused a book to be printed, by an Italian adventurer, in which the secret was revealed. The book was suppressed and the author imprisoned, for the sake of appearances. But one hundred and fifty-five copies were in circulation, and the culprit was released after six days. It became dangerous for Charles to meet parliament. The facts became known to Shaftesbury long before, and determined his course from the time of his dismissal from office, in November 1673. The scheme laid down in the Dover Treaty was a dangerous one, and after the beginning of the Dutch war there were no French troops to spare.

Charles tried another way to gain his purpose.   Both he and his brother desired to establish Catholicism for its own sake.   They were not converts, but they intended to be before they died.   The difference was that James was ready to make some sacrifice for his religion, Charles was not.   They both regarded it as the only means of putting the crown above the law.   This could be done more safely by claiming the right to dispense from penalties and disabilities imposed by parliament.   The idea, entertained as early as 1662, ripened ten years later, when the Penal Laws, as well as the intolerant legislation of Clarendon against the Puritans, which had been considered the safeguard of monarchy, were declared inoperative. The ministers, including Shaftesbury, expected to obtain the support of Nonconformists.   This calculation proved delusive.   The Dissenters, on an assurance that they would be relieved by parliament if they resisted the offers of the king, refused to accept them.   The object of his declaration was too apparent, and was indeed too openly avowed.   Just then the Duke of York became a Catholic, and although the fact was not made public, it was suspected.   Ministers advised Charles to maintain his offer of indulgence and his claim to the dispensing power.   Charles gave way and accepted his defeat.   He gave way because Lewis advised it, and promised him more French regiments than had been stipulated for, as soon as he was again at peace with the Dutch.

The House of Commons followed up its victory by passing the Test Act, excluding Catholics from office. The Duke of York resigned his post as Lord High Admiral.   It was, he said, the beginning of the scheme for depriving him of the succession to the throne.   In November 1673 Shaftesbury, who had promoted the Declaration of Indulgence, was dismissed from office and went into opposition, for the purposes of which Lewis sent him £10,000.   He learnt from Arlington the main particulars of the Treaty of Dover, and in the following month of January the secret was substantially made public in a pamphlet, which is reprinted in the *State Tracts*.

From that moment he devoted himself to the exclusion of James.

In 1676 the Duke of York made it known that he had become a Catholic. This was so gratuitous that people took it to mean that he was strong in the support which the French king gave him. He was still true to the policy of the Dover Treaty, which his brother had abandoned, and still watched his opportunity to employ force for the restoration of his Church. All this was fully understood, and his enemy, Shaftesbury, was implacable.

When he had been five years out of office, in September 1678, Titus Oates appeared. Who the people were who brought him forward, with the auxiliary witnesses, Bedloe, Dangerfield, and Turberville, the one who received £600 for his evidence against Stafford, is still unknown. Shaftesbury was not the originator. He would not have waited so many years. His part in the affair was to employ the public alarm for the destruction of the Duke of York. Therefore, from the summer of 1678 there was a second plot. The first, consisting in the Treaty of Dover, drawn up by the Catholic advisers, Arundel, Bellasis, the historian Belling, and Leighton, the great archbishop's brother. The second was the Protestant plot against the Catholics, especially the Duke of York. The indignation against the real plot, that of Dover, was essentially political.

In February 1675 the opposition proposed to James to restore his offices if he would abandon Lewis. When the imperial ambassador, in July 1677, complained of the No Popery cry, they replied that there was no question of religion, but of liberty. In the case of Oates and his comrades, the political motive faded into insignificance beside the religious. At first the evidence was unsubstantial. Oates was an ignorant man, and he obtained credit only by the excitement and distrust caused by the discovery of the premeditated *coup d'état*. Godfrey, the magistrate who conducted the inquiry, warned James that the secretary of the Duchess of York was implicated. His name was Coleman, and he had time to destroy his

papers. Some of them were seized. They spoke of a
great blow which was being prepared against the Protestants. It appeared also that he was in the pay of Lewis,
and had solicited his confessor, Père La Chaise, for a sum
of £300,000 in order to get rid of parliament. It was
argued that if such things were found in the papers he
had not burnt, there must have been worse still in those
which had perished. It showed that the scheme of Dover
was still pursued, was still a danger. At that moment
the magistrate who sent the warning disappeared. After
some days his dead body was found at the foot of Green
Berry Hill, now Primrose Hill; and one of the most
extraordinary coincidences, so interesting in the study of
historical criticism, is the fact that the men hanged for the
murder were named Green, Berry, and Hill. It was of
course suspected that Godfrey had perished because he
knew too much.

For some time the excitement rose very high. On
the day when two Jesuits were executed, one of the
Catholic envoys writes that nothing else could have saved
the lives of all the Catholics in London. Taking advantage of the state of public feeling, Shaftesbury proposed
that James should be excluded from the succession for
his religion. The crown was to go to the next heir, the
Princess of Orange. This was thrown out by the Lords.
Meantime the second Test Act expelled the Catholic
peers from the House of Lords. James withdrew from
the council, from the palace, and at last from the kingdom.

The second Exclusion Bill was founded, not on his
religion, but on his politics, that is, his treasonable connection with the King of France. The opponents of exclusion proposed limitation of the royal power, in a manner
such as that which has since prevailed. Charles preferred
this amendment to the Constitution rather than an Act
which enabled parliament to regulate the succession.
William of Orange vigorously opposed it, as the same
restraints might be retained when his wife came to the
throne. Halifax, who defeated the Exclusion Bill and
defended the Limitation Bill, assured the prince that it

would never be applied, as James had no chance whatever
of succeeding his brother.   His only purpose in proposing
his Bill was to preserve the succession, according to law,
from parliamentary control.

In order to obtain evidence that should ruin James's
prospects, it was resolved now to put the Catholic peers
on their trial.   Stafford came first.   He had not been in
the secret of the fatal Treaty.   But the plans this time
were cleverly laid.   Although Lord Stafford was entirely
innocent, Count Thun, the Austrian envoy, was profoundly
impressed by the weight of the case against him and the
weakness of the defence.   He was beheaded amid shrieks
of execration and exultation.   Arundel was to come next ;
and Arundel did know enough to compromise the duke.
But the plan had failed.   Nothing had been discovered in
Stafford's trial that could help the exclusion ; and a revul-
sion of popular feeling followed.   Monmouth was now
put forward.   If James could not be excluded he must
make way for Monmouth, if Monmouth was legitimate.
The king was pressed to acknowledge him.   A black box
was said to contain the necessary evidence of his mother's
marriage.   A bishop was spoken of who knew all about
it.   Monmouth himself accepted the idea.   When the
Duke of Plymouth died he refused to wear mourning.
He would not mourn, he said, for a brother who was
illegitimate.   After the Test Act, the Exclusion Bill, the
succession of Monmouth, the indefatigable Shaftesbury
had still one resource.   He tried an insurrection.   When
he found it impossible to draw the line between insurrection and murder, he thought the position dangerous, and
went abroad.   Russell and Sidney were put to death.
Charles was victorious over his enemies.   He owed his
victory to the French king, who gave him £700,000, and
enabled him to exist without a parliament for three years.

It was during this struggle against the overshadowing
suspicion of the Dover Treaty that the Habeas Corpus
Act was passed, and that Party took shape in England.
In general, the old cavalier families, led by the clergy and
the lawyers, acquiesced in the royal prerogative, the

doctrine of passive obedience, the absolute and irresistible authority of that which Hobbes called Leviathan, meaning the abstract notion of the State. They had a passion for order, not for oppression ; good government was as dear to them as to their opponents, and they believed that it would not be secured if the supreme authority was called in question. That was the Court Party, known as Tories. As time went on, after the Revolution, they underwent many developments. But at first they were simply defenders of royal authority against aggression, without any original ideas.

The Country Party was the party of reform. They were the people excluded from the public service by the oath in favour of non-resistance. They believed in the rightfulness of the war which the Long Parliament waged against the king, and were prepared, eventually, to make war against Charles II. That was the essential distinction between them and the Tories. They dreaded revolution, but, in an extreme case, they thought it justifiable. " Acts of tyranny," said Burnet, " will not justify the resistance of subjects, yet a total subversion of their constitution will." When Burnet and Tillotson urged this doctrine on Lord Russell, he replied that he did not see a difference between a legal and a Turkish Constitution, upon this hypothesis.

Whig history exhibits a gradual renunciation of Burnet's mitigated doctrine, that resistance is only justified by extreme provocation, and a gradual approach to the doctrine of Russell, on which the American Revolution proceeded. The final purpose of the Whigs was not distinct from that of their fathers in the Long Parliament. They desired security against injustice and oppression. The victors in the Civil War sought this security in a Republic, and in this they conspicuously failed. It was obvious that they made a mistake in abolishing the monarchy, the Established Church, and the House of Lords. For all these things came back, and were restored as it were by the force of Nature, not by the force of man.

The Whigs took this lesson of recent experience to

heart. They thought it unscientific to destroy a real political force. Monarchy, Aristocracy, Prelacy, were things that could be made innocuous, that could be adjusted, limited, and preserved. The very essence of the new Party was compromise. They saw that it is an error to ride a principle to death, to push things to an extreme, to have an eye for one thing only, to prefer abstractions to realities, to disregard practical conditions. They were a little disappointing, a little too fond of the half-way house. Their philosophy, or rather their philosopher, John Locke, is always reasonable and sensible, but diluted and pedestrian and poor. They became associated with great interests in English society, with trade, and banking, and the city, with elements that were progressive, but exclusive, and devoted to private, not to national ends. So far as they went, they were in the right, ethically as well as politically. But they proceeded slowly beyond the bare need of the moment. They were a combination of men rather than a doctrine, and the idea of fidelity to comrades was often stronger among them than the idea of fidelity to truths. General principles were so little apparent in the system that excellent writers suppose that the Whigs were essentially English, Nonconformists, associated with limited monarchy, unfit for exportation over the world. They took long to outgrow the narrow limits of the society in which they arose. A hundred years passed before Whiggism assumed the universal and scientific character. In the American speeches of Chatham and Camden, in Burke's writings from 1778 to 1783, in the *Wealth of Nations*, and the tracts of Sir William Jones, there is an immense development. The national bounds are overcome. The principles are sacred, irrespective of interests. The charter of Rhode Island is worth more than the British Constitution, and Whig statesmen toast General Washington, rejoice that America has resisted, and insist on the acknowledgment of independence. The progress is entirely consistent; and Burke's address to the colonists is the logical outcome of the principles of liberty and the notion of a higher law above municipal codes and constitutions, with which Whiggism began.

It is the supreme achievement of Englishmen, and their bequest to the nations ; but the patriarchs of the doctrine were the most infamous of men. They set up the monument to perpetuate the belief that the Catholics set fire to London. They invented the Black Box and the marriage of Lucy Waters. They prompted, encouraged, and rewarded the murderer Oates. They proclaimed that the Prince of Wales came in the warming pan. They were associated with the Rye House assassins ; that conspiracy was their ruin. Charles triumphed, and did not spare his enemies. When he died, in spite of the Dover Treaty, of his paid subserviency to France, of the deliberate scheme to subvert the liberties of England, James, the chief culprit, succeeded, with undiminished power. The prostrate Whigs were at the mercy of Jeffreys.

But forty years of agitation had produced the leaven that has leavened the world. The revolutionary system was saved, because the king threw away his advantage. The Whig party became supreme in the State by a series of events which are the most significant in English History.

XIII

THE ENGLISH REVOLUTION

THREE-QUARTERS of a century of struggling and experiment, from the fall of Bacon to the death of Charles II., had ended in failure, and the government of England had been brought into line with continental monarchy when James ascended the throne.

The House of Commons refused to listen to Seymour's warning speech, and voted, *nemine discrepante*, a revenue which, by the growth of trade, soon rose to near two millions. It was in the king's power to retain that loyal and submissive parliament as long as he chose, and he was not obliged to meet it annually. He had the control of the constituencies. The press was not free, and the proceedings of the legislature were withdrawn from public knowledge. Judges could be dismissed at will, until the bench was filled with prerogative lawyers. There was an army kept in foreign pay that could be recalled when it was wanted. Passive obedience was taught as a precept by the universities, and as a religious dogma by the Church.

It was no secret that James was resolved to be master, and to abolish the restraints and safeguards of the constitution. Penn, reporting his intentions to William of Orange, declared that he would have all or nothing. He had repeatedly avowed that he meant to do it by a standing army and by claiming the right to dispense with laws. Monmouth's rebellion gave him the standing army. Although it was unsupported either by the exclusionists or the limitationists, and although it was contemptibly managed, there had been a moment of serious danger. It was the general opinion that the night attack at Sedgemoor would have succeeded, and that the royal army would have been destroyed, if the rebels, instead of betraying their approach with musketry, had come to close quarters with axe and scythe. The king took advantage of what had happened, and he had the means of paying a force which amounted to 14,000 men.

Charles had been in perpetual want of money through the expensive scandals of his court. There were half a dozen ducal titles needing to be provided with ducal incomes, and obliging the king to become a dependent pensionary of the liberal paymaster in France. At his death all this was changed, and Catherine Sedley disappeared from Whitehall. It is true that her absence was not prolonged, and that she had obscurer rivals. But a decorous economy was observed in a branch of expenditure which had been profuse. Nevertheless Lewis XIV. hastened to make offers of pecuniary aid to the frugal James as to the extravagant Charles. He sent over a sum of £60,000 or £70,000, consisting partly of arrears already due. This was to be paid only if James found himself in difficulties after having proclaimed liberty of conscience. If there was no disturbance, there was to be no payment. And when the session ended without any measure of the kind, Lewis gave orders that the money should be returned to him. In the autumn of 1685 James proceeded to adopt his advice. He had been victorious. His birthday, in October, was celebrated more heartily than his brother's had ever been, and the atrocities of the Western Assize did not affect opinion to his disadvantage.

He made known his plans. Besides the standing army and the recall of the Habeas Corpus, he demanded the dispensing power. Nobody supposed that the head of the executive was to persecute his own religion. To admit his right of succession was to admit that the Elizabethan Code was to be practically dormant. The

Catholics desired no more.   It was enough that they
ceased to suffer oppression.   Halifax, the ablest though
not the strongest of James's ministers, agreed to that, and
did not object to a moderate number of Catholic officers.
The Prince of Orange was of the same opinion.   Toleration was therefore assured, and the era of persecution had
passed away.   That was of no use to Lewis XIV., who
in that month of October suppressed the Protestant
religion in France.   And it was of little use to James
himself, as it added nothing to his power.   He insisted
on introducing toleration by dispensing with the laws, by
right of his prerogative, and on abolishing the Test Act.
But the Test Act was a security against arbitrary power,
by depriving him of the assistance of Catholics in office.
His desire for arbitrary power was notorious, and the
country did not believe that his zeal for the liberty of
conscience was sincere.   They believed, and they believed
rightly, that he demanded more than that which would
satisfy the just and obvious necessities of his Church in
order to strengthen his prerogative, and that he was
tolerant in order that he might be absolute.   He professed
openly the maxim that toleration was the necessary condition of absolutism.   He urged Lewis, secretly, to pursue
the work of the revocation, and was reluctant to allow
collections to be made for the Huguenot fugitives.

Later, when he was himself an exile, and nothing
could be more inopportune than the profession of tolerant
sympathies at the French court, he seriously and consistently proclaimed them.   And it is very possible that
he was then sincere, and that a change had taken place.
Another change took place when he became acquainted
with the famous Rancé, who had made the abbey of La
Trappe the most edifying seat of religion in France, and
a favourite retreat for men like Bossuet and St. Simon.
James also visited him and corresponded with him, and
sixty of their letters are extant.   At Versailles people
did not understand how so much devotion could be combined with so much tolerance in religion.   The letters to
Rancé show that the religion of James, when he was on

Q

the throne, was very near the surface. Whether it was different afterwards, as they believed in France, is not quite certain. And in this connection it will be convenient to mention the assassination plot.

There was an Irish divine, Martin of Connemara, who suggested that, in time of war, it would be well that a chosen band should devote themselves to the task of falling upon the Prince of Orange and putting him to death. It would, he said, be a legitimate act of warfare. Lewis XIV. required no such arguments, and sent a miscreant named Grandval to rid him of the obnoxious prince. Berwick preferred the advice of the theologian, and, at the battle of Landen, he led a troop of 200 horsemen to the place where his kinsman stood, crying out to them to kill him. Three years later, in 1696, he was in London, communicating with the managers of the plot, who thought that it would be no murder to shoot the king on the road to Hampton Court, when surrounded by his guards. A beacon fire on Shakespeare's Cliff was to send the news across the sea, and at that signal James was to come over, in French ships. When the plot thickened, Berwick made his escape, and met his father changing horses at Clermont. Having learnt how matters stood, James pursued his way to Calais, and there, while he watched the northern horizon for the desired signal, he wrote edifying letters to the Abbé de Rancé. When the plot was betrayed he showed the deepest sympathy with the assassins, and never lamented their crime.

The series of measures by which he lost the crown form a drama in three acts. First, he tried to obtain the co-operation of the Established Church. When that failed, he turned against the Church and worked through the Dissenters. And then he brought on that quarrel with the clergy which proved fatal to him. James did not believe in the reality of Protestant religion. Sunderland assured him that in two years not a Protestant would be left in England, if compulsion ceased, and his mind was bewildered by two very remarkable facts. One of

these was the theology of recent Caroline divines.   Archbishop Bramhall could hardly be distinguished from a
Gallican.   Archbishop Leighton was in close touch with
Jansenists.   One Roman doctrine was adopted by
Montagu, another by Thorndike, a third by Isaac Barrow.
Bull received the thanks of the French clergy for his
vindication of the early fathers against the most learned
of the Jesuits.   To an ignorant and narrow-minded man
all these things pointed to one conclusion, the instability
and want of solidity in the Anglican system.   Then there
was the astounding collapse of the French Huguenots.
Lewis boasted that, in a few months, without real violence,
he had effected 800,000 conversions.   And James was
eager to believe it.   He asked himself, says Barillon, why
he could not do as much in England.   He desired the
Roman congregations to examine the question, whether
the English bishops might retain their sees.   Some said
they would be better than the Catholic clergy, who were
accused of Jansenism.   One thing he considered absolutely
certain.   The Church would never resist his authority.
The Bishop of Winchester entreated him not to rely on
the passive obedience of Churchmen.   James replied that
the bishop had lost his nerve.

Having decided to risk a quarrel with loyal Anglicans,
he assumed the dispensing power.   The judges approved.
There was precedent in his favour.   He had support not
only in the past but in the future, for William III. followed
his example.   He could claim that he was acting for the
reason of State against shameful prejudice and sordid
passion.   The greatest historic figure of the age, William
Penn, was on his side, and went over to explain the
principle of his policy to the Prince of Orange.   Lewis
XIV. urged him on.   And although the body of English
Catholics were much opposed, his immediate advisers,
who were men in the French interest, or survivors of the
Dover Treaty, Arundel, Bellasis, Dover, Tyrconnel, encouraged his fixed design.   A few men in high office, he
said, would do more for Catholicism than many hearing
mass without impediment.

We must imagine not a sinister tyrant brooding schemes of oppression, but an unintelligent absolutist, in the hands of men, some of whom were able and some sincere, plying him with plausible arguments. Therefore, when the primate and six bishops protested against the Declaration of Indulgence, James sent them to the Tower. Sunderland advised caution. The time for extreme measures, he said, had not come. The violent members of the council thought that they had their enemies at their mercy, and they prevailed.

James thought that he was triumphing, for just then the Prince of Wales was born. The future of his policy was assured. The crown was not to pass to the head of the Protestant interest in Europe. James's enemies, says the imperial envoy, gave up their cause for lost. In their despair they at once invented the lie about the warming pan. James's opportunity had now come. He could declare an amnesty for the event which had so profoundly changed his fortunes. The seven bishops could be released without a trial, and the impending catastrophe could be averted. The king, disagreeing with his advisers, with Sunderland, with the nuncio, even with Jeffreys, determined to go on. He intended that the bishops should be tried, condemned, and pardoned. With that, his victory would be complete. Instead of which, the bishops were acquitted, and the king's attack on the Church ended in defeat.

On that day Admiral Herbert, disguised as a blue-jacket, left with the invitation to the Prince of Orange to come over. It was written by Algernon Sidney's brother, and bore the signatures of seven considerable men, who were prepared to risk their lives. Several others acquiesced, and it was not the act of one party. The thing had become inevitable when the prince was born. It was delayed until the issue was decided between the crown and the Church. The associates assured William that the Prince of Wales was an imposture, and that he must come, in order to secure his own birthright, as well as the liberties of England. William of Orange had not intrigued that the crown should pass to his wife before the time, and had given his uncle much good advice. For him it was everything that England should not be against him in the struggle with Lewis XIV. For that, he had the Habsburgs on his side, and it was essential that they should still be with him if he obeyed the call of his friends. He had been preparing for it ever since he sent Dykvelt over in 1687, and had asked the States of Holland to hold twenty-five men-of-war and 9000 sailors in readiness, to meet the danger which threatened from France.

James took alarm, and warned William that the succession was not absolutely safe. Lewis, who much dreaded the prospect of having his ablest and most formidable enemy at Whitehall, wished the Princess Anne to precede her elder sister. To strengthen her claim with her father he proposed that she should become a Catholic, and sent over books of controversy for that purpose. James, on the other hand, told William that there would be no crown to inherit, but a commonwealth in England, if he did not succeed in his endeavour to make himself master. Dykvelt had conducted the secret negotiation which ended in the invitation of 30th June.

A still more delicate negotiation was pursued on the Continent. William could not allow it to appear that his expedition implied a war of religion. He would forfeit the alliance of the Emperor, which was the very pivot of his policy. Leopold was a devout and scrupulous man, and it was uncertain how he would regard an enterprise which was to substitute a Protestant dynasty for a Catholic dynasty in England. There was only one way of ensuring his assistance. In order to have the support of the Empire it was requisite to obtain the support of the Papacy. In a religious question Leopold would follow the pope. William sent one of his generals, the Prince de Vaudémont, to Rome; and, through Count Dohna, he opened a correspondence with the Vatican. He represented that the Catholics would obtain from him the toleration which they could never be sure of under James. There would be not only a serious political advantage gained by the detachment of England from the French interest, but also a positive and measurable benefit for the Church of Rome. The pope understood and assented, and took the Habsburgs with him into the camp of the Great Deliverer. This is the touch of mystery in the Revolution of 1688. James, the champion of the Church, had alienated Rome.

The pope, Innocent XI., Odescalchi, is a rare and original figure, and James said truly that no man like him had sat on the see of Rome for centuries. He began the reform of the court, which consisted in the abolition of nepotism. All through the century his predecessors had founded great princely families—Borghese, Ludovisi, Barberini, Pamphili, Chigi, Rospigliosi, Altieri. These great houses grew wealthy out of the spoils of the Church, and, as their founders died without making restitution, opponents of nepotism affirmed that they died unrepentant, and might be found in those regions of the other world where Dante delighted to exhibit the pontiffs of his time. In his zeal for a strict morality Innocent tried to rectify the teaching of the Casuists, and was involved in trouble with the Jesuits. In France he was spoken of as a Jansenist, and in England Oldmixon called him a Protestant pope. He endeavoured, as nobody had done since the Reformation, to find a remedy for the divisions of Western Christendom. The movement had not ceased since Richelieu was minister and Grotius ambassador at Paris, and it became active on both sides. Innocent sanctioned a scheme of concessions which was deemed satisfactory in the universities of Protestant Germany.

When Lewis revoked the edict of toleration the pope did not conceal his displeasure. He was compelled at last to allow Te Deums and illuminations; but he made no secret of his disbelief in the armed apostolate of missionaries in jackboots. He was bitterly opposed to the Gallican system, out of which the persecution proceeded. James II. was odious to him for many reasons. First as a promoter of French tendencies, both in politics and in religion. For James, like Lewis, was a Gallican in

Church questions.   When an Englishman defended ultramontane propositions in a disputation at Louvain, he
expressed his indignation that such an attack should have
been permitted in his presence on the plenary authority
of kings. He offended the pope by sending as his ambassador Lord Castlemaine, who was ridiculous not only
as the Duchess of Cleveland's husband, but as the author
of a book in which he pleaded for toleration on the ground
that Catholics should be as well treated in England as
Protestants in France. With great reluctance the pope
consented that his agent, D'Adda, should be appointed a
nuncio; but when James made the Jesuit Petre a privy
councillor, giving him his own apartment at Whitehall,
and represented that he would be fitter for such a position
if he was made a bishop or a cardinal, Innocent refused.

Petre laid the blame on the nuncio, and the Jesuits
asked that he should be sent out of the country.   He
would be forced, said the king, to do without the Court of
Rome. D'Adda gave the same advice as the Prince of
Orange, that the Penal Laws should not be executed, but
the Test Acts retained; and he was one of those who,
when the crisis came, maintained that there was nothing
to fear from William. After Innocent's death in 1689
there was a change, but Rome declared in favour of
taking the oath to William III.   Perth wrote from Rome
in 1695 : "The Prince of Orange has more friends here
than either in England or Holland, and the king is universally hated.   It's scandalous to hear what is said every
day, publicly, when they make comparisons betwixt an
heretical, unnatural, usurping tyrant and His Majesty."

On this state of feeling, far stronger in 1688 than in
1695, William built his plan. It was in the power of
Lewis at any moment to prevent the expedition. He
had an army ready for war, and could have held William
fast by sending it against the Netherlands. He preferred
to attack the empire on the Upper Rhine. For twenty
years it had been his desire to neutralise England by
internal broils, and he was glad to have the Dutch out
of the way while he dealt a blow at Leopold.   It was

impossible that the conflict between James and William should not yield him an opportunity. For the beginning he stood carefully aside, letting things take their course. There was no resistance, by land or sea, and it proved almost as easy to dethrone the Stuarts as it had been to restore them. The balance of parties, the lack of energetic conviction in England, had allowed things to settle down, when the real struggle began, in Ireland, in Scotland, and in the Channel. The Scots rising did not postpone the issue, but it is valuable to us for the sake of one transaction.

The deed that was done in Glencoe is familiar to us all, by a patch of Tyrian purple in the most splendid of our histories. It affords a basis for judging the character of William and of his government. They desired that some of the Highlanders should stand out, that an example might be made ; and they hoped that it might be the one Catholic clan, as they were likely to be the most dangerous Jacobites. " Who knows," wrote Stair, " but, by God's providence, they are permitted to fall into this delusion that they may only be extirpat." Four days later another writes : " The king does not care that some do it, that he may make examples of them." Accordingly, by his orders, one branch of the Macdonalds was destroyed by Campbell of Glenlyon. There is no doubt about the order. But it is not certain that William knew that the chieftain had taken the oath. The people concerned were rewarded in due proportion. One became a colonel, another a knight, a third a peer, and a fourth an earl. It was a way King William had. When the murder of De Witt made him supreme, he kept away from the Hague, but then saw that the murderers were recompensed. Eighty years later a deserter from one of our regiments was under sentence to be shot. The officer commanding the firing party, another Captain Campbell of Glenlyon, had received a reprieve, with secret orders not to produce it until the culprit stood facing the levelled muskets. At that moment, as he drew the reprieve from his pocket, his handkerchief, coming with it, fell to the ground. The soldiers took it for their signal and fired. Glenlyon exclaimed, "It is the curse of Glencoe!" and at once left the service.

When James escaped to France, he at once went over to Ireland, with a French army, while a French fleet covered the expedition and swept the Channel. James had long intended to make Ireland independent of England, that, under his Protestant successors, it might be an impregnable refuge for persecuted Catholics. He estimated that it would take five years of preparation. Tyrconnel also contemplated separation, and arranged for a French invasion, if James died. When James came over Tyrconnel thought him hopelessly incompetent, and offered his country to Lewis XIV. Sarsfield detested his treachery, and invited Berwick to undertake the government. Of James's French counsellors, one was Lauzun, who commanded the auxiliary army, and proposed to burn Dublin to the ground and ravage the open country. The other was the ambassador D'Avaux, who wished him to make short work of all the Protestants in the island.

James rejected the advice with indignation. Lewis also rejected it, but without the indignation you would expect in a most Christian king, and without thinking the adviser unworthy of his service. D'Avaux relates it all, without reserve, in his despatches, which are among the curiosities of History. They were printed at the Foreign Office, and never published. The only copy I ever saw was uncut when it came into my hands.

In spite of these discordant counsels, the Jacobite prospects in Ireland brightened when a fleet of seventy-eight ships sailed from Brest. "If they were only commanded by De Ruyter," said Louvois, whose control stopped with the shore, "there would be something to hope for." Instead of De Ruyter, Tourville defeated the combined Dutch and English at Beachy Head. The allies lost sixteen ships out of fifty-eight ; the French not one. Tourville was master of the Channel. Torrington left the Dutch to do the fighting, and kept as far as he could from the scene of danger. He had to lament the death of his favourite dog. They said that the dog died the death of an admiral, and the admiral lived the life of a dog. That 30th of June is the most disgraceful date in our naval annals.

On the following day the battle of the Boyne was won not in the legendary manner, by William, with his sword in his left hand, or Schomberg, plunging into the river to meet a soldier's death, but by the younger Schomberg, who crossed higher up and outflanked the French. Tourville's victory, after that, was entirely useless. William offered an amnesty, which was frustrated by the English hunger for Irish estates ; and the capitulation of Limerick, rejected by the Irish parliament, gave it the name of the City of the Broken Treaty.

The reign of James came to an end when he fled from the Boyne to St. Germains. He became the king of the Nonjurors. In 1693, when the French had been victorious at Steenkerk and Landen, he issued a Declaration, with the doubting approval of French divines, which the nonjuring bishops repudiated. Such concessions, they affirmed, would ruin the monarchy. Kerr was of the same opinion ; but he went on to say that when the Declaration had served its purpose and restored the king, he would not be bound to observe it. The war was unprofitable to the allies on land ; but after the victory of La Hogue the three kingdoms were safe from invasion. This is the war to which we owe the National Debt, the Bank of England, the growth of the moneyed interest.

But the agrarian interest still largely predominated, and the landlords, as the ruling class, required a reward for their share in the elevation of William. Nineteen years earlier the Corn Laws had been invented for their benefit. Protection against foreign importation did much ; but in 1689 a premium on the exportation of English-grown corn was added, and it is this which caused the immense prosperity of English agriculture in the eighteenth century, enriching the landlord with capital at the expense of the yeoman without it.

Two of our greatest writers, to speak truly, our two
greatest writers, Burke and Macaulay, have taken pains to
show that the Revolution of 1688 was not revolutionary
but conservative, that it was little more than a rectification
of recent error, and a return to ancient principles.   It was
essentially monarchical.   The king was acknowledged to
be a necessity in the then state of England.   The idea
of a Commonwealth did not appear.   The Revolution was
mainly the work of Conservatives, that is, of Churchmen who, where Church interests were not threatened,
strictly upheld authority, and reverted to their original
doctrine when the crisis was over.   No change took place
in the governing class.   The gentry who managed the
affairs of the county managed the affairs of the country
after 1688 as they had done before.   There was no
transfer of force from the aristocratic element of society
to the democratic.   The essentials of free government,
religious liberty, national education, emancipation of slaves,
freedom of trade, relief of poverty, freedom of the press,
solidarity of ministers, publicity of debates, were not
mentioned in the resolutions of the Convention or in the
Bill of Rights.   Nothing was done to determine whether
the future belonged to the Tory or the Whig.

And yet it is the greatest thing done by the English
nation.   It established the State upon a contract, and set
up the doctrine that a breach of contract forfeited the
crown—the former, in the English convention ; the latter,
in the Scottish.   Parliament gave the crown, and gave it
under conditions.   Parliament became supreme in administration as well as in legislation.   The king became its
servant on good behaviour, liable to dismissal for himself
or his ministers.   All this was not restitution, but inver-
sion.   Passive obedience had been the law of England.
Conditional obedience and the right of resistance became
the law.   Authority was limited and regulated and controlled.   The Whig theory of government was substituted
for the Tory theory on the fundamental points of political
science.   The great achievement is that this was done
without bloodshed, without vengeance, without exclusion

of entire parties, with so little definiteness in point of doctrine that it could be accepted, and the consequences could be left to work themselves out. The Act itself was narrow, spiritless, confused, tame, and unsatisfactory. It was perfectly compatible with the oppression of class by class, and of the country by the State, as the agent of a class. It was strangely imperfect.

The consequences ripened slowly, and a time came, under George III., when it seemed that they were exhausted. It was then that another and a more glorious Revolution, infinitely more definite and clear-cut, with a stronger grasp of principle, and depending less on conciliation and compromise, began to influence England and Europe.

XIV

LEWIS THE FOURTEENTH

WHILST England was traversing the revolutionary period on its arduous course towards free government, France completed, with universal applause, the structure of absolute monarchy. Neither Henry IV. nor Richelieu had done enough to secure the country against conspiracy, disorder, and invasion. There was a relapse into civil war during each minority, under Lewis XIII. and Lewis XIV.; the nobles and the magistrates turned against the crown, and a prince of the blood, Condé, commanded the Spaniards in a campaign on French soil against the royal army. With the aid of Turenne, Mazarin triumphed over every danger, and the young king was anointed in the Cathedral of Rheims.

In 1659, by the Peace of the Pyrenees, the cardinal terminated victoriously the long war with Spain, which began in the middle of the Thirty Years' War, and outlasted it, and established the supremacy of France over the Continent. The one desire of France was the concentration of power, that there might be safety abroad and order at home. To ensure this, more was required than the genius of even the most vigorous and astute ministers in the world. Neither Richelieu, who was a bishop, nor Mazarin, who was a foreigner, could be identified with the State. What was wanted had been wanting in France for half a century—the personality of the king, monarchy personified, with as much splendour, as much authority, as much ascendency, as would fill the national imagination and satisfy national pride. The

history of Charles I., the restoration of Charles II., the
outbreak of loyal sentiment, which was stronger than
religion, which was itself a religion, showed that there
was something in royalty higher than the policy of statesmen, and more fitted to inspire the enthusiasm of sacrifice.

At the death of Mazarin there was no man capable
of being his successor.   Le Tellier, Colbert, Lionne were
men of very great ability, but they were departmental
ministers.   The young monarch gave orders that, as they
had reported to the cardinal, they should now report to
himself.   He added that they were to assist him with
their advice whenever he asked for it ; and he did not
make it appear that he would trouble them often.   The
initiative of government passed into his hands.   He did
not say, " *L'état, c'est moi.*"   Those words, I believe,
were invented by Voltaire, but they are profoundly true.
It was the thing which the occasion demanded, and he
was the man suited to the occasion.

Lewis XIV. was by far the ablest man who was born
in modern times on the steps of a throne.   He was
laborious, and devoted nine hours a day to public business.
He had an excellent memory and immense fertility of
resource.   Few men knew how to pursue such complex
political calculations, or to see so many moves ahead.
He was patient and constant and unwearied, and there is
a persistent unity in his policy, founded, not on likes and
dislikes, but on the unvarying facts in the political stage
of Europe.   Every European state was included in his
system, and had its part in the game.   His management
of each was so dexterous that diplomacy often made war
superfluous, and sometimes made it successful.   Lewis
was not a born soldier like Swedish Charles and the great
Frederic.   He never exercised an actual command.   He
would appear at sieges when the psychological moment
came, and ride ceremoniously under fire, with his Jesuit
confessor close at hand.   His fame was so large a part
of the political capital of France, that a pretence was
made of believing in his generalship, and the king took it
quite seriously   He told his son to go to the wars and

prove his warlike quality, that the change, when his father died, might not be too deeply felt. In many places he was accepted as a benefactor and a friend. That was generally the case in Switzerland, in Portugal, in Denmark and Sweden, in Poland and Hungary, in parts of Germany, and in parts of Italy. For in small countries public men were poor and easily consented to accept his gifts. In this way he strove to prevent coalitions and to isolate his enemies. The enemies were Austria and the Netherlands.

Two facts governed the European situation. One was the break-up of the imperial power in Germany, after the Thirty Years' War. The effect of it was that France was fringed by a series of small territories which were too feeble to defend themselves, and which Germany was too feeble and too divided to protect. There were Belgium, Liège, Luxemburg, Lorraine, Alsace, and Franche Comté. The other overshadowing fact was the evident decay of Spain, of the royal family as well as of the nation. Belgium, Luxemburg, and Franche Comté were Spanish, and were therefore helpless. The acquisition of these provinces was an inevitable element of his policy. That was part of a far larger scheme. Philip IV. had no son. His daughter, Maria Theresa, was heir to his boundless dominions. As early as 1646 Mazarin resolved that his master should marry the Infanta, and that Spain and the Indies, Naples and the Milanese, and the remnant of the possessions of Charles the Bold, should be attached to the crown of France. When the time came, and reluctant Spain consented, at the treaty of the Pyrenees, Lewis was discovered to be in love with another lady. Her name was Marie Mancini, the youngest of three sisters, and she was the cardinal's own niece.

Mazarin, the ablest and most successful of ministers, had one damning vice. He was shamefully avaricious. He amassed, in the service of the State, therefore dishonestly, an income larger than that of the King of England or the King of Spain. The necklace of pearls which he gave to one of his nieces, and which is at Rome, is said to be still the finest in existence. But Mazarin, though he was sordid and mean, was a statesman of the highest rank. He sent his niece away, in spite of the tears of Lewis, and the Spanish princess became Queen of France. The independence of Spain, the unity of the Spanish empire, were too grand a thing to be an item in the dowry of a bride. She was compelled to renounce her rights, which were transferred to her sister. The renunciation was conditional. It was to depend on the payment, in due time, of the Infanta's fortune. As the payment was not made, the French regarded the surrender as null and void, and the interest at stake, the most splendid inheritance on earth, was one that could not be given up without a conflict. From the moment of the marriage the main object of French policy was to make the succession secure, by negotiation or force, and to take every advantage otherwise of Spanish weakness.

All these plans were doomed to a terrible disappointment. In 1665 Philip of Spain died; but he had married again, and left a son, who became king, in his cradle, under the name of Charles II. The new king was sickly and backward, and it was expected that he would die young, unmarried, and childless. Meantime, the fulfilment of French hopes was postponed for a generation, and the Spanish succession was opened, not at the beginning of Lewis's reign, but at the end. He recovered from the blow by a device to acquire part of the Spanish empire, no longer having a hope of the whole. The device was suggested by Turenne. His experience in the Fronde taught him the danger of having the Spaniards so near, in the valley of the Somme. "Whenever there is trouble in France," he said, "the enemy can be at Paris in four days." In self-defence, for security rather than aggrandisement, the frontier must be pushed back. He caused his secretary to compose a treatise, showing that, by the custom of Brabant, that province devolved on the queen, Maria Theresa. It was the custom there that the children of a first marriage should suffer no loss if their father married again. What would have been their estate, remained their estate. The fee simple passed to them

The father enjoyed a life-interest only, without the power of disposal. The French government argued that, by the analogy of the Salic Law, the principle which applied to property applied to sovereignty, and that what was good for a manor was good for a crown. And they assumed that the custom of Brabant was the law of Belgium.

This is the right of Devolution, with which the king's aggressive career began, and his first war was the war of Devolution, or, as they say in France, the war for the rights of the queen. Those rights consisted of consolation claims set up after the wreck of the dream of universal empire. They presented abundant matter for dispute, but they were worth disputing, even by the last argument of kings.

The Power most concerned was not Spain, but the Netherlands. For Spain, the Belgic provinces were an outlying dependency, involving international complications. For Holland, they were a rampart. The government of the States was in the hands of John de Witt and the Republicans. They were held in check by the partisans of the House of Orange, which, in the last generation, had put the republican leader, the real predecessor of De Witt, to death. The feud was there, faction was not appeased, and De Witt dreaded the day when the Orange party should recover power. The Prince of Orange was only seventeen. When war came in sight, the Perpetual Edict excluded him from the position which his family had occupied, by forbidding the Stadtholder from being at the same time Commander of the Forces. De Witt was not afraid of a naval war. His brother was the admiral, and it was he who sailed up the Thames. But war on land would bring the young William forward. De Witt made every possible concession, hoping to prevent it. Rather than fight the French, he was willing to agree to a partition of the Belgic provinces. Already, he was at war with England, and the sea-fights had been indecisive. Resistance to France on land was out of the question, except by means of a Coalition, and as no Coalition could be hoped for, Holland stood aside, while Turenne overran

Flanders. The Austrian Habsburgs did not interfere to protect the Spanish branch, although they were its heirs. In case his son should die, Philip IV. had left his entire monarchy to his second daughter, who was married to the Emperor Leopold. It would remain in the family; whereas, if the French queen had not renounced, it would be swallowed up in the dominions of a stranger,— that was the point of view of a Spaniard. The Austrian viewed things differently. He knew perfectly well that France would not be bound by an act which belonged not to the world of real politics, but to the waste-paper basket. Therefore, when France proposed an eventual partition, it seemed important to obtain a more serious and more binding contract than the queen's renunciation. The conditions were not unfavourable to the imperial interest. As there were several other partition treaties, none of which were carried out, the terms of this, the first, need not occupy us. The treaty was not meant to govern the future, but the present. It helped to keep the Emperor tranquil during the spoliation of his Spanish kinsman.

Within a week of the first treaty of partition, Sir William Temple concluded the Triple Alliance. Deserted by Austria, De Witt turned to England. He sent his fleet to destroy the British men-of-war in the Medway, and this catastrophe, coming so soon after the plague and the fire of London, was too much for the feeble spirit of Charles and his ministers. They made peace, allied themselves with Holland and with Sweden, and the progress of the French was arrested. The Triple Alliance was the earliest of that series of coalitions which ended by getting the better of the power of Lewis XIV., and is therefore a landmark in History. But there was nothing lasting in it; the rivalry of the two commercial countries was not to be reconciled by politicians. England was on the side of the Prince of Orange, and desired that he should become sovereign. William had resolved, during the very negotiations that prepared the alliance, that the way to ruin De Witt was to exhibit him to Lewis in the light of a friend of the English. After having been conciliatory to the edge of weakness, he had turned suddenly into an enemy. Lewis could not continue the war because of the maritime superiority of his united opponents. He made peace, restoring Franche Comté, which Condé had occupied, and contenting himself with an extended frontier in Flanders. Lille, which had been taken by Vauban, in an otherwise inglorious campaign, was converted into a great French stronghold. That was the result.

These events exhibit Lewis in his prime, while Colbert and Lionne were living, and were able to balance the sinister influence of Louvois. It was a war of ambition, undertaken after the shock of the loss of Spain and of all that belonged to it. It was not begun from a sense of right and duty. But the advantage was not pushed to the bitter end ; the terms agreed upon were reasonable ; part of the conquests were restored. Lewis proved himself capable of moderation, of self-command, even of generosity. The outrageous violence and tyranny of later years were not immediately apparent. He withdrew from the fray, preparing for another spring. Then he would avenge himself on John de Witt, and conquer Belgium in Holland. De Witt was the most enlightened statesman in Europe, but he was not a war minister. England was easily detached from him in the hope that the Prince of Orange might be supreme ; and Lewis agreed to whatever was necessary, that the English fleet might be on his side. Thus the Triple Alliance was dissolved, and the Dover Treaty took its place. The help afforded by the English fleet in the Dutch war fell short of expectation, but the effect of the agreement was to blot out England for many years.

De Witt, unable to face the storm, offered advantageous terms, which were rejected, and then resigned office. The Prince of Orange took the command of the army ; but, at the approach of the French, eighty-three Dutch fortresses opened their gates. At the Hague De Witt and his brother were torn to pieces by an Orange mob, and Holland saved itself by letting in the ocean.

William of Orange, never a very successful general, was a good negotiator, and, excepting his own uncle Charles II., he soon had Europe on his side. The French were driven over the Vosges by the Imperialists. Turenne, in his last campaign, reconquered Alsace, crossed the Rhine, and gave battle to Montecucculi. He fell, and his army retired. Lewis XIV., to mark the greatness of the loss, at once named six new marshals of France. Montecucculi resigned his command. Having had the honour, he said, of fighting Turenne, and having even defeated him, he would not risk his reputation against men who were the small change for the great man who was dead. Lewis XIV. had 220,000 men under arms. Condé defeated William at Senef. As often as Vauban defended a fortress, he held it ; as often as he besieged a fortress, it fell. The balance of victory inclined to France. England gave no assistance, and the Prince of Orange came over, married the eldest of the princesses, immensely strengthening his own position, and hastening the conclusion of peace.

The peace of Nimeguen gave to Lewis XIV. that predominant authority over Europe which he retained undiminished, and even increased, during at least ten years. He acquired a further portion of Belgium, strengthening his frontier on the threatened line ; he annexed Franche Comté and he recovered Alsace. He had shown himself to be aggressive and unscrupulous, but his military power was equal to his pretensions ; he was true to his humbler allies ; his diplomatic foresight, and the art of his combinations, were a revelation to his contemporaries. They also knew that they would never be safe from renewed attack, as the larger half of the coveted region, in the Low Countries, Luxemburg, and Lorraine, was still unabsorbed. His interest was clearly recognised. His policy had been openly declared. With so much ambition, capacity, and power, the future was easy to foretell. In the position he had acquired, and with the qualities he had shown, he would be as dangerous in peace as in war. Coalitions alone could resist him. and a coalition could only be a work of time and patience. When the alliance which had opposed him with unequal fortune was dissolved, a season of peril would ensue, for which no defensive provision could be made.

The keystone of the situation was the assured inaction of England. Whilst that lasted, at least while Charles II. lived, Lewis would defy the rest of Europe. He had nothing to fear except the Stadtholder. Whilst De Witt governed, the French attack was irresistible. But the Perpetual Edict was repealed, and William of Orange was captain-general for life. He had saved his country, driven out the French, raised Europe against them. The merchants of Amsterdam, who, in 1672, were preparing to sail for Batavia, as the Puritans sailed for New England, were now the second Power in Europe politically, and commercially by far the first. William of Orange, to whose international genius the change was due, stood very near the succession to the English throne. In the course of nature it would be his some day, by right of his wife, or by his own. And there was hope for European independence and the existence of free communities, if the resources of England passed to William earlier than the resources of Spain fell into the hands of Lewis. After the peace, that was the problem of general politics.

The treaties of Nimeguen were far from satisfying the aspirations of Lewis. He dismissed his foreign minister. Pomponne was the most honourable man in his service, and had conducted with eminent dexterity and success the negotiations for the numerous treaties with every country. Lewis says that he was deficient in the energy and the greatness requisite in executing the orders of a king of France who had not been without good fortune. Pomponne came into office in 1671 and left it in 1679, so that he was not compromised by the derisive claim of devolution, or by the yet more hollow sophistry of reunion, by which Lewis now proceeded to push his advantage. His dismissal announced to the nations what they had to look for. It meant that the profit of

Nimeguen was not enough, that the greatness of the French monarch exacted further sacrifices.

After the peace Lewis kept up his army. There were 112,000 men under arms, and there were cadres for twice as many more. With that force in hand, he proceeded to raise new claims, consequential, he said, on the late favourable treaties. He said that the territories ceded to France ought to be ceded with their dependencies, with such portions as had formerly belonged to them, and had been detached in the course of ages. And the parliaments of Lorraine, Alsace, and Franche Comté were directed to ascertain what places there were, what fragments under feudal tenure, to which that retrospective principle applied. They were called chambers, or courts, of reunion, and they enumerated certain small districts, which the French troops accordingly occupied. All this was futile skirmishing. The real object was Strasburg. Alsace was French, but Strasburg, the capital, that is, the capital of Lower Alsace, was imperial. It was the most important place on the road between Paris and Vienna, for it commanded the passage of the only river which crossed and barred the way. Situated on the left bank, it was the gate of France ; and twice in the late war it had admitted the Imperialists, and opened the way to Paris. The bishop, Fürstenberg, belonged to a great German family that was devoted to the French interest ; but the town was Protestant.

Up to that moment, 1681, religious antagonism had not added much to the acerbity of the conflict. Spain and Austria were the enemies of Lewis ; Sweden and Denmark were his allies. Brandenburg accepted his gifts, in money, in jewels, in arras. England was his humble friend. But a change was approaching ; and it began when Fürstenberg first said mass in Strasburg minster, and preached from the text " Nunc Dimittis." Vauban at once arrived, and erected an impregnable barrier, and a medal was struck bearing the inscription · " Clausa Germanis Gallia." On the same day as Strasburg, the French occupied Casale. This was a fortress closing the road between the duchy of Savoy and the duchy of Milan, and commanding the line of the Po. It belonged to Montferrat, which was a dependency of Mantua ; but the duke had his price, and he sold the right of occupation to the French. The agreement had been concluded three years before, but it had been betrayed by the duke's minister, and it had become necessary to await a more convenient occasion. The French government did not scruple to have an obstructive adversary put out of the way. Louvois gave orders that Lisola, the Austrian statesman who exposed the scheme of devolution, should be seized, and added that it would be no harm if he was killed. His son commissioned Grandval to murder William III.

The traitor of Casale met with a more terrible fate than a pistol shot or the stroke of a dagger. He suddenly disappeared, and no man ever looked upon his face again. His existence was forgotten, and when he died, long after, nobody knew who he was. In the dismal register of the dead who died in the Bastille he is entered under the name of Marchiali. Fifty years later he began to fix the attention of the world, and became a fascinating enigma. For Marchiali means Mattioli, who was the man in the Iron Mask. That is, of course, there was no man in the Iron Mask ; the material was more merciful than that ; and the name which has become so famous is as false as the one in which the victim of tyranny was buried.

Whilst Lewis pursued his career of annexation, the empire was disabled by war with the Turks and by troubles in Hungary. In 1683 the grand vizier besieged Vienna, and would have taken it but for the imperial allies, the Elector of Saxony, the Duke of Lorraine, and the King of Poland. After the relief of the capital they carried the war down the Danube, and Leopold was once more the head of a powerful military empire. It was too late to interfere with French conquests. Luxemburg was added to the series in 1684, and an armistice of twenty years practically, though not finally, sanctioned what had been done since Nimeguen. When the four great fortresses had become French,—Lille, Besançon, Strasburg, and Luxemburg, and when the empire succumbed, recognising all these acts of entirely unprovoked aggression, Lewis attained the highest level of his reign. He owed it to his army, but also to his diplomacy, which was pre-eminent. He owed it, too, to the intellectual superiority of France at the time, and to the perfection which the language reached just then. The thinking of Europe was done for it by Frenchmen, and French literature, penetrating and predominant everywhere, was a serious element of influence.

In all the work of these brilliant years there was increase of power and territorial agglomeration ; there was no internal growth or political development. The one thing wanted was that the king should be great and the country powerful. The object of interest was the State, not the nation, and prosperity did not keep pace with power. The people were oppressed and impoverished for the greater glory of France. Colbert trebled the public revenue, but he did not make it depend on the growth of private incomes or the execution of useful public works. In 1683 Colbert died, and Louvois, the son of Le Tellier, became supreme minister.

The queen's death, about the same time, caused a greater change. The king married Madame de Maintenon. He had been unfaithful to his first wife, but now he was a model husband. The second wife, who never became a queen, and was never acknowledged, ruled over his later years. She was the most cultivated, thoughtful, and observant of women. She had been a Protestant, and retained, for a long time, the zeal of a convert. She was strongly opposed to the Jansenists, and was much in the confidence of the best men among the clergy. It was universally believed that she promoted persecution, and urged the king to revoke the Edict of Nantes. Her letters are produced in evidence. But her letters have been tampered with by an editor, who was a forger and a falsifier.

The Revocation required no such specific agency, but

proceeded by consistent logic, from the tenour of the reign. The theory of government, which is that which Bossuet borrowed from Hobbes, and clothed in the language of Scripture, does not admit that a subject should have a will, a conviction, a conscience of his own, but expects that the spiritual side of him shall be sacrificed to the sovereign, like his blood and treasure. Protestant liberties, respected by Richelieu and still more entirely by Mazarin, who acknowledged the loyalty of Huguenots in the Fronde, became an exotic, an anachronism, a contradiction, and a reproach, as absolute monarchy rose to the zenith. The self-government of the Gallican Church, the administration of the clergy by the clergy, was reduced to the narrowest limits, and the division of power between Church and State was repressed in favour of the State. It could not be borne, in the long-run, that Protestants should govern themselves, while Catholics could not.

The clergy, zealous for the extinction of Jansenism, naturally extended their zeal against those who were more hostile to their Church than Jansenists. Everything else was required to give way to the governing will, and to do honour to the sovereign. The Protestants, under their protecting immunity, were a belated and contumelious remnant of quite another epoch. Exceptions which were tolerable under the undeveloped monarchy were revolting when it had grown to its radiant perfection. The one thing wanting was the Revocation, to abolish the memory of an age in which a king whose throne was insecure conceded to turbulent and disloyal subjects that which the sovereign of a loyal and submissive people would do well to revoke. To fulfil the ideal of royalty, the monument of the weakness of royalty and the strength of revolution must be ingeniously hidden away. The ardour of rising absolutism is the true cause of the Revocation.

William III. explained it in another way. He said that the purpose was to sow suspicion and dissension between Protestant and Catholic Powers, by showing that the Catholics at heart desired to extinguish the Protestant religion. Such a suspicion, properly fanned, would make alliances and coalitions impossible between them. The Waldenses then survived in one or two valleys of Piedmont, much assimilated to the Swiss Calvinists. Lewis required that they should be put down by force, and, when the Duke of Savoy hesitated, offered to supply the necessary troops. This extraordinary zeal, indicating that the spirit of persecution was common to all, and was not stimulated by causes peculiar to France, supplies the only evidence we have to sustain William's interpretation.

It is well to be rational when we can, and never, without compulsion, to attribute motives of passion, or prejudice, or ignorance as a factor in politics. But it is necessary to remember that the Plot was only six years old. The French government knew all abut it, and was in the secret of the papers destroyed by Coleman. To them it must have appeared that the English were turned into ferocious assassins by the mere force of their religious belief. There was no visible reason why such things should be in England and not in France, why a majority should be more easily carried away than a minority, or why High Church Anglicans should be more prone to murder a priest or a friar than extreme Calvinists, with whom it was a dogmatic certainty that Catholics were governed by Antichrist.

The Gallican clergy were divided. Several bishops condemned the action of the government, then or afterwards. The great majority promoted or encouraged it, not all by a revival of the persecuting spirit, but partly in the belief that the barriers were falling, and that the Churches were no longer irreconcilable. They were impressed by the fact that Protestantism had outgrown and discarded Luther, that Arminians in Holland, the Lutherans of the University of Helmstedt, the French schools of Sedan and Saumur, the Caroline divines in England, and even Puritans like Leighton and Baxter, were as much opposed as themselves to the doctrine of justification, which was the origin of the Protestant movement. At the same time, the abuses which roused Luther's opposition had disappeared, if not everywhere, at least in

France. Between Protestants in that later variation and Gallicans, the difference was not that which subsisted with Ultramontanes. Bossuet and two Englishmen, Holden and Cocker, drew up statements of what they acknowledged to be essentials in religion, which were very unlike the red-hot teaching of Salamanca and Coimbra. As the Protestants were no longer the Protestants who had seceded, the Catholics were no longer the Catholics who had cast them out. The best men of the Sorbonne were as unlike Tetzel and Prierias as Leibniz was unlike John Knox. It was unscientific, it was insincere, to regard the present controversy as a continuation of the old.

These sentiments were very heartily reciprocated among the Lutherans, and people spoke much of a misunderstanding, and represented the Reformation as the result of the unfinished theology, the defective knowledge of Church history, in the sixteenth century. Thus it was that nobody went further than Bossuet at one time in the direction of union, and nobody was more strongly in favour of the harsh measures of Louvois. If the policy of the Revocation had been to divide the European Powers, it proved a failure ; for it helped to make them coalesce.

In the following year, 1686, a league was concluded at Augsburg between the emperor, part of the empire, Spain, Sweden, and the Netherlands. This was the old story. Against nearly the same combination of discordant forces Lewis had held his own in the Dutch war and the negotiations of Nimeguen. England was wanting. William attempted to bring over his father-in-law, and, having failed by friendly arts, undertook to compel him. The Revolution threw the weight of England into the scales, and the war that ensued became the war of the Grand Alliance.

This was the turn in the fortunes of Lewis. He ravaged twenty miles of the Palatinate for the sake of a claim on the part of the Duchess of Orleans, who was a Princess Palatine. His armies were victorious, as usual, at Steenkerk and at Landen. The English were driven to the north-eastern extremity of Ireland ; and Trouville had better reason than Van Tromp to fix a broom at his masthead. And then Ireland was lost. The French fleet was destroyed, by very superior numbers, at La Hogue, and the Grand Alliance, aided at last by the ships, and the men, and the money of England, bore down the resistance of exhausted France. William was acknowledged King of England at the close of a struggle which had begun twenty-five years before. Lewis, having formally offered to support James's election to the throne of Poland, when Sobieski died, gave him up. Vauban complained that the war had been too prosperous on the Continent to justify so disastrous a termination.

From the peace of Ryswick the lengthening shadow of the Spanish succession falls upon the scene, and occupies the last years alike of William, of Leopold, and of Lewis. It was known that the King of Spain could not live long ; and as the prize came near, Europe, for four years, was hushed in expectation.

XV

THE WAR OF THE SPANISH SUCCESSION

WE come now to the last and greatest transaction in
Lewis XIV.'s reign—the acquisition of the Spanish
crown.

The idea of a predominant Power in Europe was part
of absolutism. It proceeded from the same love of
authority, the same pride of greatness, the same disregard
for the equal rights of men, the same pretension to
superiority and prerogative, international as well as
national. The position of the king in Europe was
security for his position in France itself. Subjects were
more willing to submit to one to whom foreigners submitted. In three successive wars Lewis had striven for
this advantage, and had made himself felt as the public
enemy and the vigilant disturber of the peace of Europe.
If he added Spain to his dominions by legal and pacific
means, by negotiated treaty or testamentary bequest, it
would be more legitimate than his former attempts at
mastery. His mother was a Spanish princess. His
wife was a Spanish princess. The emperor was in the
same position, but in each case the Queen of France was
the elder sister. Both of the French queens had resigned
their claims; but Lewis had not confirmed his wife's
renunciation, as her dowry was left unpaid; and it was
not confirmed by the national authorities in Spain.

In 1668, in spite of the will of Philip IV. giving the
succession to Austria, Leopold, who at that time had no
children, had been ready for an equitable partition. But
in 1689, when the Maritime Powers, that is, when William

III. had urgent need of Austria in the coalition against France, they promised the undivided monarchy of Spain to Leopold's second son.   That agreement was superseded by the peace of Ryswick.   And in the interval a new claimant was born, with evidently better right than the young archduke.   For the archduke was the son of a second marriage.   The emperor had only a daughter by his Spanish wife, who married the elector Max Emmanuel of Bavaria, and gave birth to a son in 1692.   Under the will of Philip IV., the late King of Spain, that prince was the lawful heir.   He was not the imperial candidate ; for Leopold had required his own daughter to surrender her claim, that his crowns might not pass from Habsburg to Wittelsbachs.

For the very reason that he was neither a Habsburg nor a Bourbon, the electoral Prince of Bavaria became the candidate of William, and he agreed with Lewis that he should inherit Spain and the Indies, Italy and the Low Countries to be divided.   By this, which is known as the First Partition Treaty, though in reality it was the second, England obtained nothing, except the prospect of peace through a friendly understanding with France, and it alienated the emperor and outraged Spain.   That foreigners should dispose at their own convenience of the empire which had been built up by Spanish hands, was an intolerable offence to Spaniards.   They refused to be dismembered without even having been consulted.   With all her dominions, with the united crowns of twenty-two kingdoms, Spain was unprosperous and insecure.   Her vitality was kept up by her foreign possessions.   Brabant, the Milanese, Campania, Apulia, were the richest portions of Europe, and neither France, nor the empire, nor England possessed the like.   Deprived of these, the monarchy would decline quickly ; for with all her pride, and her fame, and her unsetting sun, Spain was visibly going down.   It was their policy and their resolution that the crown, though it must pass away to strangers, should pass undiminished.   That it was about to pass away, all men knew.

On 19th September, three weeks before Lewis and William concluded their treaty, the primate assured the French ambassador that they must proceed as if the king was a dead man. The king himself knew his danger. His wife was a sister of the empress, and they were in the Austrian interest. So much so, that having made a will in favour of the Bavarian prince, Charles revoked it ; the ambassador Harrach, the Prince of Hesse who commanded in Catalonia, the queen, when her confidant was not bribed on the other side, were active for the archduke. But when the Partition Treaty became known, in November 1698, the king made another will, and publicly announced that his heir was the young prince of Bavaria. He thus took the candidate of France and England, assigning to him the whole, not a part. It was an attempt to preserve unity and avert partition by adopting the chosen claimant of the partitioning Powers. The English parliament, intent on peace, and suspicious of William's foreign policy, which was directed by him personally, with Dutch advisers, to the exclusion of ministers, reduced the army to 7000 men. William carried his distrust of Englishmen so far that he requested the imperial ambassador Wratislaw, an important man in his own country, to consult nobody but the Dutchman Albemarle. The public men of this country, he said, revealed every secret to their friends.

Six months later, both the will and the treaty were void and annulled by the death of the Bavarian prince, by small-pox, at Brussels, where his father was governor. The work had to be begun over again. The feeling of all Spanish statesmen in favour of maintaining the integrity of the monarchy was unchanged. That could be done only by choosing a Bourbon or a Habsburg. No other person could compete. The court was divided simply into an Austrian and a French party. The king's choice reverted to his nephew, the archduke. But those who had preferred the electoral prince were opposed to the Austrian, and became the partisans of France. They were a majority, and preponderant. If it could be made her interest to keep up the Spanish empire France was

better able to do it than Austria. Especially now that
England was detached from her ally the emperor. For
William concluded with Lewis a second Treaty of Partition,
giving Spain, the Indies, and the Netherlands to the archduke, the Italian possessions to France. Austria was no
party to this agreement, and openly preferred Italy to all
the rest. In England it was received with extreme cold-
ness, and in Spain with indignation. In the summer of
the year 1700 the king's illness became alarming. The
skill of his physicians being exhausted, spiritual remedies
were sought, and he was exorcised. The devil declared
that the king was possessed. Subsequently he admitted
that this was a falsehood, which surprised nobody.

The great question, whether the Spanish monarchy
should remain united or should go to pieces, reached a
preliminary conclusion on 3rd October 1700. Charles
appeared to be sinking, when he signed the last will
which Portocarrero and the friends of the French had
drawn up, with some marks of haste. He lived on four
weeks longer, but never had the strength to revoke the
act which disinherited his family. He left Spain, with all
dependencies, to the Duke of Anjou, second son of the
Dauphin, and if Anjou ever came to the throne in France,
then he should be succeeded in Spain by his younger
brother, so that the two crowns could never be united.
Failing the French line, the succession was to pass to the
archduke; and if the archduke came to the throne of
Austria, then to the Duke of Savoy. There also the union
of the crowns was provided against. The policy of all
this was obvious. The artifice consisted in the omission
of the House of Orleans. For the Duke of Orleans,
descending from Anne of Austria, was nearer than the
archduke Charles. At the same time he was farther removed from the throne of France than the Duke of Anjou,
less likely, therefore, to alarm the Powers. It might be
hoped that he would be near enough to Lewis to secure
the preservation of the Spanish empire, and not near
enough to threaten European independence. A time
came when the allies thought of him as a possible sub-

stitute, and offered him a principality between France and Spain. That is, he suggested himself as a better alternative to Anjou, and they thought of giving him Navarre and Languedoc. Put forward at a time when the Maritime Powers were not committed to the archduke, he might have been accepted. But he was not the candidate of Lewis. The object of the Spaniards was to make sure that Lewis would break his engagement with William III., that he would give up the partition and accept the succession, preferring the risk of war for so great a prize to the chance of a pacific division of the spoil. This they ensured by the provision that Spain, if it did not belong to the French line, should pass to the Austrian; that, failing Anjou and his brother, the Austrian should take his place.

The will of Charles II. shows a distinct animosity against the Maritime and Protestant Powers; and a rumour spread that it had been written under the influence of the pope, who dreaded the presence of Dutch and English sailors and factors in South America. A letter was produced purporting to contain the advice of Innocent XII. in the matter; and the following pontiff, Clement XI., was obliged to disavow it.

Before the death of Charles II. the nature of the will he had made was known at Versailles. Tallard, who had negotiated the Partition Treaty, was beside himself with anger. He convinced Torcy, he convinced Lewis himself, that they must not accept the succession. On 4th November the king sent word to William that he remained true to the scheme of Partition to which he had pledged himself. "I shall fulfil my engagements," he said, "in spite of any offers that may be made to me." He assured Leopold that he would never accept the whole succession. It was safer to be content with a share, under the auspicious sanction of the Maritime Powers. But Torcy, having shaken off the too eager Marshal Tallard, changed his mind. He urged that neither the whole succession nor a part of it could be had without fighting, as Austria was as much opposed to the

S

partition, as to the acceptance of the will by France. Torcy was not yet the great man he became during his long administration. But his argument carried conviction, and Lewis argued that his grandson should accept the proffered throne, and that the Bourbons should reign where the Habsburgs had reigned for a century and a half. He was not bound by any engagement to the emperor, who was no party to the Partition Treaty. He was bound by that treaty to King William; but it was uncertain whether William had the support of his two nations. The funds rose at Amsterdam; and in England the king observed that everybody preferred the will to the treaty. For the Partition Treaty had stipulated nothing for English interests, nothing, therefore, worth fighting for. And England had no territorial advantage to claim.

The commercial, economical, and pacific spirit was evident, both in England and Holland. On the other side, there was the strong will and the infinite dexterity of William. In the last Partition Treaty he had betrayed this weakness of his position, and had given way to the skilled diplomacy of France. Lewis did not believe that he would prevail over the public opinion of his country. And if he did prevail, his position would be less formidable than before. Lewis now had Spain on his side, and all the dependencies of Spain. He also had Bavaria and Savoy. In the last war he had been unsuccessful at sea, and in the Irish expedition, which was carried on beyond the sea, by his naval, not by his military administration. In the coming war he would trust less to his fleet than to his troops, which had never been unsuccessful in a general action. He resolved to defy the Dutch and English, and to seize every attainable advantage. The Spanish ambassador had exclaimed, "The Pyrenees have melted away." Lewis now announced that his grandson was not to renounce his right to the throne of France. In the Barrier Fortresses the Dutch held garrisons. Lewis sent them home and occupied the places himself. "Dutchmen were not wanted," he said, "to protect one Bourbon

against the other." In August 1701 he obtained for
French traders the *asiento*, the profitable and coveted
monopoly in negro slaves. In September he prohibited
English imports. Then, on the 16th, he did one thing
more, one thing too much even for a nation of economists
and calculators.

The acceptance of the Spanish succession by France
was the frustration of William's efforts during thirty years.
He had striven and made war for peace and civilisation
against wilful attack and the reign of force. That good
cause was defeated now, and the security of national
rights and international conventions was at an end. The
craving for empire and the hegemony of Europe had
prevailed. The temper of England compelled him, in
April 1701, to acknowledge Philip of Anjou. The
country, he said, could not understand the refusal to
acknowledge a king welcomed by the whole of Spain.
He advised the Emperor to have the German princes with
him, and to begin the attack. He himself would arm
meanwhile, and his own people, before long, would drive
him into war. He relied on the arrogance of the French,
and this calculation, the measures by which he brought
public opinion on to his side, are the greatest achievement of his career.

As it became apparent that England was to lose, not,
like Austria, a visionary prospect, but its commercial
existence, during the summer of 1701 the spirit of
parliament began to be roused. William, watching the
flow of the patriotic tide, concluded with Austria and
Holland the treaty of the Hague, which divided Europe,
for the first time, into a Latin and a German half.
Austria was to obtain that which it desired above all
things, dominion over Italy. The Maritime Powers were
to retain their commercial privileges in Spain, and everything they could make their own in America. France
was to be excluded from transatlantic markets; but
nothing was said as to Spain. Implicitly, Philip V.
was acknowledged. The Maritime Powers aimed much
more at prosperity than at power. Their objects were

not territorial, but commercial. The date of this treaty, which was to cost so much blood, was 7th September.

William was moving more rapidly than public opinion, but public opinion was not far behind. The country was committed to war with France at the very beginning of that fatal September. The treaty had been signed nine days, when James II. died at St. Germains. Lewis acknowledged the son as he had acknowledged the father—the one as the other, a king *in partibus*. It was a platonic engagement, involving no necessary political consequences. Since the treaty of Ryswick, Lewis treated William as king, though there was a James II. He did not cease so to treat him because there was a James III. To a prince who, the week before, had contrived a warlike coalition against him, a coalition which soon proved more formidable than all those which had preceded it, he owed no more than the letter of their agreements. The decisive step towards open hostilities was taken by the King of England, not by the King of France. Parliament had just passed the Act of Succession. Lewis's declaration in favour of the Stuarts appeared to be a defiance of the law in favour of the Guelphs. England had not dared to question the right of the Spaniards to regulate the succession. England could not permit interference with her own.

This declaration of Lewis XIV., imprudent but not unprovoked, gave to William what he wanted. It supplied a strong current of national feeling. The nation was ardent on his side. He had succeeded at last. The war with France, for the partition of the Spanish monarchy, would be carried on with determination under the coming reign. For William knew that Anne would soon be queen. It was also known at Paris, for William had consulted the French king's physician, and there were no illusions. The strange impolicy of Lewis's action may be explained by the belief that another than William of Orange would appear at the head of the allied armies in the next campaign. That the change of commander would be the greatest calamity that had befallen France since Agincourt was not foreseen.

In November 1701 Parliament was dissolved, and a majority was returned prepared for war, prepared to support the policy of the Grand Alliance. What made it formidable was that the Tories themselves were warlike. The Whigs were warlike because it was their nature, since France had declared itself for the Stuarts ; also because they and their friends were interested in pushing trade with the oceanic world, which was mainly Spanish. But it was not, at first, a Whig war. On 9th March 1702 they obtained the majority. They were 235 to 221.

William III. was dying. He had borne the accident well by which he broke his collar-bone. He sat at dinner that evening, and was expected to recover in a few weeks. But he fell asleep one day near an open window. Nobody had the courage to shut it, and he caught a chill, of which, in five days, he died. His prestige was lost to the cause of the allies. At the same time, William was a Dutch king, working with Dutchmen only, Heinsius, Bentinck, Keppel, for Dutch as much as for English objects. While he lived there was no danger that the interests of his own countrymen would be made subordinate to those of England. There was no sign of Holland taking the second place, of Holland being sacrificed to England. That security was now over. The leadership passed to England. In the field, the Dutch were far ahead. The understanding was that the English were to be 40,000, the Austrians 90,000, and the Dutch 102,000. But whereas the Dutch ultimately put 160,000 men into line, the English, in the greatest battle of the war, at Malplaquet, were under 8000, or less than one-twelfth of the whole force engaged.

What gave to this country the advantage in the war of the Spanish Succession was the genius and the overwhelming personal ascendency of Marlborough. One of the Dutch deputies, who did not love him, who was not even quite convinced as to his qualities as a soldier, describes him as perfectly irresistible, not so much by energy and visible power, as by his dexterity and charm. And this in spite of defects that were notorious and grotesque. Everybody knows, and perhaps nobody believes, the story of his blowing out the candle when he found that his visitor had no papers to read. Many years later the story was told, when an officer present stated that he was the visitor whom the duke had treated so parsimoniously. It is due to him that England became one of the great Powers of the world, and next to France, the first of the Powers. And it was not his doing, but the doing of his rivals, that the allies were sacrificed. The Dutch had no such splendid personality, and though they had their full share in the war, they lost by the result. The character of the struggle changed by the death of William and the substitution of Marlborough, who depended, more and more, on the support of the Whigs. In one of his last conversations William had said : " We seek nothing but the security which comes from the balance of power." Our policy was not maintained throughout on that exalted level.

The War of Succession began in Italy, by the attempt of Eugene to recover Milan, which reverted to the empire on the death of Charles II. It was, as it were, a private affair, involving no declaration of war, no formal breach with France. But the French were in Lombardy, and, with the support of the Duke of Savoy, they were able to check the Austrian advance. Eugene went home to Vienna to organise and direct and urge the exertions of his government. On his return, after a very memorable absence, Victor Amadeus had deserted his French alliance, and had attached himself to the Austrians. A French army laid siege to Turin, and Eugene, coming up the right bank of the Po to his rescue, defeated the French, raised the siege, and established for the first time the domination of Austria over Italy. He was repulsed in his attempt on Toulon ; but the Italian war was at an end, and the emperor triumphant. In Germany the valley of the Danube which is the road to Vienna, was

open to the French, because the elector of Bavaria was
their ally against his father-in-law the emperor. The
Imperialists were in danger, and the Dutch, more solicitous
of the Belgian frontier before them than of what went on
hundreds of miles away, on the long line from Strasburg
to the distant centre of Austria, refused to let Marlborough
take their troops away to another seat of war in Southern
Germany.

Marlborough, sheltered by the complicity of Heinsius,
politely disregarded their orders and started on his famous
march, by Ehrenbreitstein and Heilbronn, meeting Eugene
on his way. Eugene, at that moment, was the most renowned commander in Europe. Marlborough was better
known as a corrupt intriguer, who owed his elevation to
the influence of his wife at court, who would disgrace
himself for money, who had sought favour at St. Germains
by betraying the expedition to Brest. Blenheim altered
the relative position of the two men in the eyes of the
world. It was known that the day had been won, not
by the persistent slaughter of brave soldiers, but by an
inspiration of genius executed under heavy fire with all
the perfection of art. In the midst of the struggle Marlborough had suddenly changed his order of battle, gathered
his squadrons on a new line, and sent them against the
French centre, with infantry supports. He did what
Napoleon was vainly entreated to do in his last engagement. That is what suggested the simile of the angel,
and what Addison meant by the words :—

> Rides on the whirlwind and directs the storm.

The great Eugene had done well, as he always did. The
Englishman had risen in a single day to the foremost
rank of generals. And England rose with him. There
had not been such a defeat for sixty years, since Condé,
at Rocroy, established the military reputation of France.
The French retreated to the Rhine, and on that side
Austria was safe.

In Spain the issue was very different. Philip was
thoroughly safe during three years of reign, and the

archduke would have been glad to content himself with
what could be secured in Italy.   But the English felt
that their trade interests would be safer in Spain and
the Indies under a Habsburg than under a Bourbon.
They brought the archduke to Lisbon in 1703, having
concluded with the Portuguese that treaty which made
them commercial dependants on England, and which has
been the cause of so much port wine and so much gout.
It was a disastrous change of policy.   The English
destroyed the French fleet at Vigo, with many tons of
American silver.   They took Gibraltar and Minorca,
without understanding their importance.   They failed to
defend the one ; and they six times offered the other for
an exchange.   But on land they were utterly defeated, at
Almanza and Brihuega, and the archduke never actually
reigned over much more than Catalonia.   There, having
restored the Aragonese Constitution, he succeeded in inspiring a sentiment of loyalty, and repulsed his rival.   He
was never able to maintain himself at Madrid.   On that
seat of war the French had much the best of it.   They
lost Germany at Blenheim in 1704, and Italy at Turin in
1706.

The deciding campaigns were in Belgium, where there
were many fortresses, and progress was necessarily slow.
After Marlborough's victory at Ramillies in 1706 the
French lost ground, and when the princes, as they were
called, took the field together, no French marshal had a
chance.   For Marlborough was now a prince of the empire ;
and Eugene, having driven the enemy out of Germany
and Italy, was again by his side, thirsting for something
to do.   At Oudenarde, where he was present, with no
troops of his own, at a critical moment he led a successful
charge.   Together they conquered Lille ; and together
they defeated Villars at Malplaquet.   There, in the
summer of 1709, the five years of constant victory which
began at Blenheim came to an end.

After Turin and Ramillies Lewis had been willing to
treat.   He was profoundly discouraged ; and when Torcy
came to the Hague in 1709 to meet the Triumvirate,

Heinsius, Eugene, and Marlborough, he gave up almost every point. He even agreed that France should furnish men and money to drive Philip V. out of Spain, where he felt quite safe and refused every summons. Lewis, in return, asked for Naples, and Naples only, without Sicily. The allies could have everything else, and could have compelled him to restore all the ill-gotten acquisitions of his reign. They were unwilling to be at the trouble of one more campaign in the Peninsula, where they had met with so much misfortune. They required that Lewis should undo his own offending deed, and himself compel his grandson to resign the Spanish throne. Marlborough, holding a position such as no Englishman had ever enjoyed, was preponderant in their councils. He aspired to be captain-general for life, and rejected an enormous sum with which France offered to repay his advocacy of peace. The attempt to prolong war for his own private advantage is the deadliest of his crimes. Lewis, in despair, made an appeal to his people, and a thrill of genuine indignation ran through the unhappy country. The tide began to turn. At Malplaquet, the greatest battle fought in modern Europe before Napoleon, the allies lost 23,000 out of less than 100,000 ; and the French not half so many.

A much graver change was coming over the spirit of the English nation. As the Whigs offered nothing better than the continuation of war, Toryism gained ground ; and with Toryism, the Church. The Duchess of Marlborough was supplanted in the queen's favour ; the Whigs went out of office ; and the new ministers dismissed Marlborough and appointed Ormonde to command in his stead. With the aid of an obscure French priest, who acted as chaplain to the Imperial ambassador, they began a secret negotiation with Torcy. They stipulated that the Dutch should be kept out of it, and should not be listened to, if they made proposals of their own ; also that their conditions should be understood to come from the initiative of France. Torcy responded heartily. His first letter is dated five days after the death of the Emperor Joseph

By that event, the Archduke Charles succeeded to his throne. Joseph died 17th April. Four months earlier, 23rd December, Harley, by his intermediary, Gautier, informed Torcy that England would give up Spain and the Indies to the Bourbon king, and would desert the allies as soon as trade interests were provided for. The surrender of that which the English had claimed from 1703 to 1710, the return, in spite of success and glory, to the moderate policy laid down by William in 1701, was not caused by the prospect of the union of the crowns on the head of Charles. Harley was afraid that the archduke would make those terms himself. For it was known that the Austrians regarded Spain and its colonies as more burdensome than profitable. When Harley was stabbed by Guiscard, and was laid up with his wound, the secret of the negotiations passed into St. John's hands. His treatment of the allies was perfidious ; but they obtained almost as much as they really wanted.

Eugene, deserted by the English forces under Ormonde, was beaten by Villars at Denain, and afterwards, by no fault of the English, at Friedlingen. Then the emperor made his own peace at Rastadt. At Utrecht, the Dutch secured a favourable tariff, the right of garrison in a line of fortified towns, from Ghent to Namur, and the daring Torcy had so thoroughly penetrated the weakness of England, in consequence of party divisions, that he concluded a disastrous war by a triumphant negotiation. France retained her own territory, practically undiminished, recovering Lille, and acquiring, for the younger branch of the royal house, Spain and the Spanish colonies. It gained infinitely more than either Holland or England. Marshal La Feuillade asked Bolingbroke why he had let them off so easily. The answer was : Because we were no longer afraid of you. Philip V. retained all that was legitimately Spanish, in Europe and America, excepting the two fortresses conquered by England, Gibraltar and Port Mahon. He refused to give up Corunna. But he renounced his claim in the succession to his grandfather's crown. Bolingbroke betrayed the allies, and he disgraced

his country by the monopoly of the slave trade ; but the
distribution was not unfair to the contracting parties, and
the share of England was not excessive. We acquired
Newfoundland, Nova Scotia, and the Hudson Bay territory,
and, in addition to the *asiento*, the right of trading in
the possessions of the House of Bourbon—in fact, the
commerce of the world. And our revolutionary system,
the permanent exclusion of the Stuarts, received the
sanction of Europe. It was the condemnation of the
principle of non-resistance, which had carried the Tories
to power, and the perpetuation of Whiggism.

Bolingbroke did not intend that the great achievement
of his life should serve the purpose of his enemies, and
he gravitated towards the Stuarts, the true representatives
of the cause to which Sacheverell had given renewed
vitality. Harley had opened, through Berwick, negotiations with St. Germains, and had thereby secured the help
of the Jacobite organisation. Bolingbroke went further.
He believed that the Elector of Hanover could not be
prevented from coming in, but that he would soon be
driven out again. He said that he was too unintelligent
to understand and manage parties, too much accustomed
to have his own way to submit to govern under constitutional control. He promised that King James would be
restored. And the French concluded peace at Utrecht in
the belief that they were dealing with a Jacobite, that
their concession in regard to the crown of England
amounted to nothing, that, by yielding now, they would
secure hereafter the elevation of a dependent dynasty.
Under that illusion they combined with Bolingbroke to
overreach themselves and to institute party government,
under the supremacy of the Whigs.

XVI

THE HANOVERIAN SETTLEMENT

THE first thing is to consider by what steps a government came into existence entirely different from that of England in the seventeenth century, and unlike anything that had previously been known in Europe.

The old order terminates with the Bill of Rights and the Act of Settlement. What followed is not a development of that Act, but in contradiction to it. With the new dynasty there is a new departure. And the change was not effected by statute, but by that force which makes the law, and is above the law, the logic of facts and the opinion of the nation. The essential innovations, the cabinet, the premier, and government by party, are still without legislative sanction. The Act of Settlement was speedily unsettled. It separated the administration from the legislature by excluding placemen from the House of Commons; and it prohibited the king from visiting his foreign dominions without leave. And it required the king to be advised by the Privy Council, thereby rejecting a united cabinet, the exclusive organ of a party. Both William and, at that time, Marlborough preferred that all the leading men should be united in the administration. Before the Act of Settlement came into operation, during the reign of Anne, the idea of a united cabinet taken from the same party had prevailed, and at last even Harley could not be tolerated by the Jacobites. If Bolingbroke had not made it impossible for George I. to trust the loyalty of the Tories, the rising of 1715 would have been fatal to them. The new dynasty governed by

the Whigs, that is, by one party, and by a cabinet, not
by the council. As the king understood neither English
nor English affairs, he very rarely presided. The cabinet
decided in his absence, and then reported.

It is necessary to see what manner of man he was.
A branch of the ancient Guelphic House reigned at
Hanover, and had succeeded by politic and constant
effort in consolidating half a dozen territories into one
important principality. It was the most rising and
prosperous of the German Houses. It acquired the ninth
electorate in 1692; and it was manifestly appropriate
when it was designated for the English succession, because the first elector, who had accomplished the greatness of his family, had married the youngest daughter of
Elizabeth Stuart, the Princess Palatine, who in an evil
hour was Queen of Bohemia. The Electress Sophia
was a Calvinist. Her husband was a Lutheran. His
predecessor, who died in 1678, had been a convert to
Catholicism. Hanover had been the centre of reunion,
and there were Lutheran divines there who, under the
commanding influence of Leibniz, went further than
Tract No. 90 in the direction of Rome. With their easy
comprehension and impartial appreciation of religious
systems, the Guelphs of Hanover were not representative
Protestants. Some misgivings arose in the mind of
William III., and it was thought that he looked with
suspicious favour on the young Frederic William, the man
who afterwards drilled the battalions which Frederic the
Great led to victory. A Hanoverian statesman wrote, in
alarm, that William seemed to prefer the Prussian prince,
because he was a Protestant, to the Hanoverian, who was
a Lutheran. The implication is that the Lutherans
offered less resistance to Catholicism. But the fact also
was that Sophia was a Stuart by the mother's side, and
did not wish too loudly to proclaim that she was not a
legitimist. There was a little ostensible hesitation; and
the electress so managed that the crown should seem to
be forced upon her. It was part of this decorous comedy
that her son never learnt English—a circumstance of the

utmost value, afterwards, to England. The Electress
Sophia was not perhaps a very estimable, though a very
intelligent princess. But she was eighty-four when the
crown came within reach, and she died of rage at an
unfriendly letter from Queen Anne, betraying her Jacobite
propensity.

The elector, who ascended the throne of England
two months after his mother's death, was neither a tyrant,
nor a coward, nor a fool ; he was only unintellectual and
brutally selfish. There were ladies in his company who
received English titles, and offended one part of the public
by their morals and the remainder by their ugliness. One
was created Duchess of Kendal, and Walpole said of her
that she was Queen of England if ever there was one.
But she sold her influence for money, amounting sometimes to £10,000, and Walpole at last complained to his
master. The king laughed in his face, and replied, in his
dog-Latin, that no doubt his minister also was paid by
the people whom he recommended. There was a deeper
taint on his reputation. He had married the only
daughter of his neighbour and kinsman, the Duke of Celle,
thereby securing the succession to his dominions. Her
mother was not of royal birth, and she was treated so
cruelly by her husband and by the Electress Sophia that
she resolved to escape from her misery by flight. In her
despair she accepted the assistance of Count Königsmarck,
whom the envoy Stepney described as a profligate adventurer. The secret was betrayed ; the princess was
divorced, and spent the long remainder of her life at
Ahlden, a remote country house which had belonged to
her father. This was no more than had happened in
many great families tried by the temptation of irresponsible monarchy, but there was a superadded tragedy ;
for Count Königsmarck disappeared and was never seen
again. As part of the scheme to run away with the
princess, he had transferred his services to Saxony, where
he was made a general. For that reason, and still more
for the persuasive supplications of his sister, the beautiful
Aurora von Königsmarck, the Elector Augustus the

Strong caused some inquiry to be made. It led to no result. But Aurora became the mother of the Marshal of Saxony, who defeated the English at Fontenoy, and conquered the Austrian Netherlands for the French. From the marshal was descended George Sand, the most famous Frenchwoman of the last generation. The Hanoverian government issued a lying report, but attempted no defence. Nobody doubted that Königsmarck had been made away with, and that the author of the crime was the King of England, whose proper destination therefore should have been not St. James's but Newgate, and indeed not Newgate but Tyburn. Such was the character that preceded the founder of our reigning line of kings, and such were the weapons in the hands of his dynastic foes.

His most dangerous enemy was the Prince of Wales ; not the Stuart who held his court in Lorraine, but his own eldest son. For George II. believed in the prisoner of Ahlden ; believed that his mother had been cruelly treated, wrongfully accused, and unjustly divorced, and was therefore able to see his father by an exceedingly clear light. Thence arose a bitter enmity between them, and that tendency to opposition in the princes of Wales which became a family tradition and a salutary factor in the Constitution.

George I. found that, as long as he respected English institutions, things went very well with him, and he made no attempt to overturn them. The fear that a sovereign who was nominally absolute in one place could never govern under a constitution in another proved to be unnecessary. His interests, and those of his continental advisers, were mainly continental. In political science he had long had the ablest counsellor in Europe at his elbow, Leibniz, the friend of the electress. And although that great man did not enjoy unbroken favour, it was not easy to be blind to the flood of light which he poured on every subject. Leibniz had been instrumental in securing the succession, and he abounded in expositions of constitutional policy. He professed himself so good a Whig that he attributed to that cause his unpopularity with many people in England, especially at Cambridge, and most of all at Trinity. He seems not to have known that his rival, Newton, was as good a Whig as himself, and indeed a much better one. It was characteristic of his mind ever to impute the broad divisions of opinion among men to ignorance or incapacity to understand each other. With a more scientific method, he thought that many disputes could be settled, and many adversaries reconciled. For many years it was his favourite occupation to show that there was no real cause for a breach at the Reformation, and that people called themselves Protestants not knowing what was really meant by Catholic. He assured the Catholics that the Confession of Augsburg, rightly understood, was sound Catholicism ; and he assured the Lutherans that there was nothing in the Council of Trent with which they were forced, in consistency, to quarrel. With the same maxim, that men are generally right in what they affirm, and wrong in what they deny, he taught that Whig and Tory are alike necessary portions of truth, that they complete each other, that they need each other, that a true philosophy of politics includes the two. He also said that the past is a law for the future, and that the will of Providence consecrates those things which are permitted to succeed and to endure. This is pure conservatism. The Whig seeks that which ought to be elsewhere than in that which is. His standing purpose is to effect change, for the past is essentially Tory.

The influence of the most enlightened German on the new German dynasty was not favourable to party government, and would have combined better with the system of William III. They consulted an enlightened Englishman, and Lord Cowper drew up an important political paper, showing that the king ought to depend on the Whigs. Moreover, Bolingbroke, at the last moment, by his Stuart intrigue, compelled George I. to come in as the nominee of a party. To Bolingbroke's intrigues the House of Hanover owed that which it most needed, the prestige of victory. He had found comfort in the reflection that, although it might be impossible to prevent the heralds from proclaiming the new monarchy, the new monarch would soon make himself odious, and would be more easy to expel than to exclude. The mass of the people was Tory, and the majority of Tories were Jacobites. There was the assured co-operation of the sects discontented with the Union, and a part of the very small army would be held fast by the sullen anger of the Irish.

Lewis XIV., weary and inert, would not risk another war; but if he saw his opportunity to interfere, he was not likely to neglect it. The Pretender would be advised by his brother, Berwick, the victor of Almanza. The insurgent forces would be led by the Duke of Ormonde, who had succeeded Marlborough as commander-in-chief. Marlborough himself had advanced money for the Jacobite rising, and was so much suspected by the ministers that they would not let him take the command.

The hopefulness of the situation darkened somewhat before the time for action arrived. Lewis XIV. died, and the Regent, having Philip of Spain for a rival, required the good-will of England. Two miscreants, to whom James had offered £20,000 if they would shoot the king and the Prince of Wales, failed to earn their reward. The arrest of a leading Jacobite, Sir William Wyndham, so scared his partisans, that Ormonde, having sailed into Torbay, returned to St. Malo without landing. The Highlanders rose, but there was no Dundee and no Montrose to make them superior to regular troops. They fought with doubtful fortune at Sheriffmuir, while the Borderers, finding no support in Lancashire, surrendered at Preston. When James Stuart landed in Aberdeenshire, the struggle was over. Cadogan was approaching at the head of the Dutch auxiliaries, and the Pretender escaped by a back door from his own men, and made his way to Gravelines. He had proved unequal to the occasion, and was not gifted with political understanding. But he had been instructed by Fénelon, and had learnt from him the doctrine of toleration.

T

The strongest part of the case against the new order in England was the treatment of the Irish Catholics ; and James saw the whole thing in the light of a religious conflict. Bolingbroke, who had been an oppressor of Nonconformists, and had no sympathy with the prince's motives, fell into disgrace. He was made responsible for the failure, and was suspected of having told secrets to the ambassador, Stair, in order to make his peace at home. He was allowed to return, and did far more harm to the House of Hanover as a loyal subject than he had done as a manager of insurrection.

Seven peers had been taken with arms in their hands ; and, in order to avoid questions which might have injured their friends, they pleaded guilty, and threw themselves on the mercy of the king. As they were more guilty than the followers whom they had led to their destruction, they could not be pardoned. Some, amid universal applause, made their escape from the Tower, and only two were sent to the scaffold. At the last moment, when repentance did not avail, Derwentwater retracted the declarations of loyalty he had made at his trial, and died protesting his unswerving fidelity to the House of Stuart. The Tories were effectually ruined. The militant part of them had been crushed. The remainder had proved helplessly weak, and the last dying speech of their honoured champion was taken as a proof that they were traitors at heart, and that their professions of loyalty were interested and insincere. Parliament displayed an enthusiastic attachment to the dynasty and its ministers ; they were ready for any expenditure, for any armaments, and a force of 16,000 men was raised, for the better security of the Whigs.

On this state of feeling the government introduced septennial parliaments. Under the Triennial Act a general election would have fallen due in 1717, too soon for safety after the Jacobite rising. Opinion in the country had not been impressed by recent events, by the utter weakness of the rebels, the overwhelming success of the government, the significant menace of the dying leader,

so deeply as the House of Commons.   The new establishment would be in peril with the constituencies, but safe
with their representatives.   This was so certain that the
philosophic arguments, for legislative independence and
for popular control, were superfluous.   The victors secured
their victory and perpetuated their power by extending
their mandate from three years to seven.   The measure
strengthened the House of Commons, and prepared the
long reign of the Whigs.   The funds rose, and the king
took advantage of the improved situation to spend some
months in Hanover.   There he had greater scope to
devote himself to foreign affairs, and to bring the Englishmen who attended him under the influence of experienced
foreigners.   Thus, while the Tories were prostrate and
the Whigs supreme, a schism arose between the ministers
at Hanover and the ministers at home.   Walpole and
Townshend went out of office ; Stanhope and Sunderland
formed a new administration, which the South Sea Bubble
overthrew.   A great question of constitutional principle
opened between them and their former colleagues.   The
enmity between the king and the Prince of Wales made
it probable that the ministers who had the confidence
of the father would be dismissed on his son's accession.
George II., to carry out his purpose, would be obliged to
swamp the House of Lords with new peers.   To prevent
this, it was proposed to limit the power of creation and
to fix a maximum number.   As the Septennial Act had
increased the power of the commons, the Peerage Bill
would, in their turn, have increased the power of the peers,
against the crown on one hand, against the commons on
the other.   The Whigs were not prepared to diminish the
House of Commons, and not yet afraid that it would
become too powerful, exposed as it was to corruption, and
elected, on a narrow franchise, by an uneducated constitu-
ency.   Burnet, the typical Whig, had protested against
such limitations as should quite change the form of our
government, and render the crown titular and precarious.

Walpole defeated the Bill.   It deprived government of
one great means of influence, by abolishing the hope of a

peerage. He was not prepared to sacrifice a legitimate species of patronage. He came back, thereupon, to office, but not to a principal office; and he was not a member of the Cabinet when the South Sea Company undertook to reduce the National Debt. They offered only eight and a half years' purchase; but the spirit of speculation was strong, and these bad terms were widely accepted. The shares of the Company rose from 130 to 1000. As there was so much capital seeking investment, rival enterprises were started, and were opposed by the South Sea Company. Their ruin destroyed its credit; and after large sums had been won, large sums were lost. Some had been impoverished, others enriched. The country had not suffered, but the ministry fell. Walpole inherited their power. The ground was cleared for his long administration. It lasted so long that he did more than any other man to establish the new system of government. He was more zealous to retain his power than to make heroic use of it, and was a good administrator but an indifferent legislator. In his time those things were best which were done outside of parliament. Walpole made it his business to yield to public opinion, and did it consistently in the three critical moments of his career—in Wood's Halfpence, in the Excise, and in the Spanish war. The same problem presented itself to a greater man in the present century, and was decided on the opposite principle. Guizot was himself persuaded that a measure of parliamentary reform was inevitable, since the opinion of the country was in its favour. But the opinion of parliament was against it, and he preferred to fall, together with the monarchy, in obedience to parliament, rather than to triumph by public opinion.

Walpole gave way in the affair of the Halfpence, that he might not alienate those through whom he governed Ireland. The coins were good. They were to contain twice the value of metal with which we are satisfied, and it was never shown that they did not. The gains of the contractor were exorbitant. He was able to pay a heavy fee to the Duchess of Kendal; and when the contract was revoked, he obtained an excessive compensation. His Halfpence are historic because Swift, in raising a tempest over the Irish grievance, employed the language of revolution and national patriotism, as it had never been heard. Again, the Excise Bill would have saved many hundreds of thousands of pounds to the State, when a hundred thousand was more than a million is now; but Walpole, in spite of his majority, yielded to the clamour outside. And he did the same thing in regard to the Spanish war, the last great crisis he encountered.

Walpole's main idea on taking the highest office, that which he proclaimed in his first king's speech, was to divert the country from frantic speculation to the legitimate profits of industry and trade. The two great openings for trade were with the Mediterranean and with Spanish America. That with the Mediterranean was somewhat neglected, as the government relied more on the friendship of the piratical Algerines than on the solid possession of Gibraltar and Minorca. George I. had written a letter to Philip V., dated 1st June 1721, in which he distinctly assured him of his " readiness to satisfy with regard to your demand relating to the restitution of Gibraltar, promising you to make use of the first favourable opportunity to regulate this article with consent of my parliament." The English ministry were not convinced of the importance of retaining Gibraltar, and fully expected to be in a position to give it up to Spain for an equivalent. Indeed, in January 1721, Stanhope had said to the French envoy that in a year, when the financial position of England was better and the temper of parliament improved, they would certainly give up Gibraltar, for the merest shadow of an equivalent, as the place was only a burden to them. But they had not counted on the determination of the English people to hold it at all costs. Philip, however, not perhaps without some reason, always regarded the engagement as precise, and treated the continued retention as an act of bad faith. In all that I have just said about Gibraltar, I have been quoting a recent writer in the *Historical Review*.

The South American trade presented infinite possibilities. It was pursued with difficulty against the resistance of the Spaniards, who had the law on their side. It was considered worth a war, and the strength of public feeling overcame the feeble scruples of the minister. The war ended disastrously, but before the end Walpole had been driven from office. It had been no part of his policy to promote prosperity by arms, but it was part of his policy, and the deciding part of it, to let the nation, in the last instance, regulate its own affairs. Peace was a good thing; but profit was also a good thing; and Walpole had no principle that made one a question of duty and the other a question of interest.

The constant lesson of the Revolution was that England preferred monarchy. But after the fall of Walpole it was observed that there was a new growth of republican sentiment, and that the country felt itself superior to the government. This was the natural result of the time known as the Robinocracy; not because he devised liberal measures, but because he was careful to be neither wiser nor more liberal than the public. He was quite content to preserve the government of the country by the rich, in the interest of their own class. Unlike Stanhope, his predecessor, he was unmoved by the intolerance of the laws in England, and especially in Ireland. He was a friend to Free Trade; but he suffered Ireland to be elaborately impoverished, for the benefit of English landlords. Slavery and the slave trade, which Bolingbroke had promoted, were not remedied or checked by this powerful Whig. The criminal Code, in his time, grew annually more severe; and I need enter into no details as to the treatment of prisoners and of the poor. Walpole was so powerful, and was powerful so long, that much of the responsibility for all these things is at his door. On this account, and not because he governed by patronage and pensions and ribbons and bribes, he was a false Whig.

Government by Party was established in 1714, by Party acting through the Cabinet. Walpole added to this

the prime minister, the accepted head of the Party and
of the Cabinet. As the king did not preside, the minister
who did preside discharged many functions of the king.
The power of governing the country was practically
transferred. It was shared, not between the minister
and the king, but between the head of the ministry
and the head of the opposition. For Party implies the
existence of a party which is out as well as a party
that is in. There is a potential ministry ready for
office whenever the majority is shifted. As Walpole
remained twenty-one years in office, he ignored this part
of the constitutional system. He never became a leader
of opposition, and when he resigned, no such thing had
been provided. "All the talents" were opposed to him,
but they were not an organised opposition. They were
discontented and offended Whigs, assailing ministers on
no ground of principle. This form of opposition was
instituted by Pulteney, when he quarrelled with Walpole.
Pulteney founded the *Craftsman*, in which there was much
good political writing. For Bolingbroke had returned to
England, and as he was not allowed to resume his seat
in the Lords, he could make his power felt only through
his pen. As he was thoroughly cured of his Jacobite
sympathies, the doctrine he proclaimed was a Toryism
stripped of the reactionary element. He proposed to
make the State dominate over all the interests — land,
Church, trade, and the like. That this might be done,
and the government by a class for a class abolished, he
appealed to the crown. The elevation of the State over
the dominant classes had been the part of intelligent
Monarchy in every age. And it is the spell by which
Bolingbroke transformed Toryism and introduced the party
called the King's Friends, which became a power in the
middle of the century, and was put an end to by Mr. Pitt,
after losing America, and setting up an English rival to
England. After the final fall of the Stuarts in 1746, this
was the moving force of Toryism, and the illiberal spirit
was seriously curbed. Macaulay goes so far as to say
that the Tories became more liberal than the Whigs.

But it was an academic and Platonic liberality that did not strengthen the constitution.

The Whigs, having added the unwritten clauses, exclusive government by party, cabinet instead of council, and premier instead of king, did nothing to discover defects to be reformed and principles to be developed. They became Conservatives, satisfied with defending the new dynasty and the institutions that accompanied it. One supreme change was absolutely essential to complete their system. For its essence was that the object of the law, which was liberty, should prevail over the letter of the law, which was restraint. It required that public opinion should control legislation. That could not be done without the liberty of the press ; and the press was not free while it was forbidden to publish and to discuss the debates of parliament. That prohibition was strictly maintained. For near thirty years we know the debates, and even the divisions, chiefly through the reports of Bonnet the Brandenburg resident, and of Hoffmann the Austrian resident, who tell us much that is sought vainly in the meagre pages of Hansard. Then came the epoch of Dr. Johnson and his colleagues in Grub Street. But when the Whig reign ended, at the resignation of the great Commoner in 1761, the Whigs had not admitted the nation to the parliamentary debates.

The debates were made public in 1774. The unreported parliament of 1768, as it is called, is the first that was properly reported. The speeches were taken down by one of the members, Cavendish, the ancestor of the Waterparks. A portion has been printed and forgotten. The remainder is preserved in manuscript, and contains, in all, about two hundred and fifty speeches of Edmund Burke. It is of no little value to political students, inasmuch as Burke at his best is England at its best. Through him and through American influence upon him, the sordid policy of the Walpolean Whigs became a philosophy, and a combination of expedients was changed into a system of general principles.

XVII

PETER THE GREAT AND THE RISE
OF PRUSSIA

WHILST the English people, with the example and assistance of the Dutch, were carrying forward the theory of constitutional government, a still more important movement in the opposite direction was proceeding in the North, and new forces were brought into the widening circle of general history.

The Muscovite empire extended from the frontiers of Poland to the farthest extremity of China. In numbers and in extent it was the first of Christian Powers. But it played no part in the concert or the conflict of Europe, and its existence was almost unnoticed and unfelt. The people were too backward in the scale of wealth or knowledge or civilisation to obtain influence even on their neighbours. Potentially the most formidable force on earth, practically they were forgotten and unknown. In a single reign, by the action of one man, Russia passed from lethargy and obscurity to a dominant position among the nations.

The first need was intercourse with the world—intercourse of trade for its material progress, intercourse of ideas for its civilisation. The problem was too obvious to escape the earlier Romanoffs. They were a clerical dynasty, closely associated with the Church, and allowing to the Patriarch a position very near the throne. In politics they were inefficient and unsuccessful ; but their Church policy was charged with far-reaching consequences. In that, they were superior to the people about them, and they introduced certain moderate reforms, literary rather than dogmatic, in the externals of ritual, and in the liturgical books.   An illiterate clergy had allowed abuses to take root, and were excessively intolerant of change.   A schism arose between the established church with its rectified texts and improved ceremonial, and the large minority who rejected them.

Everybody knows Newman's story of the ancient priest who fell into the habit, at mass, of saying, " quod ore mumpsimus " instead of " quod ore sumpsimus," and, when admonished of his error, refused to exchange old " mumpsimus " for new " sumpsimus." Although " mumpsimus " is the very motto for the Russian schismatics, and although ignorance and superstition were the root of the matter, they combined with a dread of arbitrary change by an arbitrary power, and supplied a basis for resistance to Erastianism and the fusion of Church and State.   This was the heart of the opposition to the later reforms, to which the Church in general yielded reluctantly, and the sectaries not at all, choosing death, and even suicide by fire, to compromise.   The reforming government was driven into persecution by the fanaticism of these men.

The new spirit began to reign when the young Tsar Peter triumphed over family intrigues that were supported by the party of reaction.   He was uneducated, unmannerly, uncivilised ; but he had a clear notion of that which his people required, and the energy and force of character to achieve it.   As there were no roads in Russia, and not much material for making them, the waterway was the easy and natural line to follow.   The Russian rivers flowed to the Caspian and the Euxine, and invited to the conquest of Persia and Central Asia, or to the deliverance of the Slavonic and Greek brethren from the Turk.   Peter was not carried away by either prospect.   He did indeed send a fleet down the Volga, and another down the Don.   He conquered the Persian coast of the Caspian, but resisted the temptation of pushing his arms to the Indian Ocean.   He was repeatedly at war with the Turk ; but he contented himself with a humble measure of success.

Poland, for reasons of race and of religion, was the national enemy ; and from the death of Sobieski in 1696 there were symptoms that it was likely to break up. The next king, Augustus of Saxony, in 1702, proposed the partition of the Polish dominions. His agent, Patkul, renewed the idea at Berlin in 1704, and Austria did the same in 1712. At the height of his military success, in 1710, Peter entertained the idea, only to dismiss it. He preferred to wait. Poland would be convenient as a helpless neighbour, covering his frontier on a dangerous side ; and its constitution prevented it from becoming formidable. He was content to make sure that the feeble government should never undergo reform. He resolutely fixed his thoughts in another direction, and chose, not the easiest, but the most difficult line of attack.

Tartars, or Persians, or Zaporogue Cossacks supplied no new element that could be of service to his people. The Russians had issued from the long subjection to the Golden Horde, indigent, ignorant, prejudiced, dishonest and false. A mighty future lay before them, but they were unfit for such a destiny. The civilising influences they required could come only from contact with superior races. From them they must import the goods, they must import the men, that were needed to raise them, in the arts of peace and war, to a level with others. The route for both species of commerce was by sea. But Russia touched the sea only in the North, where it is closed by ice. The way to the countries that were most advanced, intellectually and socially, to France and England, especially to Holland and the empire behind it, was by the Baltic.

There the Swedes stopped the way. Gustavus had conquered the Baltic provinces, and all the way from Poland to Finland the coast was inaccessible to the interior of Russia. Sweden was still esteemed a great Power ; and although it was not yet discovered, the new king was, what Peter never became, a capable and am bitious commander.　The main argument of Peter's reign was the struggle for supremacy with Charles XII.

Before it broke out, he undertook a journey to make acquaintance with the foreign countries by which he intended to accomplish the elevation of his own.　That was the time of those grotesque studies in shipbuilding, tooth-drawing, and other useful arts in which he acquired a sort of technical mastery ; and it was then that he learned to think so highly of the Dutch as a practical people, worthy of imitation.　This preference was not exclusive, and he was eager to borrow what he could from others—military organisation from Austria, manners from France, clothes from England, methods of administration from Germany.　Together with the foreign customs he undertook to introduce experts who were to teach them, until the disciples became equal to their masters. The Scotsman Gordon and the Genevese Lefort were at the head of his army and navy.　Germans, such as Münnich and Ostermann, followed ; and then there came a vast army of engineers, miners, metal founders, artificers of almost all kinds, for the roads and bridges, the ships and palaces, the schools and hospitals that he called into existence.　These things were the *sine qua non* of civilisation.　It would be long before his own people understood the use of them.　They could only be obtained by importation.　To stimulate the demand for them at home it would be necessary to rely on the progress of intelligence.　That could not be done in a nation consisting mainly of serfs.　The educational part of the enterprise was the one which had least success, and which he understood least.　For such imponderables he had no scales, and he cared more for the kind of knowledge that was practically useful than for the interior improvement of the mind, which constitutes what we call a gentleman.　No such exotic could flourish at his court.　He required that those whom he honoured with his confidence should get as drunk as himself; that they should be servile and cringing, without moral courage or self-respect, happy to be insulted, kicked, and spat upon.　They might be men of resource, brave soldiers, clever administrators, but they seldom developed those elements of character which prevent a man from being corrupt. For those qualities he had no comprehension. Civilisation, as he understood it, was material, not moral. He could not imagine management of men by the nobler motives. He raised the condition of the country with great rapidity ; he did not raise it above his own level.

Whilst he was on his travels exploring Europe an insurrection broke out, and the old Russian militia, the Strelitz, mutinied, and plotted to exterminate the Germans and all the abettors of foreign innovation. The movement was crushed by Gordon, and Peter on his return was undisputed master. He then plunged into war with Sweden for the Baltic provinces—that is, for access to the sea, which was the highway to all the world. Beaten at first, but not discouraged, he organised a new army, while Charles XII. overran Poland and dictated terms of peace in the heart of Germany.

It then appeared that the Russians, like most nations when they are ably commanded, were the raw material of good soldiers. Charles came back to Russia from his Saxon campaign laden with glory, and marched on Moscow by Minsk, Mohilev, the Beresina—very much the route which Napoleon followed. At the instigation of Mazeppa he turned aside to the Ukraine, in the hope of raising the Cossacks against the Tsar. At Pultawa, near the Dnieper, he was defeated, and fled for refuge to Turkey. The work of Gustavus, who had made Sweden so great, was undone, and Russia succeeded to the vacant place among the Powers.

The supreme object of Peter's policy was attained. He was in possession of the Baltic coast north of the Dwina. Finland was restored, but he retained Livonia, Esthonia, Ingria, from Riga to Viborg. On the Neva, where the Gulf of Finland penetrates farthest inland, he fixed his capital. The place was a swamp, that swallowed the tallest trunks of trees, and the workmen perished by fever. But an island in the mouth of the river made it impregnable by sea. It was free from traditions and reactionary memories, looking only to the future and the new things that the commerce with the world would bring ; a gate for the inflow of the forces by which its founder would transform the nation. As part of the same transformation the Tsar of Muscovy became Emperor of Russia. It was a claim to the Byzantine inheritance, and a menace to the Austrian successor of the Western Empire. This was faint and distant ; and Peter remained on friendly terms with Vienna. But the title was coldly received by Europe, and was not finally recognised until forty years after his death.

The persuasions by which Peter bent Russia to his will were base and atrocious ; for, although one of the greatest men that have influenced the course of Christian history, he is undoubtedly the worst of them ; but he was not working for himself ; at Pultawa he told his troops that they were fighting for Russia, not for him. His motive was impersonal. He had grasped a great ideal, and he served it with devotion, sacrificing everything to it, and not sparing himself. The absolute State was the ideal, or rather the idol, for which he toiled, the State as it had been devised by Machiavelli and Hobbes. To raise the country by the employment of its own internal forces was an unpromising and unprofitable enterprise. He, who was himself a barbarian, could only accomplish his purpose by means of aid from outside, by the instrumentality of those who had experience of a more advanced order of things. The borrowed forces could only be applied by the powers of despot. That power, moreover, was already provided. Muscovy had never been governed otherwise than by irresponsible and irresistible authority. That authority had been inactive and not deeply felt. Now the same authority interfered to alter almost everything, except the subjection of the serf to the landowner.

To enforce the supremacy of the State over society, and of will over custom, Peter introduced his most characteristic institution. He made precedence depend on public service, and regulated it according to rank in the army in fourteen degrees, from the ensign to the marshal. A new aristocracy superseded the old, and the ancient nobles were forced to serve, in order to be somebody, when away from the ancestral home. They were important, not by their possessions or their descent, but by the position in which they stood towards the emperor. Peter had imbibed too much of the rationalism of the West to be a persecutor. He was severe with the schismatics, who existed only as opponents of change and enemies of civilisation ; and as there were no Jews in Russia, he decreed that in future there should be none. But he built churches for the foreigners whom he brought into the country, and did not attempt to sustain the domination of the Muscovite clergy, who, like the English, professed passive obedience, but obeyed without approval. When the last patriarch was dying he expressed the wish that all men of other faith—Catholic, Protestant, and Mahomedan—should be burnt, and their places of worship levelled with the ground.

Peter's schemes of change were so tremendous that most Russians recoiled and wished them no success. His own family opposed him, and became a centre of plotting opposition. He repudiated his wife, and sent her to the seclusion of a convent. His second empress was a peasant woman, whose name was Martha, but was called, in Russia, Catharine. It was uncertain whether her husband was dead. It was certain that Peter's first wife was living. Nobody minded. But Alexis, the son of the earlier marriage, took the conservative side, and became, from 1711, the hope of those who rejected Peter's anti-national, cosmopolitan, chiefly Dutch and German system of reform. He longed for the Asiatic twilight of the past, and the discontented longed for him to succeed. Peter, seeing that he was a poor creature, wished him to resign his claim. Alexis fled, and placed himself under the protection of the emperor Charles VI. He was discovered in the castle of St. Elmo at Naples, and brought back to Russia, where he was condemned to death, and died of torture. The plan had been to return to the ancient ways, and to give Petersburg back to the Swedes, with the command of the coast. The clergy were mixed up in it, and Peter now secured himself against the Church. He had left the patriarchate vacant. He now abolished it, and divided its powers.

A kindred spirit had arisen, capable of carrying out reform in the Church. Procopovitch had become a united Greek, in order to be admitted to foreign universities. He studied in Rome, and in Germany he became familiar with Lutheran theology. He came back with much of the religious culture of the West, and Peter appointed him to one of the sees. The bishops protested. They said that he was a heretic seventeen times over. And they proposed, if they were not believed, that the matter should be decided by the three eastern patriarchs. It was a scheme to disconnect the Church from the State, to merge it in the Eastern Church. Procopovitch defeated his enemies, and drew up the plan by which the Church was brought under the civil power, much on the lines of Henry VIII. It was governed, thenceforward, by the Holy Synod, which was controlled by a great official who represented the emperor. The clergy ceased to be an obstacle. The government of the Church by the Synod was part of a plan of government by boards, which had been suggested by Leibniz. The empire was governed by a Senate of eight, of ten, at one time of twenty members. Under the Senate, which made laws, were ten ministerial departments, or boards, like our Treasury or Admiralty, which executed them. And there were eleven governors of provinces, each larger than a European monarchy. Men fit for such a responsiblity could not be found in Russia, and the empire was badly governed. But it was there. The transformation was accomplished. And the gigantic force was centred in the hand of a tyrant.

The concentration was such, the destruction of resisting forces was so complete, that the machine worked well in the hands of women. For almost the whole of the seventy years after Peter's death, Russia was governed by empresses. The last of them, Catharine II., was one of the ablest and most successful rulers in modern times. For the machine which Peter created was strong enough to endure. It still exists as he made it, an amalgam of power and servility, never leading, but often supplying the deciding force in the history of the world. It was the empire of Peter the Great that destroyed the empire of Napoleon.

Such a Power, limited by feeble neighbours, would have been a danger to the whole of Europe, but that another great Power, founded in the same generation, became a bulwark against a menacing expansion. The rise of Prussia preserved the Continent from being submerged. This new phase of northern monarchy was very unlike that which we have just considered. Prussia, like Russia, was a military Power, living on the hope of expansion. But it was infinitely inferior, as to extent and population. It was not a giant but an athlete ; and its future depended, not on the intrusion of foreign elements, but on its own development and practical organisation. Nature had done nothing to promise greatness. The country was open and arid, and the inhabitants were hard, unimaginative, and poor. Religion had less power over them than over any other part of Germany. To this day the sky-line of Berlin is more unbroken by church towers than that of almost any other city. Neither their situation on the map of Europe nor hereditary endowment fitted the Prussians for empire. It was the work of the dynasty that a country which was less than Scotland, and was protected by no barrier of land or water, became greater than France.

The Prussian people, by which I mean the people of Brandenburg and its vicinity, were conscious that Nature had not favoured them excessively, and that they could prosper only by the action of their government. No people were more submissive, or more ready to suffer, for the sake of the State. And none have gone farther in asserting its omnipotence, or in abdicating in its hands. They had no silver streak, no natural barriers. As a consequence of the Reformation the dominions of the

Teutonic knights were joined in personal union under the same Hohenzollerns who reigned on the Oder and the Elbe. One was part of the empire, the other was enclosed in Poland, and they were separated by Polish territory. They did not help each other, and each was a source of danger for the other. They could only hope to exist by becoming stronger. That has been, for two centuries and a half, a fixed tradition at Berlin with the rulers and the people. They could not help being aggressive, and they worshipped the authority that could make them successful aggressors.

The dynasty entered into the spirit of the problem from 1640. One-half of the electors and kings since then have struggled intensely for the increase of their power. And they built up their state in spite of the other half, who had no enterprise or masterful energy. But before the accession of the great elector, in 1640, Brandenburg had taken a line of its own in the question of religion which was eminently favourable to territorial increase. It was more tolerant than other portions of the empire. The elector was one of the last of the German princes to join the Reformation. And Saxony retained the pre-eminence among the Protestants. Early in the seventeenth century the reigning family became Calvinists. The country was Lutheran. The position was unfavourable to the exercise of what was called the right of Reformation, the right of enforcing conformity under pain of exile ; and, between the Calvinist at the head and the Lutherans in every other office, the Catholics were able to exist. In some provinces, though not in all, they were definitely tolerated. The great elector made every effort to attract the fugitive Huguenots. Agents were sent out to show them the way, and to help them with funds. Whole districts were peopled by them, and about twenty thousand of them settled in Berlin and other towns. Like Peter the Great, the great elector derived his notion of better things from Holland, and he encouraged Dutch artisans to settle. His dominions were scattered and unlike. He introduced a system of government that was the same

for all, and was above local or social influences. The estates
lost their ancient authority, and one supreme will governed
everything, through a body of trained administrators such
as up to that time existed nowhere else.

The next elector obtained the royal crown. Prince
Eugene said that the emperor's ministers, who had advised
the grant, deserved to be hanged. But in fact they were
not less prescient than he, for they warned Leopold that
Prussia would deprive his family of the empire. The
King of Prussia became the head of the Protestant
interest in Germany. That prerogative had been forfeited
by the Elector of Saxony when he received the crown of
Poland and became a Catholic. Rome alone protested
against the Protestant king, and spoke only of a margrave
of Brandenburg until after the death of Frederic II. All
the Catholic Powers acknowledged the new title and disregarded the protest. For the first time there was a
kingdom within the empire, a kingdom, moreover, which
was Protestant. It was a step towards the break-up of
that irrational body.

The second king succeeded in 1713 and died in 1740.
He is the Peter the Great of Prussia. For him, the whole
secret of government is the increase of power at home.
His idea was that monarchy cannot be too absolute. It
requires to be wisely administered ; but it does not require
to be limited. Concentration cannot be too intense. No
enemy outside is so dangerous as public opinion within.
He announced that he would establish his power on a
rock—" *un rocher de bronze.*" He meant that the power
of the State must be independent of the changing motives
of the hour, that it must be directed by a will superior
alike to majority and minority, to interests and classes.
He spent his reign in very deliberately contriving such a
machine. The king, he said, must do his work himself,
and not shrink from trouble. He was perpetually in
harness. He was like a madman in his vehemence and
his crudity of speech. But there was method in his fury,
and calculating design and even practical wisdom. He
gave an impetus as powerful as that of the Tsar Peter ;

but he was superior to him in knowledge of detail as well as in point of character. He was a hard taskmaster, but he knew what he was about ; and it does not appear that his subjects desired to be governed in another way or that they would have been satisfied with a monarch who did not strain their strength to the uttermost.

The object in which they agreed with him—the supremacy of the Prussians in Germany—was not to be obtained if they would not go into training. There was no shrinking. He said, in 1713 : "when my son comes to the throne he must find the vaults crowded with gold," and the son, in 1740, found eight million thalers. He found, moreover, a well-equipped army of eighty-three thousand men. This was the special creation of the energetic king. He was, indeed, a peaceful ruler, and did not thirst for military glory. Among European Powers he was of little account, and kept all his violence for home use. When he laid up treasure, and organised an army that was not so large as that of France, of Austria, or of Russia, but more concentrated and better drilled, his people understood that he would some day provide territory and population to match,—an army so excessive, an army six times as large, in proportion to those of other Powers, was meant to be employed. The burden was not felt. Of the expense, one-half was borne by the domain. Of the men, a large portion was recruited abroad, and relieved the natives of Prussia. After some years, it was felt that the platoons of giants, which had cost twelve million thalers, were a wasteful toy, and that the money might have been spent to advantage among the people. The king attempted to supply their place by a levy among the agrarian population, which is reputed the remote origin of universal service. His economy was so rigid that, with an income of seven million thalers, he spent five millions on his armaments. He thus created the force which began what Napoleon completed, the dissolution of the Holy Roman Empire. For that which the father stored, the son expended ; and I hope in the next lecture to tell you how he did it.

He so eclipsed Frederic William that the latter became an obscure memory, and was spoken of with contempt and disgust by his own people. Carlyle discovered in him his own ideal, the strong man, and set him on his legs. And when the army which he created, which had been remodelled by Frederic, Scharnhorst, Roon, and Moltke, became the greatest of all armies, Germany remembered its founder and was grateful for his militarism.

They have made their choice, as we must do. Those who remember with honour men like Hampden and Washington, regard with a corresponding aversion Peter the Great and Frederic William I. But without the first Europe might be French, and without the other it might be Russian. That which arose in Northern Europe about the time of our revolution settlement was a new form of practical absolutism. Theological monarchy had done its time, and was now followed by military monarchy. Church and State had oppressed mankind together; henceforth the State oppressed for its own sake. And this was the genuine idea which came in with the Renaissance, according to which the State alone governs, and all other things obey. Reformation and Counter-Reformation had pushed religion to the front : but after two centuries the original theory, that government must be undivided and uncontrolled, began to prevail. It is a new type, not to be confounded with that of Henry VIII., Philip II., or Lewis XIV., and better adapted to a more rational and economic age. Government so understood is the intellectual guide of the nation, the promoter of wealth, the teacher of knowledge, the guardian of morality, the mainspring of the ascending movement of man. That is the tremendous power, supported by millions of bayonets, which grew up in the days of which I have been speaking at Petersburg, and was developed, by much abler minds, chiefly at Berlin ; and it is the greatest danger that remains to be encountered by the Anglo-Saxon race.

XVIII

FREDERIC THE GREAT

THE peace of Utrecht was followed by a period of languor and depression. Spain and Sweden asserted themselves unsuccessfully; whilst England under Walpole, France under Fleury, Austria under the ceremonious majesty of Charles VI., were inactive and pacific. The generation lacked initiative, and was not rich in eminent men.

In Prussia there was no repose, no leisure, but simply the tension of a tiger crouching for a spring. The king, who had devoted his life to creating the greatest army in Europe, never attempted to employ it, and left it a thunder-bolt in the hands of his son. The crown prince was a musician and a versifier, with a taste for clever men, but also for cleverish men, an epicurean student, with much loose knowledge, literary rather than scientific, and an inaccurate acquaintance with French and Latin. To Bayle, Locke, Voltaire in his first manner, he owed an abundance of borrowed ideas, conventionally rational; but to the rising literatures of his own country, which ruled the world before he died, he did not attend. Hardened by his father's heartless severity he learnt to live without sympathy, to despise mankind, to rely on himself. He was the author of a commonplace treatise against Machiavelli, partly founded on Montesquieu's *Grandeur et Décadence*. This unamiable youth, with the aspirations and the vanity of a minor poet, was the most consummate practical genius that, in modern times, has inherited a throne.

In the same year, 1740, in which Frederic II. succeeded his father, the Emperor Charles VI. died, leaving his hereditary dominions to his daughter Maria Theresa, wife of the Grand Duke of Tuscany, of the House of Lorraine. By an instrument called the Pragmatic Sanction, which was the subject of protracted negotiations, the Powers had agreed to acknowledge her right. She was a sensible and reasonable woman, much the best that had ever reigned; but she was without culture or superior talent, and her husband was not able to supply the deficiency. Frederic at once made himself master of Silesia. There were certain territorial claims. The succession was about to be disputed, and a scramble might be expected. The death of the Russian empress, Anne, made it improbable that Austria would be protected on that side. Frederic was ambitious, and he was strong enough to gratify his ambition. No accepted code regulated the relations between States. It could not be exactly the same as that between men; and in what respect it differed was not determined. States were absolute, and acknowledged no law over them. Grave and disinterested men would have admitted that that may be done for the State which could not be done for the individual; that robbery was not robbery, that murder was not murder, if it was committed in the public interest. There might be a want of generosity, a want of delicacy about it; but if conquest by unprovoked attack was a crime, in the same sense or the same degree as poisoning a man to obtain his property, history must undergo a fundamental revision, and all respect for sovereign authority must be banished from the world. How far that revision has been accomplished or that respect has departed, at the present day, may be hard to say. At that time, Frederic was much more widely applauded for his prompt success than detested or despised for his crime.

At Molwitz, his first battle, the Austrian cavalry carried all before them, and Schwerin got the king to quit the field before the solid infantry of Brandenburg won the day. Voltaire, who hated him behind a mask of flattery, said that he had never known what it was to be grateful, except to the horse that carried him out of fire at Molwitz. That humiliation taught Frederic to remodel and increase his cavalry, and he afterwards owed to it much of his success. Nobody again advised him to ride out of the way of danger. He was soon known and dreaded as an invariable victor, and Maria Theresa ended the war by surrendering the contested province. Frederic concluded a treaty of alliance with France, which was to last fifteen years, and did last until, in 1756, Kaunitz effected the great change in the attitude of European Powers.

On the extinction of the Habsburg dynasty of emperors, the Bavarian House of Wittelsbach claimed the succession ; and the French, supported by Frederic, traversed Germany and invaded Bohemia. Maria Theresa was loyally defended by Hungary in both the Silesian wars, and maintained her right, without recovering the country she had lost. She was ineffectively supported by England against the superiority of French arms in the Netherlands. That good understanding now came to an end.

The Seven Years' War, otherwise called the Third Silesian War, because it finally settled the question whether Silesia should be Austrian or Prussian, though it involved almost every European Power, was an episode in a far larger controversy. French and English were at peace in the old world, but a feud had broken out in the backwoods of the new, where their strife was for the grandest prize ever disputed by man, dominion over America from the Atlantic ultimately to the Golden Gates of the Pacific, and for the future of the world. The French were masters of the lake region and the St. Lawrence, and also of the Mississippi basin. They claimed the intervening country by right of discovery, and they began, in 1748, to establish an effective occupation of the valley of the Ohio. The English might retain the Atlantic fringe ; the French would possess the hinterland from Louisbourg to New Orleans. They planted a chain of posts, choosing the place for them with superb intuition. One is now Detroit, another Chicago. And under the inland slope of the Alleghanies, where the waters fall towards the Gulf of Mexico, at the confluence of the Monongahela with the Ohio, a French officer, Duquesne, built a fort, the most important of all, which closed the interior to our colonies, but which has undergone a significant change of name, for Fort Duquesne is called after Pitt, and is the Birmingham of America.

This annexation of debatable land was an act of aggression to which the colonists were not bound to submit. The first to understand that it was a question of existence was the man on whose head the destinies of the country rested. Washington twice led expeditions against Duquesne, the second time with Regulars under Braddock, and was each time defeated. The question of the possession of the interior was left to be decided on the Heights of Abraham. It was worth more to the English people than any continental issue. The quarrel spread to the ocean, and we made no scruple to assail French ships wherever the conditions were favourable.

Kaunitz, the minister of Maria Theresa, saw his opportunity for a grand stroke of policy. By transplanting the struggle from the New World to the Old, and from sea to land, he would obtain a French alliance against Prussia. Ostensibly his purpose was the recovery of the lost province ; but the circumstances seemed promising, and he spoke of reducing Frederic to the position of a margrave of Brandenburg. He asked, at first, for no assistance in the field. If France would set up an army of observation on the frontier, the house of Hanover would be disabled from joining Prussia. France was glad, in a quiet way, to check the House of Hanover. By degrees a complete understanding was achieved, and Lewis XV. undertook to help Austria with an army in the field and a vast sum of money. Belgium was to be the price of it, partly for France, partly for the Bourbon, who was Duke of Parma, in exchange for his Italian dominions. This change of front was much facilitated by the civilities of Kaunitz to the person whom the Austrian envoy described as the French Prime Minister, Madame de Pompadour.

He was equally successful with Russia.   There the
government had come to the conclusion that the danger
to the empire was not from Austria, which was expanding
towards the Mediterranean, and had just lost its northern
province, but from Prussia, which was aspiring and aggressive, and on the watch for opportunities.   Therefore the
Russians were only too eager for the attack to begin,
and had to be restrained by the Austrians, who could
only bring France into line by a negotiation in several
stages.   The Russian government agreed, reluctantly, to
wait for the spring of 1757.   But the hereditary grand-
duke was an admirer of Frederic ; the chancellor, Bernstorff, was secured by the English ; and the action of the
Russians was half-hearted throughout.

The first half of 1756 was spent by the three great
military Powers in preparing the attack for next year.
Nobody could blame the Austrians for plotting to reconquer what had belonged to them, and it is at Vienna
that their initiative has been demonstrated.   At Berlin,
the discovery has been received with some resistance.
They were proud of the great Frederic as a warrior and
a conqueror ; they were not ready to admire him as a
quaker, and the victim of designing foes.   He had been
quite willing to commence a new war when the occasion
should warrant it.   He hoped, some day, to conquer
Bohemia as he had conquered Silesia, and to exchange
it for Saxony.   But the conditions needed for such an
enterprise did not exist, and he was in no hurry.   He
concluded a very harmless Convention at Westminster, in
January 1756 ; but he was not arming at a time when
the scheme of Kaunitz was about completed.   It was
midsummer before he knew the danger that threatened
him.   Certain despatches which were opened as they
passed through the Prussian Post Office, others which
were stolen, revealed the whole plot.   Without an ally,
except the House of Hanover, and such confederates from
North-western Germany as English gold might induce to
join, he had to defend himself against Austria, Russia,
France, great part of Germany, and eventually Sweden

and Spain. The help of England was assured, for, in May, war had been declared between England and France. But the English had not been preparing for a very formidable effort. They at once lost Minorca, the advanced post in the Mediterranean, from which they watched the Gulf of Lyons and the naval arsenal of Toulon, and felt the loss so acutely that they shot the admiral who had failed to relieve the place. Calcutta too was taken, and the English perished in the Black Hole. In the Lake region the French, at first, had the best of it.

Frederic underrated the value of the alliance, and mismanaged it badly. He knew that there was a Whig dogma against letting England be taken in tow by Hanover. The great propounder of the doctrine was William Pitt, who now rose to power. Frederic did not know that this turgid declaimer was as able, as powerful, as ambitious as himself, and did not divine that he would make the German quarrel and the compulsory defence of Hanover the means of occupying the military forces of France until the contest for oceanic empire was decided in favour of England. Pitt declared that he would conquer America in Germany. He armed one hundred and forty-eight ships of the line and fifty frigates, with which he swept the Atlantic, and Montcalm, for many months, received neither instructions nor supplies. But Frederic required that the army in English pay, which was to defend Hanover, and thus to cover his right flank, should be commanded by the Duke of Cumberland. Upon this Pitt went out of office. The duke did not justify the king's choice of him. He was beaten by d'Estrées, and agreed to dissolve his force. But Pitt, who had soon returned to power, rejected the Convention, gave Frederic a subsidy of £670,000 a year, and maintained a force against the French, under Ferdinand of Brunswick, who did his work well. There was more of English gold in his camp than of English steel. One of our commanders was court-martialled. When the Marquis of Granby did better, at Warburg, the joy was great, and he became a popular hero. His hat and wig were blown off as he led the charge, and his portrait, bareheaded, in a high wind, is at Trinity, and was on the sign of many an inn, especially of a well-known one at Dorking, in Mr. Pickwick's time.

On 21st July, 1756, when Frederic II. discovered the whole of the peril that confronted him, although it was far more than he had dreamt of, he lost neither hope nor courage. His army of 145,000 men was not the largest, but was much the best. Three or four of his generals, his brother Henry, the Prince of Brunswick, Schwerin, who had served under Eugene at Blenheim, and had followed Charles XII. into Turkey, above all, Seydlitz, were superior to the men on the other side, so far as these were known. There were three millions in ready money, which was enough for two campaigns in those economical days. The Russians had a long march before them, in order to come within range ; the French might be left to the army of English mercenaries. The king might hope, by energy and rapidity, to crush the Austrians in the valley of the Elbe, which is Bohemia, or the valley of the Oder, which is Silesia, before their friends came to aid them. Nearer still than Austria were the Saxons, whose elector was King of Poland, and whose minister, Brühl, like Beust in 1866, was the centre of anti-Prussian politics.

Frederic began by seizing Dresden, and carrying off the secret papers of his enemies. The Saxon army held out for some weeks, and was then forced to serve in the ranks of their conqueror, who thus altered the proportion of numbers, by moving 20,000 men from one side to the other. The Saxon officers remonstrated when called on to take the oath of allegiance to their enemy. They said that such a thing was unexampled. He replied that he was not afraid of being original. Their resistance had compelled him to withdraw from Bohemia, after an indecisive action. In 1757 he won a great battle at Prague, where he sacrificed 18,000 men and Schwerin was killed. The main Austrian army was shut up in the city, and Frederic expected them to surrender ; but a relieving

force, under Daun, defeated him at Kollin, and he withdrew to his own country, that is, he withdrew into
Saxony, which he had made his home, Dresden being
then the most civilised and luxurious place in Germany.
For six years he did not see Berlin, which was twice
occupied by the enemy. Up to that midsummer of
1757 his success in war, like that of Marlborough, had
been unbroken. Kollin was the first of three great battles
which he lost. In the following year he was again
defeated by Daun, in a night attack at Hochkirch, with
the loss of 100 guns. And in 1759, which is the turning
of the tide, the Russians beat him at Kunersdorf. And
yet it is to this chequered year 1757, not to the preceding
career of incessant victory, that Frederic the Great owes
the immensity of his military fame.

The French had triumphed on the western side of the
seat of war, and had driven Cumberland before them,
when Frederic attacked them with a much smaller force,
at Rossbach, in Saxony. With hardly any resistance
and hardly any loss, he gained a complete victory over
them and their Imperialist allies. Then he hurried to
Silesia, where the Austrians were masters. He defeated
them at Leuthen, a month after Rossbach, recovered
Breslau, and made 38,000 prisoners. Nothing like it
had been seen in war. The defeat of the French made
him a national hero. Previously, his enemies were
Germans, and the French were his allies. That was forgotten and rectified. That Germany had so much to
suffer at his hands was forgiven. And the victory was so
complete, so artistic, that he was not less admired in
France, where they laughed at their unsuccessful marshals.
Not long before he was spoken of in Paris as one who
had just missed being a great man. Such language was
never used again. And the tremendous reduction of
Austrian forces at Leuthen and Breslau was a still greater
surprise. A man who could do that might do anything,
and was out of proportion with the ordinary race of
men.

There is an undefinable quantity in military genius

which makes the event uncertain. At the beginning the emperor had written that Frederic's secret had been discovered, and consisted in what was called the oblique order—that is, to make one wing much stronger than the other, to refuse with the weak wing, and to attack with overwhelming force with the strong. That method did not originate with him, but he repeatedly employed it. Then there was his innovation in the use of cavalry. He had learnt its value, against the musket of those days, by experience; and he believed that Seydlitz, in the open, at the head of seventy squadrons, was a thing which no infantry could resist. Then there was the impetus his troops derived from the extraordinary renown of their king, that there was nothing to counterbalance on the other side. This was evident, was matter of common knowledge. But even in his own army, on his own staff, in the royal family, there were two opinions. There was a school which taught that actual fighting must not be resorted to until the use of brains has been exhausted, that the battle comes in when the manœuvre has failed, that the seizure of a strategic position, or a scientific retreat, like that of Wellington into Portugal, of Barclay in 1812 before Napoleon, of Johnston before Sherman, is the first defence of armies, so that a force which is tactically inferior may be strategically superior. Frederic was, I believe, the first great soldier to reject this doctrine, and to act on the principle that nothing can destroy the enemy except a pitched battle, and that the destruction of the enemy, not the weakening of the enemy, is the right object of war. His battles were very numerous and very sanguinary, and not always decisive. Napoleon followed in his footsteps, manœuvring less, as he grew older, and fighting more. It is the adopted teaching of the Prussian school, since Clausewitz and Moltke.

During the French campaign of 1814 Napoleon said to Marmont: "We are still 100,000." "No!" said the marshal; "only 60,000." "Exactly," Napoleon replied; "60,000 and myself, that is 100,000." Something of this kind must be allowed in the person of the great

king ; and it kept up his hopes after his enemies began
to prevail in 1759. In 1760 he was still successful at
Liegnitz and at Torgau.   But his country was exhausted ;
his ranks were thinned by the wasteful expenditure of
life ; there was nothing to look forward to, unless the
Turk effected a diversion on the Danube ; and Frederic
was repeatedly on the point of taking poison.   In 1755
he had written that war must always be aggressive.
Even a successful defence weakens the victor.

The zeal of his only ally was beginning to cool.   Pitt
had accomplished more than he intended when he offered
his subsidies to Prussia.   Our fleet commanded the ocean.
The Mediterranean squadron had been defeated at Lagos,
the Atlantic squadron at Quiberon; Canada had been
conquered, and with Canada the interior of North America,
with its population of savages and its inexhaustible
resources.   Bengal was English, and the rivalry of the
French in India had ceased to be formidable.   In four
years England had grown into a boundless empire, offering, what no other war had done, compensation for
expenditure and increase of debt.   Trade had learnt to
follow the flag, and Pitt's profusion was not waste.   Much of
this success was due to the Prussian alliance.   The vicissitudes of the French army had hampered the French navy.
Frederic, who was several times very near destruction, had
been saved by his ally.   He had retained his disputed
province, while England annexed dominions as vast as
Europe.   His genius and his power had been made so
manifest that he was not again attacked during the
remainder of his reign.   England possessed that which,
if it had been duly husbanded and developed, would
make her mistress of the world.   The object of each, in
concluding their alliance, had been gained, but there was
no proportion between them.   In 1760 Pitt rejected peace
with France when it would have damaged his treaty with
Prussia.   But when there was no prospect of a final
triumph, and Frederic was only thinking of the terms
on which he might obtain peace, Pitt advised him to
negotiate.   Then, in the autumn of 1761, under a new

king, he was expelled from office. The subsidy came to
an end, and Bute opened negotiations.

Frederic had resolved that he would not wear a diminished crown ; that he would disappear from the scene if
he could not preserve by treaty of peace the full integrity
of the monarchy which he no longer hoped to preserve by
war. But he stood alone. The change of reign, the fall
of Pitt, the termination of the subsidy, the pacific disposition of Bute, somewhat exaggerated by those through
whom he heard of it, weakened him so seriously that he
allowed the struggle to languish while he sounded the
courts, and especially sounded the Turk, as to his feelings
towards his Austrian neighbour. Then, in an instant, the
scene was entirely transformed. Elizabeth, the last of the
children of Peter the Great, died in January 1762. She
had been his bitter enemy throughout, personally as well
as on grounds of pure policy, by which he was held to be
the menacing obstruction to the expansion of Russia in
Europe. Her heir was a German prince, married to a
German princess, the famous Catharine, and they at once
offered terms of peace.

Meanwhile Spain went to war with England, and the
government began to treat apart from Frederic. Newcastle would have renewed the subsidy, but Bute refused,
and Newcastle thereupon resigned, while Bute concluded
peace. Frederic, quite unable to continue active operations, retained Silesia, but gave up his conquest, Saxony.
Therefore, at the price of immense suffering to his people,
he emerged from the unequal contest victorious and
successful.

William III., Lewis XIV., Peter of Russia, had been
great and able sovereigns ; but none had left on the world
such an impression of his genius. When Frederic appeared
at the Te Deum at Charlottenburg in all his glory, he
broke down utterly and burst into tears. He had been
the victor, but it was England that carried away the prize.
He had acquired in his campaigns immeasurable authority
and renown, but his people had been decimated and
impoverished, and he had gained no accession of territory

In the first years of peace that followed, it appeared that there was a neighbouring country in which that deficiency might be repaired, and the disappointing issue of the war might be made good by the art of the statesman. The republic of Poland covered an enormous territory, but was the most backward of the civilised nations. It was governed, socially and politically, by the aristocratic class, and it was their prerogative that any minority, or even a single noble, might exert the right of veto on the proceedings of the Diet. The political conditions were those of the eleventh century. The government was the weakest in Europe. The Poles had been the earliest people to establish religious toleration ; but they had succumbed to the Counter-Reformation, and they still refused liberty of conscience to the Dissidents, mainly of the Greek Church. It was the plain policy of Russia to maintain the grievance and the occasion for intervention, and to frustrate every attempt of intelligent Poles to reform their constitution and create a regular government.

In the reign of Catharine in Russia, and of her admirer Stanislas Poniatowski in Poland, the republic became a Russian dependency. The empress desired that this convenient situation should continue, and esteemed that a partition would be injurious to her interests. From the same point of view it appeared desirable to Austria and Prussia. Poland, undivided as it was, was useless to anybody but Catharine. Poland divided among friends would strengthen each of them at the expense of Catharine What they succeeded in appropriating would be so much taken from the sphere of Russian power. The Russian empress endeavoured to turn their thoughts elsewhere. She pointed to Turkey, which was a dreadful blot on the map of Christendom, and proposed that Austria should rectify its frontier on that side. But Turkey could defend itself, and could not be subjected to spoliation without a struggle, which Austria would have to carry on. That was a wretched bargain compared with Poland, which must yield if the three Powers showed their teeth. And Turkey could be of no use to Frederic the Great. There-

x

fore Kaunitz proposed that he should give back Silesia, and compensate himself richly out of Polish territory, where Austria also had some local claims to enforce.

Frederic was ready to annex part of Poland, but he saw no reason for giving up anything that he possessed. If Austria wished to enlarge her boundaries, Poland was extensive enough to satisfy her demands as well as his own. There would be no difficulty, no obstacle on the spot, no resistance of European opinion. England had already proposed the Polish solution of territorial controversy. In France there would be some genuine or affected displeasure. But Poland was a Catholic country, much influenced by prelates. The men who guided French thought would be easily consoled for its disappearance from the political stage. It was not modern enough to interest them, and its treatment of the Dissidents was a glaring offence. Therefore, although Catharine annexed as much as both the others together, the partition was accomplished in opposition to her real policy. About one-third of Poland was thus taken. The reckoning proved correct. Europe remained unmoved. By a series of treaties it had condoned the seizure of Silesia. It was too late to complain of the dismemberment of Poland. The work was completed, under very different conditions, twenty years later. It was overthrown by Napoleon ; but, as he was without a Polish policy, and was disgusted by the obtrusive Liberalism of the Poles in his time, it was revived and sanctioned by the wisdom of united Europe at the Congress of Vienna.

The years which followed the Seven Years' War were a time of peace for a great part of the Continent, in the course of which a memorable change took place in European polity. It was the age of what may be called the Repentance of Monarchy. That which had been selfish, oppressive, and cruel became impersonal, philanthropic, and beneficent. The strong current of eighteenth-century opinion left the State omnipotent, but obliged it to take account of public, as distinct from dynastic, interests. It was employed more or less intelligently, for the good of the people. Humanity contended for the mastery with ambition. It was still a despotism, but an enlightened despotism. The competent expert more than ever was supreme, but he was influenced by great writers, —Locke, Montesquieu, Turgot, Beccaria, Adam Smith. There was a serious tendency to increase popular education, to relieve poverty, to multiply hospitals, to promote wealth by the operations of the engineer, to emancipate the serf, to abolish torture, to encourage academies, observatories, and the like. Prisons had never been so bad—attempts were made to reform them. The slave trade had never been so prosperous; people began to doubt whether it was moral. Laws were codified, and though the codes were surprisingly bad, the laws were improved by them. The movement was almost universal, from Spain to Denmark and Russia. Piedmont dealt successfully with the feudal and social question, which baffled the National Assembly in France. The rich plain of the Milanese was administered by a proconsul of Maria Theresa, in a manner which made it the example of Europe. A strenuous disciple of the economists governed Baden. Würzburg and Bamberg, under the last Prince Bishop, were considered the happiest region in the empire. Turgot, Bernstorff, Firmian, were admired and imitated as Lewis XIV. had been in a former phase of absolute monarchy. Society was enjoyable, apart from politics, and was studied like a fine art in the homes of luxury, —Paris, Brussels, Rome, and Venice. Things went very well in those days with any man who was not a Whig, and had no views as to what makes governments legitimate and averts revolution.

In that age of the enlightenment of despotism the most enlightened despot was Frederic II. Of all rulers and reformers he was the most laborious and incessant. " A king," said he, " is the first servant of the State." He did more work and had fewer pleasures than any of them. The dominant influence was philosophy, not religion, emancipation of the State from the Church. That corresponded well with Frederic's temper. He was tolerant, and on the whole consistently tolerant. In those days the Jesuits were suppressed, first by the secular power in Bourbon countries, then by the Papacy. The Jesuits peculiarly represented the old order that was changing, and the authority of the ecclesiastical law that was being restrained. When they ceased to exist in Catholic countries, they sought a refuge in England, and at Petersburg; but their best and most determined protector was Frederic the Great. The only one of all the princes of that generation who saw farther, and understood that the time of absolute monarchy, enlightened or unenlightened, was very near its end, was Leopold of Tuscany, ancestor of the Austrian dynasty. That was a thing which Frederic never perceived. The great change that came over Europe in his time did not make for political freedom. We shall see how that greater change was to come from beyond the Atlantic.

XIX

THE AMERICAN REVOLUTION

THE rational and humanitarian enlightenment of the eighteenth century did much for the welfare of mankind, but little to promote the securities of freedom. Power was better employed than formerly, but it did not abdicate.

In England, politically the most advanced country, the impetus which the Revolution gave to progress was exhausted, and people began to say, now that the Jacobite peril was over, that no issue remained between parties which made it worth while for men to cut each others' throats. The development of the Whig philosophy was checked by the practical tendency to compromise. Compromise distinguished the Whig from the Roundhead, the man who succeeded from the man who failed, the man who was the teacher of politics to the civilised world from the man who left his head on Temple Bar.

The Seven Years' War renewed the interrupted march by involving America in the concerns of Europe, and causing the colonies to react on the parent state. That was a consequence which followed the Conquest of Canada and the accession of George III. The two events, occurring in quick succession, raised the American question. A traveller who visited America some years earlier reports that there was much discontent, and that separation was expected before very long. That discontent was inoperative whilst a great military power held Canada. Two considerations reconciled the colonists to the disadvantages attending the connection with England. The English fleet guarded the sea against pirates ; the English army guarded the land against the French. The former was desirable ; the latter was essential to their existence. When the danger on the French side disappeared, it might become very uncertain whether the patrol of the Atlantic was worth the price that America had to pay for it. Therefore Montcalm foretold that the English, if they conquered the French colonies, would lose their own. Many Frenchmen saw this, with satisfaction ; and the probability was so manifest that Englishmen saw it too. It was their interest to strengthen their position with new securities, in the place of that one supreme security which they had lost by their victory at Quebec. That victory, with the vast acquisition of territory that followed, would be no increase of imperial power if it loosened the hold on Atlantic colonies. Therefore, the policy of the hour was to enforce the existing claims and to obtain un-equivocal recognition of English sovereignty. The most profitable method of doing it was in the shape of heavier taxation ; but taxes were a small matter in comparison with the establishment of undisputed authority and un-questioning submission. The tax might be nominal, if the principle was safe. Ways and means would not be wanting in an empire which extended from Hudson's Bay to the Gulf of Mexico. For the moment the need was not money but allegiance. The problem was new, for the age of expansion had come suddenly, in East and West, by the action of Pitt ; and Pitt was no longer in office, to find the solution.

Among the Whigs, who were a failing and discredited party, there were men who already knew the policy by which since then the empire has been reared—Adam Smith, Dean Tucker, Edmund Burke. But the great mass went with the times, and held that the object of politics is power, and that the more dominion is extended, the more it must be retained by force. The reason why free trade is better than dominion was a secret obscurely buried in the breast of economists.

Whilst the expulsion of the French from their Trans-atlantic empire governed the situation, the immediate difficulty was brought on by the new reign. The right of searching houses and ships for contraband was conveyed by certain warrants called Writs of Assistance, which required no specified designation, no oath or evidence, and enabled the surprise visit to be paid by day or night. They were introduced under Charles II., and had to be renewed within six months of the demise of the crown. The last renewal had been at the death of George II.; and it was now intended that they should be efficacious, and should protect the revenue from smugglers. Between 1727 and 1761 many things had changed, and the colonies had grown to be richer, more confident, more self-respecting. They claimed to extend to the Mississippi, and had no French or Spaniards on their borders. Practically, there was no neighbour but England, and they had a patrimony such as no Englishman had dreamt of. The letter of the law, the practice of the last generation, were no argument with the heirs of unbounded wealth and power, and did not convince them that they ought to lose by the aid which they had given against France. The American jurists argued that this was good by English law, but could not justly be applied to America, where the same constitutional safeguards did not exist—where the cases would be tried by judges without a jury, by judges who could be dismissed at pleasure, by judges who were paid by fees which increased with the amount of the property confiscated, and were interested in deciding against the American importer, and in favour of the revenue. That was a technical and pedestrian argument which every lawyer could understand, without passing the limits of accustomed thought.

Then James Otis spoke, and lifted the question to a different level, in one of the memorable speeches in political history. Assuming, but not admitting, that the Boston custom-house officers were acting legally, and within the statute, then, he said, the statute was wrong. Their action might be authorised by parliament; but if so, parliament had exceeded its authority, like Charles with his shipmoney, and James with the dispensing power.

There are principles which override precedents. The laws of England may be a very good thing, but there is such a thing as a higher law.

The court decided in favour of the validity of the writs ; and John Adams, who heard the judgment, wrote long after that in that hour the child Independence was born. The English view triumphed for the time, and the governor wrote home that the murmurs soon ceased. The States, and ultimately the United States, rejected general warrants ; and since 1817 they are in agreement with the law of England. On that point, therefore, the colonies were in the right.

Then came the larger question of taxation. Regulation of external traffic was admitted. England patrolled the sea and protected America from the smuggler and the pirate. Some remuneration might be reasonably claimed ; but it ought to be obtained in such a way as not to hamper and prohibit the increase of wealth. The restrictions on industry and trade were, however, contrived for the benefit of England and to the injury of her colonies. They demanded that the arrangement should be made for their mutual advantage. They did not go so far as to affirm that it ought to be to their advantage only, irrespective of ours, which is our policy with our colonies at the present time. The claim was not originally excessive. It is the basis of the imputation that the dispute, on both sides, was an affair of sordid interest. We shall find it more just to say that the motive was empire on one side and self-government on the other. It was a question between liberty and authority, government by consent and government by force, the control of the subject by the State, and the control of the State by the subject. The issue had never been so definitely raised. In England it had long been settled. It had been settled that the legislature could, without breach of any ethical or constitutional law, without forfeiting its authority or exposing itself to just revolt, make laws injurious to the subject for the benefit of English religion or English trade. If that principle was abandoned in America it could not well be maintained in Ireland, and the green flag might fly on Dublin Castle.

This was no survival of the dark ages. Both the oppression of Ireland and the oppression of America was the work of the modern school, of men who executed one king and expelled another. It was the work of parliament, of the parliaments of Cromwell and of William III. And the parliament would not consent to renounce its own specific policy, its right of imposing taxes. The crown, the clergy, the aristocracy, were hostile to the Americans; but the real enemy was the House of Commons. The old European securities for good government were found insufficient protection against parliamentary oppression. The nation itself, acting by its representatives, had to be subjected to control. The political problem raised by the New World was more complicated than the simple issues dealt with hitherto in the Old. It had become necessary to turn back the current of the development of politics, to bind and limit and confine the State, which it was the pride of the moderns to exalt. It was a new phase of political history. The American Revolution innovated upon the English Revolution, as the English Revolution innovated on the politics of Bacon or of Hobbes. There was no tyranny to be resented. The colonists were in many ways more completely their own masters than Englishmen at home. They were not roused by the sense of intolerable wrong. The point at issue was a very subtle and refined one, and it required a great deal of mismanagement to make the quarrel irreconcilable.

Successive English governments shifted their ground. They tried the Stamp Act; then the duty on tea and several other articles; then the tea duty alone; and at last something even less than the tea duty. In one thing they were consistent: they never abandoned the right of raising taxes. When the colonists, instigated by Patrick Henry, resisted the use of stamps, and Pitt rejoiced that they had resisted, parliament gave way on that particular measure, declaring that it retained the disputed right.

Townshend carried a series of taxes on imports, which produced about three hundred pounds, and were dropped by Lord North. Then an ingenious plan was devised, which would enforce the right of taxation, but which would not be felt by American pockets, and would, indeed, put money into them, in the shape of a bribe. East Indiamen were allowed to carry tea to American ports without paying toll in England. The Navigation Laws were suspended, that people in New England might drink cheap tea, without smuggling. The duty in England was a shilling a pound. The duty in America was three-pence a pound. The shilling was remitted, so that the colonies had only a duty of threepence to pay instead of a duty of fifteenpence. The tea-drinker at Boston got his tea cheaper than the tea-drinker at Bristol. The revenue made a sacrifice, it incurred a loss, in order to gratify the discontented colonials. If it was a grievance to pay more for a commodity, how could it be a grievance to pay less for the same commodity? To gild the pill still further, it was proposed that the threepence should be levied at the British ports, so that the Americans should perceive nothing but the gift, nothing but the welcome fact that their tea was cheaper, and should be spared entirely the taste of the bitterness within. That would have upset the entire scheme. The government would not hear of it. America was to have cheap tea, but was to admit the tax. The sordid purpose was surrendered on our side, and only the constitutional motive was retained, in the belief that the sordid element alone prevailed in the colonies.

That threepence broke up the British empire. Twelve years of renewed contention, ever coming up in altered shape under different ministers, made it clear that the mind of the great parent State was made up, and that all variations of party were illusory. The Americans grew more and more obstinate as they purged the sordid question of interest with which they had begun. At first they had consented to the restrictions imposed under the Navigation Laws. They now rejected them.

One of the tea ships in Boston harbour was boarded at night, and the tea chests were flung into the Atlantic. That was the mild beginning of the greatest Revolution that had ever broken out among civilised men. The dispute had been reduced to its simplest expression, and had become a mere question of principle. The argument from the Charters, the argument from the Constitution, was discarded. The case was fought out on the ground of the Law of Nature, more properly speaking, of Divine Right. On that evening of 16th December 1773, it became, for the first time, the reigning force in History. By the rules of right, which had been obeyed till then, England had the better cause. By the principle which was then inaugurated, England was in the wrong, and the future belonged to the colonies.

The revolutionary spirit had been handed down from the seventeenth-century sects, through the colonial charters. As early as 1638 a Connecticut preacher said : " The choice of public magistrates belongs unto the people, by God's own allowance. They who have the power to appoint officers and magistrates, it is in their power, also, to set the bounds and limitations of the power and place unto which they call them." In Rhode Island, where the Royal Charter was so liberal that it lasted until 1842, all power reverted annually to the people, and the authorities had to undergo re-election. Connecticut possessed so finished a system of self-government in the towns, that it served as a model for the federal Constitution. The Quakers of Pennsylvania managed their affairs without privilege, or intolerance, or slavery, or oppression. It was not to imitate England that they went into the desert. Several colonies were in various ways far ahead of the mother country ; and the most advanced statesman of the Commonwealth, Vane, had his training in New England.

After the outrage on board the *Dartmouth* in Boston harbour the government resolved to coerce Massachusetts, and a continental Congress met to devise means for its protection. The king's troops were sent to destroy military stores that had been collected at Concord; and at Lexington, on the outward march, as well as all the way back, they were assailed by militia. The affair at Lexington, 19th April 1775, was the beginning of the War of Independence, which opened with the siege of Boston. Two months later the first action was fought at Bried's Hill, or Bunker Hill, which are low heights overlooking the town, and the colonials were repulsed with very little loss.

The war that followed, and lasted six years, is not illustrious in military annals, and interests us chiefly by the result. After the first battle the colonies declared themselves independent. Virginia, acting for herself only, led the way. Then the great revolutionist, who was the Virginian leader, Jefferson, drew up the Declaration of Independence, which was adopted by the remaining states. It was too rhetorical to be scientific; but it recited the series of ideas which the controversy had carried to the front.

Thirty thousand German soldiers, most of them from Hesse Cassel, were sent out, and were at first partially successful; for they were supported by the fleet, which the estuaries carried far inland. Where the European army had not that advantage things went badly. The Americans attacked Canada, expecting to be welcomed by the French inhabitants who had been so recently turned into British subjects. The attack failed dramatically by the death of General Montgomery, under the walls of Quebec, and the French colonists remained loyal. But an expedition sent from Canada against New York, under Burgoyne, miscarried. Burgoyne had scarcely reached the Hudson when he was forced to surrender at Saratoga. The Congress of the States, which feebly directed operations, wished that the terms of surrender should not be observed, and that the 5000 English and German prisoners, instead of being sent home, should be detained until they could be exchanged. Washington and his officers made known that if this was done they would resign.

The British defeat at Saratoga is the event which

determined the issue of the conflict. It put an end to the vacillation of France. The French government had to recover the position it had lost in the last war, and watched the course of events for evidence that American resistance was not about to collapse. At the end of 1777 the victory of Saratoga supplied the requisite proof. Volunteers had been allowed to go over, and much war material was furnished through the agency of a comic poet. Now a treaty of alliance was concluded, a small army was sent to sea, and in March 1778 England was informed that France was at war with her. France was followed by Spain, afterwards by Holland.

It was evident from the first that the combination was more than England could hope to meet. Lord North at once gave way. He offered to satisfy the American demands, and he asked that Chatham should take office. From the moment that his old enemy, France, appeared on the scene, Chatham was passionately warlike. The king agreed that he should be asked to join the ministry, but refused to see him. America declined the English overtures, in fulfilment of her treaty with France. The negotiation with Chatham became impossible. That was no misfortune, for he died a few weeks later, denouncing the government and the opposition.

Then came that phase of war during which the navy of France, under d'Orvilliers in the Channel, under Suffren in the east, under d'Estaing and De Grasse in the west, proved itself equal to the navy of England. It was by the fleet, not by the land forces, that American independence was gained. But it was by the army officers that American ideas, sufficient to subvert every European state, were transplanted into France. When De Grasse drove the English fleet away from Virginian waters, Cornwallis surrendered the army of the south at Yorktown, as Burgoyne had surrendered with the northern army at Saratoga.

The Whigs came in and recognised the independence of the colonies, as North would have done four years earlier, when France intervened. Terms of peace with European Powers were made more favourable by the final success of Rodney at Dominica and of Elliot at Gibraltar ; but the warlike repute of England fell lower than at any time since the Revolution.

The Americans proceeded to give themselves a Constitution which should hold them together more effectively than the Congress which carried them through the war, and they held a Convention for the purpose at Philadelphia during the summer of 1787. The difficulty was to find terms of union between the three great states—Virginia, Pennsylvania, Massachusetts—and the smaller ones, which included New York. The great states would not allow equal power to the others ; the small ones would not allow themselves to be swamped by mere numbers. Therefore one chamber was given to population, and the other, the Senate, to the states on equal terms. Every citizen was made subject to the federal government as well as to that of his own state. The powers of the states were limited. The powers of the federal government were actually enumerated, and thus the states and the union were a check on each other. That principle of division was the most efficacious restraint on democracy that has been devised ; for the temper of the Constitutional Convention was as conservative as the Declaration of Independence was revolutionary.

The Federal Constitution did not deal with the question of religious liberty. The rules for the election of the president and for that of the vice-president proved a failure. Slavery was deplored, was denounced, and was retained. The absence of a definition of State Rights led to the most sanguinary civil war of modern times. Weighed in the scales of Liberalism the instrument, as it stood, was a monstrous fraud. And yet, by the development of the principle of Federalism, it has produced a community more powerful, more prosperous, more intelligent, and more free than any other which the world has seen.

APPENDIX I

THE following letter was sent out to the contributors to
the Cambridge History. It will interest many, as
giving characteristic expression to Acton's ideals as
a historian. The paragraphs are left as in the
original.

[*From the Editor of the Cambridge Modern History.*]

1. Our purpose is to obtain the best history of modern
times that the published or unpublished sources of information admit.

The production of material has so far exceeded the use
of it in literature that very much more is known to students
than can be found in historians, and no compilation at
second hand from the best works would meet the scientific
demand for completeness and certainty.

In our own time, within the last few years, most of the
official collections in Europe have been made public, and
nearly all the evidence that will ever appear is accessible
now.

As archives are meant to be explored, and are not
meant to be printed, we approach the final stage in the
conditions of historical learning.

The long conspiracy against the knowledge of truth
has been practically abandoned, and competing scholars
all over the civilised world are taking advantage of the
change.

By dividing our matter among more than one hundred
writers we hope to make the enlarged opportunities of
research avail for the main range of modern history.

Froude spoke of 100,000 papers consulted by him in manuscript, abroad and at home ; and that is still the price to be paid for mastery, beyond the narrow area of effective occupation.

We will endeavour to procure transcripts of any specified documents which contributors require from places out of reach.

2. It is intended that the narrative shall be such as will serve all readers, that it shall be without notes, and without quotations in foreign languages.

In order to authenticate the text and to assist further research, it is proposed that a selected list of original and auxiliary authorities shall be supplied in each volume, for every chapter or group of chapters dealing with one subject.

Such a bibliography of modern history might be of the utmost utility to students, and would serve as a substitute for the excluded references.

We shall be glad if each contributor will send us, as early as he finds it convenient, a preliminary catalogue of the works on which he would rely ; and we enclose a specimen, to explain our plan, and to show how we conceive that books and documents might be classified.

3. Our scheme requires that nothing shall reveal the country, the religion, or the party to which the writers belong.

It is essential not only on the ground that impartiality is the character of legitimate history, but because the work is carried on by men acting together for no other object than the increase of accurate knowledge.

The disclosure of personal views would lead to such confusion that all unity of design would disappear.

4. Some extracts from the editor's Report to the Syndics will show the principles on which the Cambridge History has been undertaken.

" The entire bulk of new matter which the last forty years have supplied amounts to many thousands of volumes. The honest student finds himself continually deserted, retarded, misled by the classics of historical literature, and has to hew his own way through multitudinous transactions, periodicals, and official publications, where it is difficult to sweep the horizon or to keep abreast. By the judicious division of labour we should be able to do it, and to bring home to every man the last document, and the ripest conclusions of international research. . . .

" All this does not apply to our own time, and the last volumes will be concerned with secrets that cannot be learned from books, but from men. . . .

" The recent Past contains the key to the present time. All forms of thought that influence it come before us in their turn, and we have to describe the ruling currents, to interpret the sovereign forces, that still govern and divide the world. . . .

" By Universal History I understand that which is distinct from the combined history of all countries, which is not a rope of sand, but a continuous development, and is not a burden on the memory, but an illumination of the soul. It moves in a succession to which the nations are subsidiary. Their story will be told, not for their own sake, but in reference and subordination to a higher series, according to the time and the degree in which they contribute to the common fortunes of mankind. . . .

" If we treat History as a progressive science, and lean specially on that side of it, the question will arise, how we justify our departure from ancient ways, and how we satisfy the world that there is reason and method in our innovations. . . .

" To meet this difficulty we must provide a copious, accurate, and well-digested catalogue of authorities. . . .

" Our principle would be to supply help to students, not material to historians. But in critical places we must indicate minutely the sources we follow, and must refer not only to the important books, but to articles in periodical works, and even to original documents, and to transcripts in libraries. The result would amount to an ordinary volume, presenting a conspectus of historical literature, and enumerating all the better books, the newly acquired sources, and the last discoveries. It would exhibit in the clearest light the vast difference between history, original and authentic, and history, antiquated and lower than high-water mark of present learning. . . .

"We shall avoid the needless utterance of opinion, and the service of a cause.

"Contributors will understand that we are established, not under the Meridian of Greenwich, but in Long. 30° W.; that our Waterloo must be one that satisfies French and English, Germans and Dutch alike; that nobody can tell, without examining the list of authors, where the Bishop of Oxford laid down the pen, and whether Fairbairn or Gasquet, Liebermann or Harrison took it up."

CAMBRIDGE,
March 12, 1898.

APPENDIX II

NOTES TO THE INAUGURAL LECTURE ON THE STUDY OF HISTORY

[1] No political conclusions of any value for practice can be arrived at by direct experience. All true political science is, in one sense of the phrase, *a priori*, being deduced from the tendencies of things, tendencies known either through our general experience of human nature, or as the result of an analysis of the course of history, considered as a progressive evolution.—MILL, *Inaugural Address*, 51.

[2] Contemporary history is, in Dr. Arnold's opinion, more important than either ancient or modern ; and in fact superior to it by all the superiority of the end to the means.—SEELEY, *Lectures and Essays*, 306.

[3] The law of all progress is one and the same, the evolution of the simple into the complex by successive differentiations.—*Edinburgh Review*, clvii. 428. Die Entwickelung der Völker vollzieht sich nach zwei Gesetzen. Das erste Gesetz ist das der Differenzierung. Die primitiven Einrichtungen sind einfach und einheitlich, die der Civilisation zusammengesetzt und geteilt, und die Arbeitsteilung nimmt beständig zu.—SICKEL, *Goettingen Gelehrte Anzeigen*, 1890, 563.

[4] Nous risquons toujours d'être influencés par les préjugés de notre époque ; mais nous sommes libres des préjugés particuliers aux époques antérieures.—E. NAVILLE, *Christianisme de Fénelon*, 9.

[5] La nature n'est qu'un écho de l'esprit. L'idée est la mère du fait, elle façonne graduellement le monde à son image.—FEUCHTERSLEBEN, in CARO, *Nouvelles Études Morales*, 132. Il n'est pas d'étude morale qui vaille l'histoire d'une idée.—LABOULAYE, *Liberté Religieuse*, 25.

[6] Il y a des savants qui raillent le sentiment religieux. Ils ne savent pas que c'est à ce sentiment, et par son moyen, que la science historique doit d'avoir pu sortir de l'enfance. . . . Depuis des siècles les âmes indépendantes discutaient les textes et les traditions de l'église, quand les lettrés n'avaient pas encore eu l'idée de porter un regard critique sur les textes de l'antiquité mondaine.—*La France Protestante*, ii. 17.

[7] In our own history, above all, every step in advance has been at the same time a step backwards. It has often been shown how our latest constitution is, amidst all external differences, essentially the same as our earliest, how every struggle for right and freedom, from the thirteenth century onwards, has simply been a struggle for recovering something old.—FREEMAN, *Historical Essays*, iv. 253. Nothing but a thorough knowledge of the social system, based upon a regular study of its growth, can give us the power we require to affect it.—HARRISON, *Meaning of History*, 19. Eine Sache wird nur völlig auf dem Wege verstanden, wie sie selbst entsteht.—In dem genetischen Verfahren sind die Gründe der Sache, auch die Gründe des Erkennens.—TRENDELENBURG, *Logische Untersuchungen*, ii. 395, 388.

[8] Une telle liberté . . . n'a rien de commun avec le savant système de garanties qui fait libres les peuples modernes.—BOUTMY, *Annales des Sciences Politiques*, i. 157. Les trois grandes réformes qui ont renouvelé l'Angleterre, la

liberté religieuse, la réforme parlementaire, et la liberté économique, out été obtenues sous la pression des organisations extra-constitutionnelles.—OSTRO-GORSKI, *Revue Historique*, lii. 272.

[9] The question which is at the bottom of all constitutional struggles, the question between the national will and the national law.—GARDINER, *Documents*, xviii. Religion, considered simply as the principle which balances the power of human opinion, which takes man out of the grasp of custom and fashion, and teaches him to refer himself to a higher tribunal, is an infinite aid to moral strength and elevation.—CHANNING, *Works*, iv. 83. Je tiens que le passé ne suffit jamais au présent. Personne n'est plus disposé que moi à profiter de ses leçons ; mais en même temps, je le demande, le présent ne fournit-il pas toujours les indications qui lui sont propres?—MOLÉ, in FALLOUX, *Études et Souvenirs*, 130. Admirons la sagesse de nos pères, et tachons de l'imiter, en faisant ce qui convient à notre siècle.—GALIANI, *Dialogues*, 40.

[10] Ceterum in legendis Historiis malim te ductum animi, quam anxias leges sequi. Nullae sunt, quae non magnas habeant utilitates; et melius haerent, quae libenter legimus. In universum tamen, non incipere ab antiquissimis, sed ab his, quae nostris temporibus nostraeque notitiae propius cohaerent, ac paulatim deinde in remotiora eniti, magis è re arbitror.—GROTIUS, *Epistolae*, 18.

[11] The older idea of a law of degeneracy, of a " fatal drift towards the worse," is as obsolete as astrology or the belief in witchcraft. The human race has become hopeful, sanguine.—SEELEY, *Rede Lecture*, 1887. *Fortnightly Review*, July 1887, 124.

[12] Formuler des idées générales, c'est changer le salpêtre en poudre.—A. DE MUSSET, *Confessions d'un Enfant du Siècle*, 15. Les révolutions c'est l'avènement des idées libérales. C'est presque toujours par les révolutions qu'elles prévalent et se fondent, et quand les idées libérales en sont véritablement le principe et le but, quand elles leur ont donné naissance, et quand elles les couronnent à leur dernier jour, alors ces révolutions sont légitimes—RÉMUSAT, 1839, in *Revue des Deux Mondes*, 1875, vi. 335. Il y a même des personnes de piété qui prouvent par raison qu'il faut renoncer à la raison ; que ce n'est point la lumière, mais la foi seule qui doit nous conduire, et que l'obéissance aveugle est la principale vertu des chrétiens. La paresse des inférieurs et leur esprit flatteur s'accommode souvent de cette vertu prétendue, et l'orgueil de ceux qui commandent en est toujours très content. De sorte qu'il se trouvera peut-être des gens qui seront scandalisés que je fasse cet honneur à la raison, de l'élever au-dessus de toutes les puissances, et qui s'imagineront que je me révolte contre les autorités légitimes à cause que je prends son parti et que je soutiens que c'est à elle à décider et à regner.—MALEBRANCHE, *Morale*, i. 2, 13. That great statesman (Mr. Pitt) distinctly avowed that the application of philosophy to politics was at that time an innovation, and that it was an innovation worthy to be adopted. He was ready to make the same avowal in the present day which Mr. Pitt had made in 1792.—CANNING, 1st June 1827. *Parliamentary Review*, 1828, 71. American history knows but one avenue of success in American legislation, freedom from ancient prejudice. The best lawgivers in our colonies first became as little children.—BANCROFT, *History of the United States*, i. 494. Every American, from Jefferson and Gallatin down to the poorest squatter, seemed to nourish an idea that he was doing what he could to overthrow the tyranny which the past had fastened on the human mind.—ADAMS, *History of the United States*, i. 175.

[13] The greatest changes of which we have had experience as yet are due to our increasing knowledge of history and nature. They have been produced by a few minds appearing in three or four favoured nations, in comparatively a short period of time. May we be allowed to imagine the minds of men everywhere working together during many ages for the completion of our knowledge? May not the increase of knowledge transfigure the world?—JOWETT, *Plato*, i. 414. Nothing, I believe, is so likely to beget in us a spirit of enlightened liberality, of Christian forbearance, of large-hearted moderation, as the careful study of the history of doctrine and the history of interpretation.—PEROWNE, *Psalms*, i. p. xxxi.

[14] Ce n'est guère avant la seconde moitié du XVIIᵉ siècle qu'il devint impossible

de soutenir l'authenticité des fausses décrétales, des Constitutions apostoliques, des Récognitions Clémentines, du faux Ignace, du pseudo-Dionys, et de l'immense fatras d'œuvres anonymes ou pseudonymes qui grossissait souvent du tiers ou de la moitié l'héritage littéraire des auteurs les plus considérables.—DUCHESNE, *Témoins anténicéens de la Trinité*, 1883, 36.

[15] A man who does not know what has been thought by those who have gone before him is sure to set an undue value upon his own ideas.—M. PATTISON, *Memoirs*, 78.

[16] Travailler à discerner, dans cette discipline, le solide d'avec le frivole, le vrai d'avec le vraisemblable, la science d'avec l'opinion, ce qui forme le jugement d'avec ce qui ne fait que charger la mémoire.—LAMY, *Connoissance de soi-même*, v. 459.

[17] All our hopes of the future depend on a sound understanding of the past.—HARRISON, *The Meaning of History*, 6.

[18] The real history of mankind is that of the slow advance of resolved deed following laboriously just thought ; and all the greatest men live in their purpose and effort more than it is possible for them to live in reality.—The things that actually happened were of small consequence—the thoughts that were developed are of infinite consequence.—RUSKIN.   Facts are the mere dross of history.   It is from the abstract truth which interpenetrates them, and lies latent among them like gold in the ore, that the mass derives its value.—MACAULAY, *Works*, v. 131.

[19] Die Gesetze der Geschichte sind eben die Gesetze der ganzen Menschheit, gehen nicht in die Geschicke eines Volkes, einer Generation oder gar eines Einzelnen auf.   Individuen und Geschlechter, Staaten und Nationen, können zerstäuben, die Menschheit bleibt.—A. SCHMIDT, *Züricher Monatsschrift*, i. 45.

[20] Le grand péril des âges démocratiques, soyez-en sûr, c'est la destruction ou l'affaiblissement excessif des parties du corps social en présence du tout.   Tout ce qui relève de nos jours l'idée de l'individu est sain.—TOCQUEVILLE, 3rd January 1840, *Œuvres*, vii. 97.   En France, il n'y a plus d'hommes.   On a systématiquement tué l'homme au profit du peuple, des masses, comme disent nos législateurs écervelés.   Puis un beau jour, on s'est aperçu que ce peuple n'avait jamais existé qu'en projet, que ces masses étaient un troupeau mi-partie de moutons et de tigres.   C'est une triste histoire.   Nous avons à relever l'âme humaine contre l'aveugle et brutale tyrannie des multitudes. — LANFREY, 23rd March 1855. M. DU CAMP, *Souvenirs Littéraires*, ii. 273.   C'est le propre de la vertu d'être invisible, même dans l'histoire, à tout autre œil que celui de la conscience.—VACHEROT, *Comptes Rendus de l'Institut*, lxix. 319.   Dans l'histoire où la bonté est la perle rare, qui a été bon passe presque avant qui a été grand.—V. HUGO, *Les Misérables*, vii. 46.   Grosser Maenner Leben und Tod der Wahrheit gemaess mit Liebe zu schildern, ist zu allen Zeiten herzerhebend ; am meisten aber dann, wenn im Kreislauf der irdischen Dinge die Sterne wieder aehnlich stehen wie damals als sie unter uns lebten.—LASAULX, *Sokrates*, 3.   Instead of saying that the history of mankind is the history of the masses, it would be much more true to say that the history of mankind is the history of its great men.—KINGSLEY, *Lectures*, 329.

[21] Le génie n'est que la plus complète émancipation de toutes les influences de temps, de mœurs et de pays.—NISARD, *Souvenirs*, ii. 43.

[22] Meine kritische Richtung zieht mich in der Wissenschaft durchaus zur Kritik meiner eigenen Gedanken hin, nicht zu der der Gedanken Anderer.—ROTHE, *Ethik*, i. p. xi.

[23] When you are in young years the whole mind is, as it were, fluid, and is capable of forming itself into any shape that the owner of the mind pleases to order it to form itself into.—CARLYLE, *On the Choice of Books*, 131.   Nach allem erscheint es somit unzweifelhaft als eine der psychologischen Voraussetzungen des Strafrechts, ohne welche der Zurechnungsbegriff nicht haltbar wäre, dass der Mensch für seinen Charakter verantwortlich ist und ihn muss abändern können.—RÜMELIN, *Reden und Aufsätze*, ii. 60.   An der tiefen und verborgenen Quelle, woraus der Wille entspringt, an diesem Punkt, nur hier steht die Freiheit, und führt das Steuer und lenkt den Willen.   Wer nicht bis zu dieser Tiefe in sich einkehren und seinen natürlichen Charakter von hier aus bemeistern kann, der

hat nicht den Gebrauch seiner Freiheit, der ist nicht frei, sondern unterworfen.
dem Triebwerk seiner Interessen, und dadurch in der Gewalt des Weltlaufs, worin
jede Begebenheit und jede Handlung eine nothwendige Folge ist aller vorherge-
henden.—FISCHER, *Problem der Freiheit*, 27.

[24] I must regard the main duty of a Professor to consist, not simply in communicating information, but in doing this in such a manner, and with such an
accompaniment of subsidiary means, that the information he conveys may be the
occasion of awakening his pupils to a vigorous and varied exertion of their
faculties.—SIR W. HAMILTON, *Lectures*, i. 14.   No great man really does his
work by imposing his maxims on his disciples, he evokes their life.   The pupil
may become much wiser than his instructor, he may not accept his conclusions,
but he will own, "You awakened me to be myself; for that I thank you."—
MAURICE, *The Conscience*, 7, 8.

[25] Ich sehe die Zeit kommen, wo wir die neuere Geschichte nicht mehr auf die
Berichte selbst nicht der gleichzeitigen Historiker, ausser in so weit ihnen neue
originale Kenntniss beiwohnte, geschweige denn auf die weiter abgeleiteten Bear-
beitungen zu gründen haben, sondern aus den Relationen der Augenzeugen und
der ächten und unmittelbarsten Urkunden aufbauen werden.—RANKE, *Reformation*, Preface, 1838.   Ce qu'on a trouvé et mis en œuvre est considérable en soi :
c'est peu de chose au prix de ce qui reste à trouver et à mettre en œuvre.—
AULARD, *Études sur la Révolution*, 21.

[26] N'attendez donc pas les leçons de l'expérience ; elles coûtent trop cher aux
nations.—O. BARROT, *Mémoires*, ii. 435.   Il y a des leçons dans tous les temps,
pour tous les temps ; et celles qu'on emprunte à des ennemis ne sont pas les
moins précieuses.—LANFREY, *Napoléon*, v. p. ii.   Old facts may always be fresh,
and may give out a fresh meaning for each generation.—MAURICE, *Lectures*, 62.
The object is to lead the student to attend to them ; to make him take interest in
history not as a mere narrative, but as a chain of causes and effects still unwind-
ing itself before our eyes, and full of momentous consequences to himself and his
descendants—an unremitting conflict between good and evil powers, of which
every act done by any one of us, insignificant as we are, forms one of the
incidents ; a conflict in which even the smallest of us cannot escape from taking
part, in which whoever does not help the right side is helping the wrong.—MILL,
Inaugural Address, 59.

[27] I hold that the degree in which Poets dwell in sympathy with the Past,
marks exactly the degree of their poetical faculty.—WORDSWORTH, in C. FOX,
Memoirs, June 1842.   In all political, all social, all human questions whatever,
history is the main resource of the inquirer.—HARRISON, *Meaning of History*, 15.
There are no truths which more readily gain the assent of mankind, or are more
firmly retained by them, than those of an historical nature, depending upon the
testimony of others.—PRIESTLEY, *Letters to French Philosophers*, 9.   Improvement
consists in bringing our opinions into nearer agreement with facts ; and we shall
not be likely to do this while we look at facts only through glasses coloured by
those very opinions.—MILL, *Inaugural Address*, 25.

[28] He who has learnt to understand the true character and tendency of many
succeeding ages is not likely to go very far wrong in estimating his own.—LECKY,
Value of History, 21.   C'est à l'histoire qu'il faut se prendre, c'est le fait que
nous devons interroger, quand l'idée vacille et fuit à nos yeux.—MICHELET, *Disc.
d'Ouverture*, 263.   C'est la loi des faits telle qu'elle se manifeste dans leur
succession.   C'est la règle de conduite donnée par la nature humaine et indiquée
par l'histoire.   C'est la logique, mais cette logique qui ne fait qu'un avec
l'enchaînement des choses.   C'est l'enseignement de l'expérience.—SCHERER,
Mélanges, 558.   Wer seine Vergangenheit nicht als seine Geschichte hat und
weiss wird und ist characterlos Wem ein Ereigniss sein Sonst plötzlich abreisst
von seinem Jetzt wird leicht wurzellos.—KLIEFOTH, *Rheinwalds Repertorium*,
xlv. 20.   La politique est une des meilleures écoles pour l'esprit.   Elle force à
chercher la raison de toutes choses, et ne permet pas cependant de la chercher
hors des faits.—RÉMUSAT, *Le Temps Passé*, i. 31.   It is an unsafe partition that
divides opinions without principle from unprincipled opinions.—COLERIDGE,
Lay Sermons, 373.

Wer nicht von drei tausend Jahren sich weiss Rechenschaft zu geben,
Bleib' im Dunkeln unerfahren, mag von Tag zu Tage leben !
GOETHE.

What can be rationally required of the student of philosophy is not a preliminary
and absolute, but a gradual and progressive, abrogation of prejudices.—SIR W.
HAMILTON, *Lectures*, iv. 92.

[29] Die Schlacht bei Leuthen ist wohl die letzte, in welcher diese religiösen
Gegensätze entscheidend eingewirkt haben. — RANKE, *Allgemeine Deutsche
Biographie*, vii. 70.

[30] The only real cry in the country is the proper and just old No Popery cry.—
Major Beresford, July 1847.   Unfortunately the strongest bond of union amongst
them is an apprehension of Popery.—*Stanley*, 12th September 1847.   The great
Protectionist party having degenerated into a No Popery, No Jew Party, I am
still more unfit now than I was in 1846 to lead it.—*G. Bentinck*, 26th December
1847 ; *Croker's Memoirs*, iii. 116, 132, 157.

[31] In the case of Protestantism, this constitutional instability is now a simple
matter of fact, which has become too plain to be denied.   The system is not
fixed, but in motion ; and the motion is for the time in the direction of complete
self-dissolution.—We take it for a transitory scheme, whose breaking up is to
make room in due time for another and far more perfect state of the Church.—
The new order in which Protestantism is to become thus complete cannot be
reached without the co-operation and help of Romanism.—NEVIN, *Mercersburg
Review*, iv. 48.

[32] Diese Heiligen waren es, die aus dem unmittelbaren Glaubensleben und den
Grundgedanken der christlichen Freiheit zuerst die Idee allgemeiner Menschenrechte abgeleitet und rein von Selbstsucht vertheidigt haben.—WEINGARTEN,
Revolutionskirchen, 447.   Wie selbst die Idee allgemeiner Menschenrechte, die
in dem gemeinsamen Character der Ebenbildlichkeit Gottes gegründet sind, erst
durch das Christenthum zum Bewusstsein gebracht werden, während jeder andere
Eifer für politische Freiheit als ein mehr oder weniger selbstsüchtiger und
beschränkter sich erwiesen hat.—NEANDER, *Pref. to Uhden's Wilberforce*, p. v.
The rights of individuals and the justice due to them are as dear and precious as
those of states ; indeed the latter are founded on the former, and the great end
and object of them must be to secure and support the rights of individuals, or
else vain is government.—CUSHING, in CONWAY, *Life of Paine*, i. 217.   As it is
owned the whole scheme of Scripture is not yet understood ; so, if it ever comes
to be understood, before the restitution of all things, and without miraculous
interpositions, it must be in the same way as natural knowledge is come at—
by the continuance and progress of learning and liberty.—BUTLER, *Analogy*,
ii. 3.

[33] Comme les lois elles-mêmes sont faillibles, et qu'il peut y avoir une autre
justice que la justice écrite, les sociétés modernes ont voulu garantir les droits de
la conscience à la poursuite d'une justice meilleure que celle qui existe ; et là est
le fondement de ce qu'on appelle liberté de conscience, liberté d'écrire, liberté de
pensée.—JANET, *Philosophie Contemporaine*, 308.   Si la force matérielle a
toujours fini par céder à l'opinion, combien plus ne sera-t-elle pas contrainte de
céder à la conscience ? Car la conscience, c'est l'opinion renforcée par le sentiment
de l'obligation.—VINET, *Liberté Religieuse*, 3.

[34] Après la volonté d'un homme, la raison d'état ; après la raison d'état, la
religion ; après la religion, la liberté.   Voilà toute la philosophie de l'histoire.—
FLOTTES, *La Souveraineté du Peuple*, 1851, 192.   La répartition plus égale des
biens et des droits dans ce monde est le plus grand objet que doivent se proposer
ceux qui mènent les affaires humaines.   Je veux seulement que l'égalité en politique
consiste à être également libre.—TOCQUEVILLE, 10th September 1856.   *Mme.
Swetchine*, i. 455.   On peut concevoir une législation très simple, lorsqu'on
voudra en écarter tout ce qui est arbitraire, ne consulter que les deux premières
lois de la liberté et de la propriété, et ne point admettre de lois positives qui ne
tirent leur raison de ces deux lois souveraines de la justice essentielle et absolue.—
LETROSNE, *Vues sur la Justice Criminelle*, 16.   Summa enim libertas est, ad
optimum recta ratione cogi.—Nemo optat sibi hanc libertatem, volendi quae velit,

sed potius volendi optima.—LEIBNIZ, *De Fato*. TRENDELENBURG, *Beiträge zur Philosophie*, ii. 190.

[35] All the world is, by the very law of its creation, in eternal progress ; and the cause of all the evils of the world may be traced to that natural, but most deadly error of human indolence and corruption, that our business is to preserve and not to improve.—ARNOLD, *Life*, i. 259. In whatever state of knowledge we may conceive man to be placed, his progress towards a yet higher state need never fear a check, but must continue till the last existence of society.—HERSCHEL, *Prel. Dis.* 360. It is in the development of thought as in every other development ; the present suffers from the past, and the future struggles hard in escaping from the present.—MAX MÜLLER, *Science of Thought*, 617. Most of the great positive evils of the world are in themselves removable, and will, if human affairs continue to improve, be in the end reduced within narrow limits. Poverty in any sense implying suffering may be completely extinguished by the wisdom of society combined with the good sense and providence of individuals.—All the grand sources, in short, of human suffering are in a great degree, many of them almost entirely, conquerable by human care and effort.—J. S. MILL, *Utilitarianism*, 21, 22. The ultimate standard of worth is personal worth, and the only progress that is worth striving after, the only acquisition that is truly good and enduring, is the growth of the soul.—BIXBY, *Crisis of Morals*, 210. La science, et l'industrie qu'elle produit, ont, parmi tous les autres enfants du génie de l'homme, ce privilège particulier, que leur vol non-seulement ne peut pas s'interrompre, mais qu'il s'accélère sans cesse.—CUVIER, *Discours sur la Marche des Sciences*, 24 Avril 1816. Aucune idée parmi celles qui se réfèrent à l'ordre des faits naturels, ne tient de plus près à la famille des idées religieuses que l'idée du progrès, et n'est plus propre à devenir le principe d'une sorte de foi religieuse pour ceux qui n'en ont pas d'autres. Elle a, comme la foi religieuse, la vertu de relever les âmes et les caractères.—COURNOT, *Marche des Idées*, ii. 425. Dans le spectacle de l'humanité errante, souffrante et travaillant toujours à mieux voir, à mieux penser, à mieux agir, à diminuer l'infirmité de l être humain, à apaiser l'inquiétude de son cœur, la science découvre une direction et un progrès.—A SOREL, *Discours de Réception*, 14. Le jeune homme qui commence son éducation quinze ans après son père, à une époque où celui-ci, engagé dans une profession spéciale et active, ne peut que suivre les anciens principes, acquiert une supériorité théorique dont on doit tenir compte dans la hiérarchie sociale. Le plus souvent le père n'est-il pas pénétré de l'esprit de routine, tandis que le fils représente et défend la science progressive? En diminuant l'écart qui existait entre l'influence des jeunes générations et celle de la vieillesse ou de l'âge mûr, les peuples modernes n'auraient donc fait que reproduire dans leur ordre social un changement de rapports qui s'était déjà accompli dans la nature intime des choses.— BOUTMY, *Revue Nationale*, xxi. 393. Il y a dans l'homme individuel des principes de progrès viager ; il y a, en toute société, des causes constantes qui transforment ce progrès viager en progrès héréditaire. Une société quelconque tend à progresser tant que les circonstances ne touchent pas aux causes de progrès que nous avons reconnues, l'imitation des dévanciers par les successeurs, des étrangers par les indigènes.—LACOMBE, *L'Histoire comme Science*, 292. Veram creatae mentis beatitudinem consistere in non impedito progressu ad bona majora. —LEIBNIZ to WOLF, 21st February 1705. In cumulum etiam pulchritudinis perfectionisque universalis operum divinorum progressus quidam perpetuus liberrimusque totius universi est agnoscendus, ita ut ad majorem semper cultum procedat.—LEIBNIZ ed. Erdmann, 150a. Der Creaturen und also auch unsere Vollkommenheit bestehen in einem ungehinderten starken Forttrieb zu neuen und neuen Vollkommenheiten.—LEIBNIZ, *Deutsche Schriften*, ii. 36. Hegel, welcher annahm, der Fortschritt der Neuzeit gegen das Mittelalter sei dieser, dass die Principien der Tugend und des Christenthums, welche im Mittelalter sich allein im Privatleben und der Kirche zur Geltung gebracht hätten, nun auch anfingen, das politische Leben zu durchdringen.—FORTLAGE, *Allg. Monatsschrift*, 1853, 777. Wir Slawen wissen, dass die Geister einzelner Menschen und ganzer Völker sich nur durch die Stufe ihrer Entwicklung unterscheiden.—MICKIEWICZ, *Slawische Literatur*, ii. 436. Le progrès ne disparait jamais, mais il se déplace

souvent. Il va des gouvernants aux gouvernés. La tendance des révolutions est de le ramener toujours parmi les gouvernants. Lorsqu'il est à la tête des sociétés, il marche hardiment, car il conduit. Lorsqu'il est dans la masse, il marche à pas lents, car il lutte.—NAPOLEON III., *Des Idées Napoléoniennes.* La loi du progrès avait jadis l'inexorable rigueur du destin ; elle prend maintenant de jour en jour la douce puissance de la Providence. C'est l'erreur, c'est l'iniquité, c'est le vice, que la civilisation tend à emporter dans sa marche irrésistible ; mais la vie des individus et des peuples est devenue pour elle une chose sacrée. Elle transforme plutôt qu'elle ne détruit les choses qui s'opposent à son développement ; elle procède par absorption graduelle plutôt que par brusque exécution ; elle aime à conquérir par l'influence des idées plutôt que par la force des armes, un peuple, une classe, une institution qui résiste au progrès. — VACHEROT, *Essais de Philosophie Critique,* 443. Peu à peu l'homme intellectuel finit par effacer l'homme physique.—QUETELET, *De l'Homme,* ii. 285, In dem Fortschritt der ethischen Anschauungen liegt daher der Kern des geschichtlichen Fortschritts überhaupt.—SCHÄFER, *Arbeitsgebiet der Geschichte,* 24. Si l'homme a plus de devoirs à mesure qu'il avance en âge, ce qui est mélancolique, mais ce qui est vrai, de même aussi l'humanité est tenue d'avoir une morale plus sévère à mesure qu'elle prend plus de siècles.—FAGUET, *Revue des Deux Mondes,* 1894, iii. 871. Si donc il y a une loi de progrès, elle se confond avec la loi morale, et la condition fondamentale du progrès, c'est la pratique de cette loi.—CARRAU, *Ib.* 1875, v 585. L'idée du progrès, du développement, me paraît être l'idée fondamentale contenue sous le mot de civilisation.—GUIZOT, *Cours d'Histoire,* 1828, 15. Le progrès n'est sous un autre nom, que la liberté en action.—BROGLIE, *Journal des Débats,* 28th January 1869. Le progrès social est continu. Il a ses périodes de fièvre ou d'atonie, de surexcitation ou de léthargie ; il a ses soubresauts et ses haltes, mais il avance toujours.—DE DECKER, *La Providence,* 174. Ce n'est pas au bonheur seul, c'est au perfectionnement que notre destin nous appelle ; et la liberté politique est le plus puissant, le plus énergique moyen de perfectionne-ment que le ciel nous ait donné.—B. CONSTANT, *Cours de Politique,* ii. 559. To explode error, on whichever side it lies, is certainly to secure progress. — MARTINEAU, *Essays,* i. 114. Die sämmtlichen Freiheitsrechte, welche der heutigen Menschheit so theuer sind, sind im Grunde nur Anwendungen des Rechts der Entwickelung. — BLUNTSCHLI, *Kleine Schriften,* i. 51. Geistiges Leben ist auf Freiheit beruhende Entwicklung, mit Freiheit vollzogene That und geschichtlicher Fortschritt.—*Münchner Gel. Anzeigen,* 1849, ii. 83. Wie das Denken erst nach und nach reift, so wird auch der freie Wille nicht fertig geboren, sondern in der Entwickelung erworben. — TRENDELENBURG, *Logische Unter-suchungen,* ii. 94. Das Liberum Arbitrium im vollen Sinne (die vollständig aktuelle Macht der Selbstbestimmung) lässt sich seinem Begriff zufolge schlech-terdings nicht unmittelbar geben ; es kann nur erworben werden durch das Subjekt selbst, in sich moralisch hervorgebracht werden kraft seiner eigenen Entwickelung. — ROTHE, *Ethik,* I. 360. So gewaltig sei der Andrang der Erfindungen und Entdeckungen, dass " Entwicklungsperioden, die in früheren Zeiten erst in Jahrhunderten durchlaufen wurden, die im Beginn unserer Zeit-periode noch der Jahrzehnte bedurften, sich heute in Jahren vollenden, häufig schon in voller Ausbildung ins Dasein treten."—PHILIPPOVICH, *Fortschritt und Kulturentwicklung,* 1892, i., quoting SIEMENS, 1886. Wir erkennen dass dem Menschen die schwere körperliche Arbeit, von der er in seinem Kampfe um's Dasein stets schwer niedergedrückt war und grossenteils noch ist, mehr und mehr durch die wachsende Benutzung der Naturkräfte zur mechanischen Arbeitsleistung abgenommen wird, dass die ihm zufallende Arbeit immer mehr eine intellektuelle wird.—SIEMENS, 1886, *Ib.* 6.

[36] Once, however, he wrote :—Darin könnte man den idealen Kern der Geschichte des menschlichen Geschlechtes überhaupt sehen, dass in den Kämpfen, die sich in den gegenseitigen Interessen der Staaten und Völker vollziehen, doch immer höhere Potenzen emporkommen, die das Allgemeine demgemäss um gestalten und ihm wieder einen anderen Charakter verleihen.—RANKE, *Welt-geschichte,* iii. 1, 6.

[37] Toujours et partout, les hommes furent de plus en plus dominés par

l'ensemble de leurs prédécesseurs, dont ils purent seulement modifier l'empire nécessaire.—COMTE, *Politique Positive*, iii. 621.

[38] La liberté est l'âme du commerce.—Il faut laisser faire les hommes qui s'appliquent sans peine à ce qui convient le mieux ; c'est ce qui apporte le plus d'avantage.—COLBERT, in *Comptes Rendus de l'Institut*, xxxix. 93.

[39] Il n'y a que les choses humaines exposées dans leur vérité, c'est-à-dire avec leur grandeur, leur variété, leur inépuisable fécondité, qui aient le droit de retenir le lecteur et qui le retiennent en effet. Si l'écrivain paraît une fois, il ennuie ou fait sourire de pitié les lecteurs sérieux.—THIERS to STE. BEUVE, *Lundis*, iii. 195. Comme l'a dit Taine, la disparition du style, c'est la perfection du style.— FAGUET, *Revue Politique*, lii. 67.

[40] Ne m'applaudissez pas ; ce n'est pas moi qui vous parle ; c'est l'histoire qui parle par ma bouche.—*Revue Historique*, xli. 278.

[41] Das Evangelium trat als Geschichte in die Welt, nicht als Dogma—wurde als Geschichte in der christlichen Kirche deponirt.—ROTHE, *Kirchengeschichte*, ii. p. x. Das Christenthum ist nicht der Herr Christus, sondern dieser macht es. Es ist sein Werk, und zwar ein Werk, das er stets unter der Arbeit hat.—Er selbst, Christus der Herr, bleibt, der er ist in alle Zukunft, dagegen liegt es ausdrücklich im Begriffe seines Werks, des Christenthums, dass es nicht so bleibt, wie es anhebt. —ROTHE, *Allgemeine kirchliche Zeitschrift*, 1864, 299. Diess Werk, weil es dem Wesen der Geschichte zufolge eine Entwickelung ist, muss über Stufen hinweggehen, die einander ablösen, und von denen jede folgende neue immer nur unter der Zertrümmerung der ihr vorangehenden Platz greifen kann.—ROTHE, *Ib.* 19th April 1865. Je grösser ein geschichtliches Princip ist, desto langsamer und über mehr Stufen hinweg entfaltet es seinen Gehalt ; desto langlebiger ist es aber ebendeshalb auch in diesen seinen unaufhörlichen Abwandelungen.—ROTHE, *Stille Stunden*, 301. Der christliche Glaube geht nicht von der Anerkennung abstracter Lehrwahrheiten aus, sondern von der Anerkennung einer Reihe vor Thatsachen, die in der Erscheinung Jesu ihren Mittelpunkt haben.—NITZSCH, *Dogmengeschichte*, i. 17. Der Gedankengang der evangelischen Erzählung gibt darum auch eine vollständige Darstellung der christlichen Lehre in ihren wesent- lichen Grundzügen ; aber er gibt sie im allseitige lebendigen Zusammenhange mit der Geschichte der christlichen Offenbarung, und nicht in einer theoretisch zusammenhängenden Folgenreihe von ethischen und dogmatischen Lehrsätzen.— DEUTINGER, *Reich Gottes*, i. p. v.

[42] L'Univers ne doit pas estre considéré seulement dans ce qu'il est ; pour le bien connoître, il faut le voir aussi dans ce qu'il doit estre. C'est cet avenir surtout qui a été le grand objet de Dieu dans la création, et c'est pour cet avenir seul que le présent existe.—D'HOUTEVILLE, *Essai sur la Providence*, 273. La Providence emploie les siècles à élever toujours un plus grand nombre de familles et d'individus à ces biens de la liberté et de l'égalité légitimes que, dans l'enfance des sociétés, la force avait rendus le privilège de quelques-uns.—GUIZOT, *Gouvernement de la France*, 1820, 9. La marche de la Providence n'est pas assujettie à d'étroites limites ; elle ne s'inquiète pas de tirer aujourd'hui la conséquence du principe qu'elle a posé hier ; elle la tirera dans des siècles, quand l'heure sera venue ; et pour raisonner lentement selon nous, sa logique n'est pas moins sûre.—GUIZOT, *Histoire de la Civilisation*, 20. Der Keim fortschreitender Entwicklung ist, auch auf göttlichem Geheisse, der Menschheit eingepflanzt. Die Weltgeschichte ist der blosse Ausdruck einer vorbestimmten Entwicklung.—A. HUMBOLDT, 2nd January 1842, *Im Neuen Reich*, 1872, i. 197. Das historisch grosse ist religiös gross ; es ist die Gottheit selbst, die sich offenbart.—RAUMER, April 1807, *Erinnerungen*, i. 85.

[43] Je suis arrivé à l'âge où je suis, à travers bien des évènements différents, mais avec une seule cause, celle de la liberté régulière.—TOCQUEVILLE, 1st May 1852, *Œuvres Inédites*, ii. 185. Me trouvant dans un pays où la religion et le libéralisme sont d'accord, j'avais respiré.—J'exprimais ce sentiment, il y a plus de vingt ans, dans l'avant-propos de la *Démocratie*. Je l'éprouve aujourd'hui aussi vivement que si j'étais encore jeune, et je ne sais s'il y a une seule pensée qui ait été plus constamment présente à mon esprit.—5th August 1857, *Œuvres*, vi. 395. Il n'y a que la liberté (j'entends la modérée et la régulière) et la religion, qui pai

un effort combiné, puissent soulever les hommes au-dessus du bourbier où l'égalité démocratique les plonge naturellement.—1st December 1852, *Œuvres*, vii. 295. L un de mes rêves, le principal en entrant dans la vie politique, était de travailler à concilier l'esprit libéral et l'esprit de religion, la société nouvelle et l'église.— 15th November 1843, *Œuvres Inédites*, ii. 121. La véritable grandeur de l'homme n'est que dans l'accord du sentiment libéral et du sentiment religieux.—17th September 1853, *Œuvres Inédites*, ii. 228. Qui cherche dans la liberté autre chose qu'elle-même est fait pour servir.—*Ancien Régime*, 248. Je regarde, ainsi que je l'ai toujours fait, la liberté comme le premier des biens ; je vois toujours en elle l'une des sources les plus fécondes des vertus mâles et des actions grandes. Il n'y a pas de tranquillité ni de bien-être qui puisse me tenir lieu d'elle.—7th January 1856, *Mᵐᵉ Swetchine*, i. 452. La liberté a un faux air d'aristocratie ; en donnant pleine carrière aux facultés humaines, en encourageant le travail et l'économie, elle fait ressortir les supériorités naturelles ou acquises.—LABOULAYE, *L'État et ses Limites*, 154. Dire que la liberté n'est point par elle-même, qu'elle dépend d'une situation, d'une opportunité, c'est lui assigner une valeur négative. La liberté n'est pas dès qu'on la subordonne. Elle n'est pas un principe purement négatif, un simple élément de contrôle et de critique. Elle est le principe actif, créateur organisateur par excellence. Elle est le moteur et la règle, la source de toute vie, et le principe de l'ordre. Elle est, en un mot, le nom que prend la conscience souveraine, lorsque, se posant en face du monde social et politique, elle émerge du moi pour modeler les sociétés sur les données de la raison.— BRISSON, *Revue Nationale*, xxiii. 214. Le droit, dans l'histoire, est le développement progressif de la liberté, sous la loi de la raison.—LERMINIER, *Philosophie du Droit*, i. 211. En prouvant par les leçons de l'histoire que la liberté fait vivre les peuples et que le despotisme les tue, en montrant que l'expiation suit la faute et que la fortune finit d'ordinaire par se ranger du côté de la vertu, Montesquieu n'est ni moins moral ni moins religieux que Bossuet.—LABOULAYE, *Œuvres de Montesquieu*, ii. 109. Je ne comprendrais pas qu'une nation ne plaçât pas les libertés politiques au premier rang, parce que c'est des libertés politiques que doivent découler toutes les autres.—THIERS, *Discours*, x. 8, 28th March 1865. Nous sommes arrivés à une époque où la liberté est le but sérieux de tous, où le reste n'est plus qu'une question de moyens.—J. LEBEAU, *Observations sur le Pouvoir Royal:* Liège, 1830, p. 10. Le libéralisme, ayant la prétention de se fonder uniquement sur les principes de la raison, croit d'ordinaire n'avoir pas besoin de tradition. Là est son erreur. L'erreur de l'école libérale est d'avoir trop cru qu'il est facile de créer la liberté par la réflexion, et de n'avoir pas vu qu'un établissement n'est solide que quand il a des racines historiques.—RENAN, 1858, *Nouvelle Revue*, lxxix. 596. Le respect des individus et des droits existants est autant au-dessus du bonheur de tous, qu'un intérêt moral surpasse un intérêt purement temporel.—RENAN, 1858, *Ib.* lxxix. 597. Die Rechte gelten nichts, wo es sich handelt um das Recht, und das Recht der Freiheit kann nie verjähren, weil es die Quelle alles Rechtes selbst ist.—C. FRANTZ, *Ueber die Freiheit*, 110. Wir erfahren hienieden nie die ganze Wahrheit : wir geniessen nie die ganze Freiheit.—REUSS, *Reden*, 56. Le gouvernement constitutionnel, comme tout gouvernement libre, présente et doit présenter un état de lutte permanent. La liberté est la perpétuité de la lutte.—DE SERRE. BROGLIE, *Nouvelles Études*, 243. The experiment of free government is not one which can be tried once for all. Every generation must try it for itself. As each new generation starts up to the responsibilities of manhood. there is, as it were, a new launch of Liberty, and its voyage of experiment begins afresh.—WINTHROP, *Addresses*, 163. L'histoire perd son véritable caractère du moment que la liberté en a disparu ; elle devient une sorte de physique sociale. C'est l'élément personnel de l'histoire qui en fait la réalité.—VACHEROT, *Revue des Deux Mondes*, 1869, iv. 215. Demander la liberté pour soi et la refuser aux autres, c'est la définition du despotisme.—LABOULAYE, 4th December 1874. Les causes justes profitent de tout, des bonnes intentions comme des mauvaises, des calculs personnels comme des dévouements courageux, de la démence, enfin, comme de la raison.—B. CONSTANT, *Les Cent Jours*, ii. 29. Sie ist die Kunst, das Gute der schon weit gediehenen Civilisation zu sichern.—BALTISCH, *Politische Freiheit*, 9. In einem Volke, welches sich zur bürgerlichen Gesellschaft, überhaupt zum Bewusstseyn der Unendlichkeit des Freien—entwickelt hat, ist nur die constitutionelle Monarchie möglich.—HEGEL's *Philosophie des Rechts*, § 137, *Hegel und Preussen*, 1841, 31.   Freiheit ist das höchste Gut.   Alles andere ist nur das Mittel dazu : gut falls es ein Mittel dazu ist, übel falls es dieselbe hemmt.—FICHTE, *Werke*, iv. 403.   You are not to inquire how your trade may be increased, nor how you are to become a great and powerful people, but how your liberties can be secured.   For liberty ought to be the direct end of your government.—PATRICK HENRY, 1788 ; WIRT, *Life of Henry*, 272.

 ⁴⁴ Historiae ipsius praeter delectationem utilitas nulla est, quam ut religionis Christianae veritas demonstretur, quod aliter quam per historiam fieri non potest. —LEIBNIZ, *Opera*, ed. Dutens, vi. 297.   The study of Modern History is, next to Theology itself, and only next in so far as Theology rests on a divine revelation, the most thoroughly religious training that the mind can receive.   It is no paradox to say that Modern History, including Medieval History in the term, is co-extensive in its field of view, in its habits of criticism, in the persons of its most famous students, with Ecclesiastical History.—STUBBS, *Lectures*, 9.   Je regarde donc l'étude de l'histoire comme l'étude de la providence.—L'histoire est vraiment une seconde philosophie.—Si Dieu ne parle pas toujours, il agit toujours en Dieu. —D'AGUESSEAU, *Œuvres*, xv. 34, 31, 35.   Für diejenigen, welche das Wesen der menschlichen Freiheit erkannt haben, bildet die denkende Betrachtung der Weltgeschichte, besonders des christlichen Weltalters, die höchste, und umfassendste Theodicee.—VATKE, *Die Menschliche Freiheit*, 1841, 516.   La théologie, que l'on regarde volontiers comme la plus étroite et la plus stérile des sciences, en est, au contraire, la plus étendue et la plus féconde.   Elle confine à toutes les études et touche à toutes les questions.   Elle renferme tous les éléments d'une instruction libérale.—SCHERER, *Mélanges*, 522.   The belief that the course of events and the agency of man are subject to the laws of a divine order, which it is alike impossible for any one either fully to comprehend or effectually to resist—this belief is the ground of all our hope for the future destinies of mankind.—THIRL-WALL, *Remains*, iii. 282.   A true religion must consist of ideas and facts both ; not of ideas alone without facts, for then it would be mere philosophy ; nor of facts alone without ideas, of which those facts are the symbols, or out of which they are grounded ; for then it would be mere history.—COLERIDGE, *Table Talk*, 144. It certainly appears strange that the men most conversant with the order of the visible universe should soonest suspect it empty of directing mind ; and, on the other hand, that humanistic, moral and historical studies—which first open the terrible problems of suffering and grief, and contain all the reputed provocatives of denial and despair—should confirm, and enlarge rather than disturb, the pre-possessions of natural piety.—MARTINEAU, *Essays*, i. 122.   Die Religion hat nur dann eine Bedeutung für den Menschen, wenn er in der Geschichte einen Punkt findet, dem er sich völlig unbedingt hingeben kann.—STEFFENS, *Christliche Religionsphilosophie*, 440, 1839.   Wir erkennen darin nur eine Thätigkeit des zu seinem ächten und wahren Leben, zu seinem verlornen, objectiven Selbstverständnisse sich zurücksehnenden christlichen Geistes unserer Zeit, einen Ausdruck für das Bedürfniss desselben, sich aus den unwahren und unächten Verkleidungen, womit ihn der moderne, subjective Geschmack der letzten Entwicklungsphase des theologischen Bewusstseyns umhüllt hat, zu seiner historischen allein wahren und ursprünglichen Gestalt wiederzugebären, zu derjenigen Bedeutung zurückzukehren, die ihm in dem Bewusstseyn der Geschichte allein zukommt und deren Verständniss in dem wogenden luxuriösen Leben der modernen Theologie längst untergegangen ist.—GEORGII, *Zeitschrift für Hist. Theologie*, ix. 5, 1839.

⁴⁵ Liberty, in fact, means just so far as it is realised, the right man in the right place.—SEELEY, *Lectures and Essays*, 109.

⁴⁶ In diesem Sinne ist Freiheit und sich entwickelnde moralische Vernunft und Gewissen gleichbedeutend.   In diesen Sinne ist der Mensch frei, sobald sich das Gewissen in ihm entwickelt.—SCHEIDLER, *Ersch und Gruber*, xlix. 20.   Aus der unendlichen und ewigen Geltung der menschlichen Persönlichkeit vor Gott, aus der Vorstellung von der in Gott freien Persönlichkeit, folgt auch der Anspruch

auf das Recht derselben in der weltlichen Sphäre, auf bürgerliche und politische Freiheit, auf Gewissen und Religionsfreiheit, auf freie wissenschaftliche Forschung u.s.w., und namentlich die Forderung, dass niemand lediglich zum Mittel für andere diene.—MARTENSEN, *Christliche Ethik*, i. 50.

[47] Es giebt angeborne Menschenrechte, weil es angeborne Menschenpflichten giebt.—WOLFF, *Naturrecht* ; LOEPER, *Einleitung zu Faust*, lvii.

[48] La constitution de l'état reste jusqu'à un certain point à notre discrétion. La constitution de la société ne dépend pas de nous ; elle est donnée par la force des choses, et si l'on veut élever le langage, elle est l'œuvre de la Providence.— RÉMUSAT, *Revue des Deux Mondes*, 1861, v. 795.

[49] Die Freiheit ist bekanntlich kein Geschenk der Götter, sondern ein, Gut das jedes Volk sich selbst verdankt und das nur bei dem erforderlichen Mass moralischer Kraft und Würdigkeit gedeiht.—IHERING, *Geist des Römischen Rechts*, ii. 290. Liberty, in the very nature of it, absolutely requires, and even supposes, that people be able to govern themselves in those respects in which they are free ; otherwise their wickedness will be in proportion to their liberty, and this greatest of blessings will become a curse.—BUTLER, *Sermons*, 331. In each degree and each variety of public development there are corresponding institutions, best answering the public needs ; and what is meat to one is poison to another. Freedom is for those who are fit for it.—PARKMAN, *Canada*, 396. Die Freiheit ist die Wurzel einer neuen Schöpfung in der Schöpfung.—SEDERHOLM, *Die ewigen Thatsachen*, 86.

[50] La liberté politique, qui n'est qu'une complexité plus grande, de plus en plus grande, dans le gouvernement d'un peuple, à mesure que le peuple lui-même contient un plus grand nombre de forces diverses ayant droit et de vivre et de participer à la chose publique, est un fait de civilisation qui s'impose lentement à une société organisée, mais qui n'apparaît point comme un principe à une société qui s'organise.—FAGUET, *Revue des Deux Mondes*, 1889, ii. 942.

[51] Il y a bien un droit du plus sage, mais non pas un droit du plus fort.—La justice est le droit du plus faible.—JOUBERT, *Pensées*, i. 355, 358.

[52] Nicht durch ein pflanzenähnliches Wachsthum, nicht aus den dunklen Gründen der Volksempfindung, sondern durch den männlichen Willen, durch die Ueberzeugung, durch die That, durch den Kampf entsteht, behauptet, entwickelt sich das Recht. Sein historisches Werden ist ein bewusstes, im hellen Mittagslicht der Erkenntniss und der Gesetzgebung.—*Rundschau*, November 1893, **13**. Nicht das Normale, Zahme, sondern das Abnorme, Wilde, bildet überall die Grundlage und den Anfang einer neuen Ordnung.—LASAULX, *Philosophie der Geschichte*, 143.

[53] Um den Sieg zu vervollständigen, erübrigte das zweite Stadium oder die Aufgabe : die Berechtigung der Mehrheit nach allen Seiten hin zur gleichen Berechtigung aller zu erweitern, d.h. bis zur Gleichstellung aller Bekenntnisse im Kirchenrecht, aller Völker im Völkerrecht, aller Staatsbürger im Staatsrecht und aller socialen Interessen im Gesellschaftsrecht fortzuführen.—A. SCHMIDT, *Züricher Monatschrift*, i. 68.

[54] Notre histoire ne nous enseignait nullement la liberté. Le jour où la France voulut être libre, elle eut tout à créer, tout à inventer dans cet ordre de faits.— Cependant il faut marcher, l'avenir appelle les peuples. Quand on n'a point pour cela l'impulsion du passé, il faut bien se confier à la raison.—DUPONT WHITE, *Revue des Deux Mondes*, 1861, vi. 191. Le peuple français a peu de goût pour le développement graduel des institutions. Il ignore son histoire, il ne s'y reconnaît pas, elle n'a pas laissé de trace dans sa conscience.—SCHERER, *Études Critiques*, i. 100. Durch die Revolution befreiten sich die Franzosen von ihrer Geschichte.—ROSENKRANZ, *Aus einem Tagebuch*, 199.

[55] The discovery of the comparative method in philology, in mythology—let me add in politics and history and the whole range of human thought—marks a stage in the progress of the human mind at least as great and memorable as the revival of Greek and Latin learning.—FREEMAN, *Historical Essays*, iv. 301. The diffusion of a critical spirit in history and literature is affecting the criticism of the Bible in our own day in a manner not unlike the burst of intellectual life in the fifteenth and sixteenth centuries.—JOWETT, *Essays and Reviews*, 346. As

the revival of literature in the sixteenth century produced the Reformation, so the growth of the critical spirit, and the change that has come over mental science, and the mere increase of knowledge of all kinds, threaten now a revolution less external but not less profound.—HADDAN, *Replies*, 348.

⁵⁶ In his just contempt and detestation of the crimes and follies of the Revolutionists, he suffers himself to forget that the revolution itself is a process of the Divine Providence, and that as the folly of men is the wisdom of God, so are their iniquities instruments of His goodness.—COLERIDGE, *Biographia Literaria*, ii. 240. In other parts of the world, the idea of revolutions in government is, by a mournful and indissoluble association, connected with the idea of wars, and all the calamities attendant on wars. But happy experience teaches us to view such revolutions in a very different light—to consider them only as progressive steps in improving the knowledge of government, and increasing the happiness of society and mankind.—J. WILSON, 26th November 1787, *Works*, iii. 293. La Révolution, c'est-à-dire l'œuvre des siècles, ou, si vous voulez, le renouvellement progressif de la société, ou encore, sa nouvelle constitution.—RÉMUSAT, *Correspondance*, 11th October 1818. A ses yeux loin d'avoir rompu le cours naturel des évènements, ni la Révolution d'Angleterre, ni la nôtre, n'ont rien dit, rien fait, qui n'eût été dit, souhaité, fait, ou tenté cent fois avant leur explosion. "Il faut en ceci," dit-il, "tout accorder à leurs adversaires, les surpasser même en sévérité, ne regarder à leurs accusations que pour y ajouter, s'ils en oublient ; et puis les sommer de dresser, à leur tour, le compte des erreurs, des crimes, et des maux de ces temps et de ces pouvoirs qu'ils ont pris sous leur garde."—*Revue de Paris*, xvi. 303, on Guizot. Quant aux nouveautés mises en œuvre par la Révolution Française on les retrouve une à une, en remontant d'âge en âge, chez les philosophes du XVIIIᵉ siècle, chez les grands penseurs du XVIᵉ, chez certains Pères d'Église et jusque dans la République de Platon.—En présence de cette belle continuité de l'histoire, qui ne fait pas plus de sauts que la nature, devant cette solidarité nécessaire des révolutions avec le passé qu'elles brisent.—KRANTZ, *Revue Politique*, xxxiii. 264. L'esprit du XIXᵉ siècle est de comprendre et de juger les choses du passé. Notre œuvre est d'expliquer ce que le XVIIIᵉ siècle avait mission de nier.—VACHEROT, *De la Démocratie*, pref., 28.

⁵⁷ La commission recherchera, dans toutes les parties des archives pontificales, les pièces relatives à l'abus que les papes ont fait de leur ministère spirituel contre l'autorité des souveraines et la tranquillité des peuples.—DAUNOU, *Instructions*, 3rd January 1811. LABORDE, *Inventaires*, p. cxii.

⁵⁸ Aucun des historiens remarquables de cette époque n'avait senti encore le besoin de chercher les faits hors des livres imprimés, aux sources primitives, la plupart inédites alors, aux manuscrits de nos bibliothèques, aux documents de nos archives.—MICHELET, *Histoire de France*, 1869, i. 2.

⁵⁹ Doch besteht eine Grenze, wo die Geschichte aufhört und das Archiv anfängt, und die von der Geschichtschreibung nicht überschritten werden sollte. *Unsere Zeit*, 1866, ii. 635. Il faut avertir nos jeunes historiens à la fois de la nécessité inéluctable du document et, d'autre part, du danger qu'il présente.— M. HANOTAUX.

⁶⁰ This process consists in determining with documentary proofs, and by minute investigations duly set forth, the literal, precise, and positive inferences to be drawn at the present day from every authentic statement, without regard to commonly received notions, to sweeping generalities, or to possible consequences. —HARRISSE, *Discovery of America*, 1892, p. vi. Perhaps the time has not yet come for synthetic labours in the sphere of History. It may be that the student of the Past must still content himself with critical inquiries.—*Ib.* p. v. Few scholars are critics, few critics are philosophers, and few philosophers look with equal care on both sides of a question.—W. S. LANDOR in HOLYOAKE'S *Agitator's Life*, ii. 15. Introduire dans l'histoire, et sans tenir compte des passions politiques et religieuses, le doute méthodique que Descartes, le premier, appliqua à l'étude de la philosophie, n'est-ce pas là une excellente méthode ? n'est-ce pas même la meilleure ?—CHANTELAUZE, *Correspondant*, 1883, i. 129. La critique historique ne sera jamais populaire. Comme elle est de toutes les sciences la plus

délicate, la plus déliée, elle n'a de crédit qu'auprès des esprits cultivés.—
CHERBULIEZ, *Revue des Deux Mondes*, xcvii. 517. Nun liefert aber die Kritik,
wenn sie rechter Art ist, immer nur einzelne Data, gleichsam die Atome des
Thatbestandes, und jede Kombination, jede Zusammenfassung und Schluss-
folgerung, ohne die es doch einmal nicht abgeht, ist ein subjektiver Akt des
Forschers. Demnach blieb Waitz, bei des eigenen Arbeit wie bei jener des
anderen, immer höchst mistrauisch gegen jedes Résumé, jede Definition, jedes
abschliessende Wort.—SYBEL, *Historische Zeitschrift*, lvi. 484. Mit blosser
Kritik wird darin nichts ausgerichtet, denn die ist nur eine Vorarbeit, welche da
aufhört, wo die echte historische Kunst anfängt.—LASAULX, *Philosophie der
Künste*, 212.

[61] The only case in which such extraneous matters can be fairly called in is
when facts are stated resting on testimony; then it is not only just, but it is
necessary for the sake of truth, to inquire into the habits of mind of him by whom
they are adduced.—BABBAGE, *Bridgewater Treatise*, p. xiv.

[62] There is no part of our knowledge which it is more useful to obtain at first
hand—to go to the fountain-head for—than our knowledge of History.—J. S.
MILL, *Inaugural Address*, 34. The only sound intellects are those which, in the
first instance, set their standard of proof high.—J. S. MILL, *Examination of
Hamilton's Philosophy*, 525.

[63] There are so few men mentally capable of seeing both sides of a question; so
few with consciences sensitively alive to the obligation of seeing both sides; so
few placed under conditions either of circumstance or temper, which admit of their
seeing both sides.—GREG, *Political Problems*, 1870, 173. Il n'y a que les
Allemands qui sachent être aussi complètement objectifs. Ils se dédoublent, pour
ainsi dire, en deux hommes, l'un qui a des principes très arrêtés et des passions
très vives, l'autre qui sait voir et observer comme s'il n'en avait point.—
LAVELEYE, *Revue des Deux Mondes*, 1868, i. 431. L'écrivain qui penche trop
dans le sens où il incline, et qui ne se défie pas de ses qualités presque autant que
ses défauts, cet écrivain tourne à la manière.—SCHERER, *Mélanges*, 484. Il faut
faire volteface, et vivement, franchement, tourner le dos au moyen âge, à ce passé
morbide, qui, même quand il n'agit pas, influe terriblement par la contagion de la
mort. Il ne faut ni combattre, ni critiquer, mais oublier. Oublions et marchons !
—MICHELET, *La Bible de l'Humanité*, 483. It has excited surprise that
Thucydides should speak of Antiphon, the traitor to the democracy, and the
employer of assassins, as ''a man inferior in virtue to none of his contemporaries.''
But neither here nor elsewhere does Thucydides pass moral judgments.—JOWETT,
Thucydides, ii. 501.

[64] Non theologi provinciam suscepimus ; scimus enim quantum hoc ingenii
nostri tenuitatem superet : ideo sufficit nobis τὸ ὅτι fideliter ex antiquis auctoribus
retulisse.—MORINUS, *De Poenitentia*, ix. 10.—Il faut avouer que la religion
chrétienne a quelque chose d'étonnant ! C'est parce que vous y êtes né, dira-t-on.
Tant s'en faut, je me roidis contre par cette raison-là même, de peur que cette
prévention ne me suborne.—PASCAL, *Pensées*, xvi. 7.—I was fond of Fleury for
a reason which I express in the advertisement ; because it presented a sort of
photograph of ecclesiastical history without any comment upon it. In the event,
that simple representation of the early centuries had a good deal to do with
unsettling me.—NEWMAN, *Apologia*, 152.—Nur was sich vor dem Richterstuhl
einer ächten, unbefangenen, nicht durch die Brille einer philosophischen oder
dogmatischen Schule stehenden Wissenschaft als wahr bewährt, kann zur
Erbauung, Belehrung und Warnung tüchtig seyn.—NEANDER, *Kirchengeschichte*,
i. p. vii. Wie weit bei katholischen Publicisten bei der Annahme der Ansicht
von der Staatsanstalt apologetische Gesichtspunkte massgebend gewesen sind,
mag dahingestellt bleiben. Der Historiker darf sich jedoch nie durch apologetische Zwecke leiten lassen ; sein einziges Ziel soll die Ergründung der Wahrheit
sein.—PASTOR, *Geschichte der Päbste*, ii. 545. Church history falsely written is
a school of vainglory, hatred, and uncharitableness ; truly written, it is a discipline
of humility, of charity, of mutual love.—SIR W. HAMILTON, *Discussions*, 506.
The more trophies and crowns of honour the Church of former ages can be shown
to have won in the service of her adorable head, the more tokens her history can

be brought to furnish of his powerful presence in her midst, the more will we be pleased and rejoice, Protestant though we be.—NEVIN, *Mercersburg Review*, 1851, 168. S'il est une chose à laquelle j'ai donné tous mes soins, c'est à ne pas laisser influencer mes jugements par les opinions politiques ou religieuses ; que si j'ai quelquefois péché par quelque excès, c'est par la bienveillance pour les œuvres de ceux qui pensent autrement que moi.—MONOD, *R. Hist.* xvi. 184. Nous n'avons nul intérêt à faire parler l'histoire en faveur de nos propres opinions. C'est son droit impresc.iptible que le narrateur reproduise tous les faits sans aucune réticence et range toutes les évolutions dans leur ordre naturel. Notre récit restera complètement en dehors des préoccupations de la dogmatique et des déclamations de la polémique. Plus les questions auxquelles nous aurons à toucher agitent et passionnent de nos jours les esprits, plus il est du devoir de l'historien de s'effacer devant les faits qu'il veut faire connaître.—REUSS, *Nouvelle Revue de Théologie*, vi. 193, 1860. To love truth for truth's sake is the principal part of human perfection in this world, and the seed-plot of all other virtues.— LOCKE, *Letter to Collins*. Il n'est plus possible aujourd'hui à l'historien d'être national dans le sens étroit du mot. Son patriotisme à lui c'est l'amour de la vérité. Il n'est pas l'homme d'une race ou d'un pays, il est l'homme de tous les pays, il parle au nom de la civilisation générale.—LANFREY, *Hist. de Nap.* iii. 2, 1870. Juger avec les parties de soi-même qui sont le moins des formes du tempérament, et le plus des facultés pénétrées et modelées par l'expérience, par l'étude, par l'investigation, par le non-moi.—FAGUET, *R. de Paris*, i. 151. Aucun critique n'est aussi impersonnel que lui, aussi libre de partis pris et d'opinions préconçues, aussi objectif.—Il ne mêle ou paraît mêler à ses appréciations ni inclinations personnelles de goût ou d'humeur, ou théories d'aucune sorte. G. MONOD, of Faguet, *Revue Historique*, xlii. 417. On dirait qu'il a peur, et généralisant ses observations, en systématisant ses connaissances, de mêler de lui-même aux choses.—Je lis tout un volume de M. Faguet, sans penser une fois à M. Faguet : je ne vois que les originaux qu'il montre.—J'envisage toujours une réalité objective, jamais l'idée de M. Faguet, jamais la doctrine de M. Faguet.— LANSON, *Revue Politique*, 1894, i. 98.

[65] It should teach us to disentangle principles first from parties, and again from one another ; first of all as showing how imperfectly all parties represent their own principles, and then how the principles themselves are a mingled tissue. —ARNOLD, *Modern History*, 184. I find it a good rule, when I am contemplating a person from whom I want to learn, always to look out for his strength, being confident that the weakness will discover itself.—MAURICE, *Essays*, 305. We may seek for agreement somewhere with our neighbours, using that as a point of departure for the sake of argument. It is this latter course that I wish here to explain and defend. The method is simple enough, though not yet very familiar.—It aims at conciliation ; it proceeds by making the best of our opponent's case, instead of taking him at his worst.—The most interesting part of every disputed question only begins to appear when the rival ideals admit each other's right to exist.—A. SIDGWICK, *Distinction and the Criticism of Beliefs*, 1892, 211. That cruel reticence in the breasts of wise men which makes them always hide their deeper thought.—RUSKIN, *Sesame and Lilies*, i. 16. Je offener wir die einzelnen Wahrheiten des Sozialismus anerkennen, desto erfolgreicher können wir seine fundamentalen Unwahrheiten widerlegen.—ROSCHER, *Deutsche Vierteljahrschrift*, 1849, i. 177.

[66] Dann habe ihn die Wahrnehmung, dass manche Angaben in den historischen Romanen Walter Scott's, mit den gleichzeitigen Quellen im Widerspruch standen, "mit Erstaunen" erfüllt, und ihn zu dem Entschlusse gebracht, auf das Gewissenhafteste an der Ueberlieferung der Quellen festzuhalten.—SYBEL, *Gedächtnissrede auf Ranke. Akad. der Wissenschaften*, 1887, p. 6. Sich frei zu halten von allem Widerschein der Gegenwart, sogar, soweit das menschenmöglich, von dem der eignen subjectiven Meinung in den Dingen des Staates, der Kirche und der Gesellschaft.—A. DOVE, *Im Neuen Reich*, 1875, ii. 967. Wir sind durchaus nicht für die leblose und schemenartige Darstellungsweise der Ranke'schen Schule eingenommen ; es wird uns immer kühl bis ans Herz heran, wenn wir derartige Schilderungen der Reformation und der Revolution lesen, welche so ganz im

kühlen Element des Pragmatismus sich bewegen und dabei so ganz Undinenhaft sind und keine Seele haben.—Wir lassen es uns lieber gefallen, dass die Männer der Geschichte hier und dort gehofmeistert werden, als dass sie uns mit Glasaugen ansehen, so meisterhaft immer die Kunst sein mag, die sie ihnen eingesetzt hat.—GOTTSCHALL, *Unsere Zeit*, 1866, ii. 636, 637.   A vivre avec des diplomates, il leur a pris des qualités qui sont un défaut chez un historien.   L'historien n'est pas un témoin, c'est un juge ; c'est à lui d'accuser et de condamner au nom du passé opprimé et dans l'intérêt de l'avenir.—LABOULAYE on RANKE ; *Débats*, 12th January 1852.

[67] Un théologien qui a composé une éloquente histoire de la Réformation, rencontrant à Berlin un illustre historien qui, lui aussi, a raconté Luther et le XVIᵉ siècle, l'embrassa avec effusion en le traitant de confrère.   " Ah ! permettez," lui répondit l'autre en se dégageant, "il y a une grande différence entre nous : vous êtes avant tout chrétien, et je suis avant tout historien."—CHERBULIEZ, *Revue des Deux Mondes*, 1872, i. 537.

[68] Nackte Wahrheit ohne allen Schmuck ; gründliche Erforschung des Einzelnen ; das Uebrige, Gott befohlen.—*Werke*, xxxiv. 24.   Ce ne sont pas les théories qui doivent nous servir de base dans la recherche des faits, mais ce sont les faits qui doivent nous servir de base pour la composition des théories.—VINCENT, *Nouvelle Revue de Théologie*, 1859, ii. 252.

[69] Die zwanglose Anordnungs—die leichte und leise Andeutungskunst des grossen Historikers voll zu würdigen, hinderte ihn in früherer Zeit sein Bedürfniss nach scharfer begrifflicher Ordnung und Ausführung, später, und in immer zunehmenden Grade, sein Sinn für strenge Sachlichkeit, und genaue Erforschung der ursächlichen Zusammenhänge, noch mehr aber regte sich seine geradherzige Offenheit seine männliche Ehrlichkeit, wenn er hinter den fein verstrichenen Farben der Rankeschen Erzählungsbilder die gedeckte Haltung des klugen Diplomaten zu entdecken glaubte.—HAYM, *Duncker's Leben*, 437.   The ground of criticism is indeed, in my opinion, nothing else but distinct attention, which every reader should endeavour to be master of.—HARE, December 1736 ; *Warburton's Works*, xiv. 98.   Wenn die Quellenkritik so verstanden wird, als sei sie der Nachweis, wie ein Autor den andern benutzt hat, so ist das nur ein gelegentliches Mittel—eins unter anderen—ihre Aufgabe, den Nachweis der Richtigkeit zu lösen oder vorzubereiten.—DROYSEN, *Historik*, 18.

[70] L'esprit scientifique n'est autre en soi que l'instinct du travail et de la patience, le sentiment de l'ordre, de la réalité et de la mesure.—PAPILLON, *R. des Deux Mondes*, 1873, v. 704.   Non seulement les sciences, mais toutes les institutions humaines s'organisent de même, et sous l'empire des mêmes idées régulatrices.—COURNOT, *Idées Fondamentales*, i. 4.   There is no branch of human work whose constant laws have not close analogy with those which govern every other mode of man's exertion.   But more than this, exactly as we reduce to greater simplicity and surety any one group of these practical laws, we shall find them passing the mere condition of connection or analogy, and becoming the actual expression of some ultimate nerve or fibre of the mighty laws which govern the moral world.—RUSKIN, *Seven Lamps*, 4.   The sum total of all intellectual excellence is good sense and method.   When these have passed into the instinctive readiness of habit, when the wheel revolves so rapidly that we cannot see it revolve at all, then we call the combination genius.   But in all modes alike, and in all professions, the two sole component parts, even of genius, are good sense and method.—COLERIDGE, June 1814, *Mem. of Coleorton*, ii. 172.   Si l'exercice d'un art nous empêche d'en apprendre un autre, il n'en est pas ainsi dans les sciences : la connoissance d'une vérité nous aide à en découvrir une autre.—Toutes les sciences sont tellement liées ensemble qu'il est bien plus facile de les apprendre toutes à la fois que d'en apprendre une seule en la détachant des autres.—Il ne doit songer qu'à augmenter les lumières naturelles de sa raison, non pour résoudre telle ou telle difficulté de l'école, mais pour que dans chaque circonstance de la vie son intelligence montre d'avance à sa volonté le parti qu'elle doit prendre.—DESCARTES, *Œuvres Choisies*, 300, 301.   *Règles pour la Direction de l'Esprit.*   La connaissance de la méthode qui a guidé l'homme de génie n'est pas moins utile au progrès de la science et

même à sa propre gloire, que ses découvertes.—LAPLACE, *Système du Monde*, ii. 371. On ne fait rien sans idées préconçues, il faut avoir seulement la sagesse de ne croire à leurs déductions qu'autant que l'expérience les confirme. Les idées préconçues, soumises au contrôle sévère de l'expérimentation, sont la flamme vivante des sciences d'observation ; les idées fixes en sont le danger.—PASTEUR, in *Histoire d'un Savant*, 284. Douter des vérités humaines, c'est ouvrir la porte aux découvertes ; en faire des articles de foi, c'est la fermer.—DUMAS, *Discours*, i. 123.

[71] We should not only become familiar with the laws of phenomena within our own pursuit, but also with the modes of thought of men engaged in other discussions and researches, and even with the laws of knowledge itself, that highest philosophy.—Above all things, know that we call you not here to run your minds into our moulds. We call you here on an excursion, on an adventure, on a voyage of discovery into space as yet uncharted.—ALLBUTT, *Introductory Address at St. George's*, October 1889. Consistency in regard to opinions is the slow poison of intellectual life.—DAVY, *Memoirs*, 68.

[72] Ce sont vous autres physiologistes des corps vivants, qui avez appris à nous autres physiologistes de la société (qui est aussi un corps vivant) la manière de l'observer et de tirer des conséquences de nos observations.—J. B. SAY to DE CANDOLLE, 1st June 1827 ; DE CANDOLLE, *Mémoires*, 567.

[73] Success is certain to the pure and true : success to falsehood and corruption, tyranny and aggression, is only the prelude to a greater and an irremediable fall. —STUBBS, *Seventeen Lectures*, 20. The Carlylean faith, that the cause we fight for, so far as it is true, is sure of victory, is the necessary basis of all effective activity for good.—CAIRD, *Evolution of Religion*, ii. 43. It is the property of truth to be fearless, and to prove victorious over every adversary. Sound reasoning and truth, when adequately communicated, must always be victorious over error.—GODWIN, *Political Justice* (Conclusion). Vice was obliged to retire and give place to virtue. This will always be the consequence when truth has fair play. Falsehood only dreads the attack, and cries out for auxiliaries. Truth never fears the encounter ; she scorns the aid of the secular arm, and triumphs by her natural strength.—FRANKLIN, *Works*, ii. 292. It is a condition of our race that we must ever wade through error in our advance towards truth : and it may even be said that in many cases we exhaust almost every variety of error before we attain the desired goal.—BABBAGE, *Bridgewater Treatise*, 27. Les hommes ne peuvent, en quelque genre que ce soit, arriver à quelque chose de raisonnable qu'après avoir, en ce même genre, épuisé toutes les sottises imaginables. Que de sottises ne dirions-nous pas maintenant, si les anciens ne les avaient pas déjà dites avant nous, et ne nous les avaient, pour ainsi dire, enlevées !— FONTENELLE. Without premature generalisations the true generalisation would never be arrived at.—H. SPENCER, *Essays*, ii. 57. The more important the subject of difference, the greater, not the less, will be the indulgence of him who has learned to trace the sources of human error,—of error, that has its origin not in our weakness and imperfection merely, but often in the most virtuous affections of the heart.—BROWN, *Philosophy of the Human Mind*, i. 48, 1824. Parmi les châtiments du crime qui ne lui manquent jamais, à côté de celui que lui inflige la conscience, l'histoire lui en inflige un autre encore, éclatant et manifeste, l'impuissance.—COUSIN, *Phil. Mod.* ii. 24. L'avenir de la science est garanti ; car dans le grand livre scientifique tout s'ajoute et rien ne se perd. L'erreur ne fonde pas ; aucune erreur ne dure très longtemps.—RENAN, *Feuilles Détachées*, xiii. Toutes les fois que deux hommes sont d'un avis contraire sur la même chose, à coup sûr, l'un ou l'autre se trompe ; bien plus, aucun ne semble posséder la vérité ; car si les raisons de l'un étoient certaines et évidentes, il pourroit les exposer à l'autre de telle manière qu'il finiroit par le convaincre également.—DESCARTES, *Règles ; Œuvres Choisies*, 302. Le premier principe de la critique est qu'une doctrine ne captive ses adhérents que par ce qu'elle a de légitime.—RENAN, *Essais de Morale*, 184. Was dem Wahn solche Macht giebt ist wirklich nicht er selbst, sondern die ihm zu Grunde liegende und darin nur verzerrte Wahrheit.—FRANTZ, *Schelling's Philosophie*, i. 62. Quand les hommes ont vu une fois la vérité dans son éclat, ils ne peuvent plus l'oublier

Elle reste debout, et tôt ou tard elle triomphe, parce qu'elle est la pensée de Dieu et le besoin du monde.—MIGNET, *Portraits*, ii. 295. C'est toujours le sens commun inaperçu qui fait la fortune des hypothèses auxquelles il se mêle.— COUSIN, *Fragments Phil.* i. 51, Preface of 1826. Wer da sieht, wie der Irrthum selbst ein Träger mannigfaltigen und bleibenden Fortschritts wird, der wird auch nicht so leicht aus dem thatsächlichen Fortschritt der Gegenwart auf Unumstösslichkeit unserer Hypothesen schliessen.—Das richtigste Resultat der geschichtlichen Betrachtung ist die akademische Ruhe, mit welcher unsere Hypothesen und Theorieen ohne Feindschaft und ohne Glauben als das betrachtet werden, was sie sind ; als Stufen in jener unendlichen Annäherung an die Wahrheit, welche die Bestimmung unserer intellectuellen Entwickelung zu sein scheint.—LANGE, *Geschichte des Materialismus*, 502, 503. Hominum errores divina providentia reguntur, ita ut saepe male jacta bene cadant.—LEIBNIZ, ed. Klopp, i. p. lii. Sainte-Beuve n'était même pas de la race des libéraux, c'est-à-dire de ceux qui croient que, tout compte fait, et dans un état de civilisation donné, le bien triomphe du mal à armes égales, et la vérité de l'erreur.— D'HAUSSONVILLE, *Revue des Deux Mondes*, 1875, i. 567. In the progress of the human mind, a period of controversy amongst the cultivators of any branch of science must necessarily precede the period of unanimity.—TORRENS, *Essay on the Production of Wealth*, 1821, p. xiii. Even the spread of an error is part of the wide-world process by which we stumble into mere approximations to truth.— L. STEPHEN, *Apology of an Agnostic*, 81. Errors, to be dangerous, must have a great deal of truth mingled with them ; it is only from this alliance that they can ever obtain an extensive circulation.—S. SMITH, *Moral Philosophy*, 7. The admission of the few errors of Newton himself is at least of as much importance to his followers in science as the history of the progress of his real discoveries.— YOUNG, *Works*, iii. 621. Error is almost always partial truth, and so consists in the exaggeration or distortion of one verity by the suppression of another, which qualifies and modifies the former.—MIVART, *Genesis of Species*, 3. The attainment of scientific truth has been effected, to a great extent, by the help of scientific errors.—HUXLEY : WARD, *Reign of Victoria*, ii. 337. Jede neue tief eingreifende Wahrheit hat meiner Ansicht nach erst das Stadium der Einseitigkeit durchzumachen.—IHERING, *Geist des R. Rechts*, ii. 22. The more readily we admit the possibility of our own cherished convictions being mixed with error, the more vital and helpful whatever is right in them will become.—RUSKIN, *Ethics of the Dust*, 225. They hardly grasp the plain truth unless they examine the error which it cancels.—CORY, *Modern English History*, 1880, i. 109. Nur durch Irrthum kommen wir, der eine kürzeren und glücklicheren Schrittes, als der andere, zur Wahrheit ; und die Geschichte darf nirgends diese Verirrungen übergehen, wenn sie Lehrerin und Warnerin für die nachfolgenden Geschlechter werden will.—*München Gel. Anzeigen*, 1840, i. 737.

[74] Wie die Weltgeschichte das Weltgericht ist, so kann in noch allgemeinerem Sinne gesagt werden, dass das gerechte Gericht, d.h. die wahre Kritik einer Sache, nur in ihrer Geschichte liegen kann. Insbesondere in der Hinsicht lehrt die Geschichte denjenigen, der ihr folgt, ihre eigene Methode, dass ihr Fortschritt niemals ein reines Vernichten, sondern nur ein Aufheben im philosophischen Sinne ist.—STRAUSS, *Hallische Jahrbücher*, 1839, 120.

[75] Dans tous les livres qu'il lit, et il en dévore des quantités, Darwin ne note que les passages qui contrarient ses idées systématiques.—Il collectionne les difficultés, les cas épineux, les critiques possibles.—VERNIER, *Le Temps*, 6th Décembre 1887. Je demandais à un savant célèbre où il en était de ses recherches. "Cela ne marche plus," me dit-il, "je ne trouve plus de faits contradictoires." Ainsi le savant cherche à se contredire lui-même pour faire avancer sa pensée.—JANET, *Journal des Savants*, 1892, 20. Ein Umstand, der uns die Selbständigkeit des Ganges der Wissenschaft anschaulich machen kann, ist auch der : dass der Irrthum, wenn er nur gründlich behandelt wird, fast ebenso fördernd ist als das Finden der Wahrheit, denn er erzeugt fortgesetzten Widerspruch.—BAER, *Blicke auf die Entwicklung der Wissenschaft*, 120. It is only by virtue of the opposition which it has surmounted that any truth can stand in the human mind.—ARCHBISHOP TEMPLE ; KINGLAKE, *Crimea*, *Winter*

Troubles, app. 104. I have for many years found it expedient to lay down a rule for my own practice, to confine my reading mainly to those journals the general line of opinions in which is adverse to my own.—HARE, *Means of Unity*, i. 19. Kant had a harder struggle with himself than he could possibly have had with any critic or opponent of his philosophy.—CAIRD, *Philosophy of Kant*, 1889, i. p. ix.

76 The social body is no more liable to arbitrary changes than the individual body.—A full perception of the truth that society is not a mere aggregate, but an organic growth, that it forms a whole, the laws of whose growth can be studied apart from those of the individual atom, supplies the most characteristic postulate of modern speculation.—L. STEPHEN, *Science of Ethics*, 31.   Wie in dem Leben des einzelnen Menschen kein Augenblick eines vollkommenen Stillstandes wahrgenommen wird, sondern stete organische Entwicklung, so verhält es sich auch in dem Leben der Völker, und in jedem einzelnen Element, woraus dieses Gesammtleben besteht.   So finden wir in der Sprache stete Fortbildung und Entwicklung, und auf gleiche Weise in dem Recht.   Und auch diese Fortbildung steht unter demselben Gesetz der Erzeugung aus innerer Kraft und Nothwendigkeit, unabhängig von Zufall und individueller Willkür, wie die ursprüngliche Entstehung.—SAVIGNY, *System*, i. 16, 17.   Seine eigene Entdeckung, dass auch die geistige Produktion, bis in einem gewissen Punkte wenigstens, unter dem Gesetze der Kausalität steht, dass jedeiner nur geben kann, was er hat, nur hat, was er irgendwoher bekommen, muss auch für ihn selber gelten.—BEKKER, *Das Recht des Besitzes bei den Römern*, 3, 1880.   Die geschichtliche Wandlung des Rechts, in welcher vergangene Jahrhunderte halb ein Spiel des Zufalls und halb ein Werk vernünftelnder Willkür sahen, als gesetzmässige Entwickelung zu begreifen, war das unsterbliche Verdienst der von Männern wie Savigny, Eichhorn und Jacob Grimm geführten historischen Rechtsschule.—GIERKE, *Rundschau*, xviii. 205.

77 The only effective way of studying what is called the philosophy of religion, or the philosophical criticism of religion, is to study the history of religion.   The true science of war is the history of war, the true science of religion is, I believe, the history of religion.—M. MÜLLER, *Theosophy*, 3, 4.   La théologie ne doit plus être que l'histoire des efforts spontanés tentés pour résoudre le problème divin.   L'histoire, en effet, est la forme nécessaire de la science de tout ce qui est soumis aux lois de la vie changeante et successive.   La science de l'esprit humain, c'est de même, l'histoire de l'esprit humain.—RENAN, *Averroès*, Pref. vi.

78 Political economy is not a science, in any strict sense, but a body of systematic knowledge gathered from the study of common processes, which have been practised all down the history of the human race in the production and distribution of wealth.—BONAMY PRICE, *Social Science Congress*, 1878.   Such a study is in harmony with the best intellectual tendencies of our age, which is, more than anything else, characterised by the universal supremacy of the historical spirit.   To such a degree has this spirit permeated all our modes of thinking, that with respect to every branch of knowledge, no less than with respect to every institution and every form of human activity, we almost instinctively ask, not merely what is its existing condition, but what were its earliest discoverable germs, and what has been the course of its development.—INGRAM, *History of Political Economy*, 2.   Wir dagegen stehen keinen Augenblick an, die Nationalökonomie für eine reine Erfahrungswissenschaft zu erklären, und die Geschichte ist uns daher nicht Hülfsmittel, sondern Gegenstand selber. — ROSCHER, *Deutsche Vierteljahrschrift*, 1849, i. 182.   Der bei weitem grösste Theil menschlicher Irrthümer beruhet darauf, dass man zeitlich und örtlich Wahres oder Heilsames für absolut wahr oder heilsam ausgiebt.   Für jede Stufe der Volksentwickelung passt eine besondere Staatsverfassung, die mit allen übrigen Verhältnissen des Volks als Ursache und Wirkung auf's Innigste verbunden ist ; so passt auch für jede Entwickelungsstufe eine besondere Landwirthschaftsverfassung.—ROSCHER, *Archiv f. p. Oek.* viii. 2 Heft 1845.   Seitdem vor allen Roscher, Hildebrand und Knies den Werth, die Berechtigung und die Nothwendigkeit derselben unwiderleglich dargethan, hat sich immer allgemeiner der Gedanke Bahn gebrochen, dass diese Wissenschaft, die bis dahin nur auf die Gegenwart, auf die Erkenntniss der bestehenden Verhältnisse und die in ihnen sichtbaren Gesetze den

Blick gerichtet hatte, auch in die Vergangenheit, in die Erforschung der bereits hinter uns liegenden wirthschaftlichen Entwicklung der Völker sich vertiefen müsse. — SCHONBERG, *Jahrbücher f. Nationalökonomie und Statistik*, Neue Folge, 1867, i. 1. Schmoller, moins dogmatique et mettant comme une sorte de coquetterie à être incertain, démontre, par les faits, la fausseté ou l'arbitraire de tous ces postulats, et laisse l'économie politique se dissoudre dans l'histoire.—BRETON, *R. de Paris*, ix. 67. Wer die politische Oekonomie Feuerlands unter dieselben Gesetze bringen wollte mit der des heutigen Englands, würde damit augenscheinlich nichts zu Tage fördern als den allerbanalsten Gemeinplatz. Die politische Oekonomie ist somit wesentlich eine historische Wissenschaft. Sie behandelt einen geschichtlichen, das heisst einen stets wechselnden Stoff. Sie untersucht zunächst die besondern Gesetze jeder einzelnen Entwicklungsstufe der Produktion und des Austausches, und wird erst am Schluss dieser Untersuchung die wenigen, für Produktion und Austausch überhaupt geltenden, ganz allgemeinen Gesetze aufstellen können.—ENGELS, *Dührings Umwälzung der Wissenschaft*, 1878, 121.

[79] History preserves the student from being led astray by a too servile adherence to any system.—WOLOWSKI. No system can be anything more than a history, not in the order of impression, but in the order of arrangement by analogy. — DAVY, *Memoirs*, 68. Avec des matériaux si nombreux et si importants, il fallait bien du courage pour résister à la tentation de faire un système. De Saussure eut ce courage, et nous en ferons le dernier trait et le trait principal de son éloge.—CUVIER, *Éloge de Saussure*, 1810.

[80] C'était, en 1804, une idée heureuse et nouvelle, d'appeler l'histoire au secours de la science, d'interroger les deux grandes écoles rivales au profit de la vérité.—COUSIN, *Fragments Littéraires*, 1843, 95, on Dégerando. No branch of philosophical doctrine, indeed, can be fairly investigated or apprehended apart from its history. All our systems of politics, morals, and metaphysics would be different if we knew exactly how they grew up, and what transformations they have undergone ; if we knew, in short, the true history of human ideas. — CLIFFE LESLIE, *Essays in Political and Moral Philosophy*, 1879, 149. The history of philosophy must be rational and philosophic. It must be philosophy itself, with all its elements, in all their relations, and under all their laws represented in striking characters by the hands of time and of history, in the manifested progress of the human mind.—SIR WILLIAM HAMILTON, *Edin. Rev.* l. 200, 1829. Il n'est point d'étude plus instructive, plus utile que l'étude de l'histoire de la philosophie ; car on y apprend à se désabuser des philosophes, et l'on y désapprend la fausse science de leurs systèmes. — ROYER COLLARD, *Œuvres de Reid*, iv. 426. On ne peut guère échapper à la conviction que toutes les solutions des questions philosophiques n'aient été développées ou indiquées avant le commencement du dix-neuvième siècle, et que par conséquent il ne soit très difficile, pour ne pas dire impossible, de tomber, en pareille matière, sur une idée neuve de quelque importance. Or si cette conviction est fondée, il s'ensuit que la science est faite.—JOUFFROY, in DAMIRON, *Philosophie du XIXᵉ Siècle*, 363. Le but dernier de tous mes efforts, l'âme de mes écrits et de tout mon enseignement, c'est l'identité de la philosophie et de son histoire.—COUSIN, *Cours de 1829*. Ma route est historique, il est vrai, mais mon but est dogmatique ; je tends à une théorie, et cette théorie je la demande à l'histoire.—COUSIN, *Ph. du XVIIIᵉ Siècle*, 15. L'histoire de la philosophie est contrainte d'emprunter d'abord à la philosophie la lumière qu'elle doit lui rendre un jour avec usure.—COUSIN, *Du Vrai*, 1855, 14. M. Cousin, durant tout son professorat de 1816 à 1829, a pensé que l'histoire de la philosophie était la source de la philosophie même. Nous ne croyons pas exagérer en lui prêtant cette opinion.—B. ST. HILAIRE, *Victor Cousin*, i. 302, Il se hâta de convertir le fait en loi, et proclama que la philosophie, étant identique à son histoire, ne pouvait avoir une loi différente, et était vouée à jamais à l'évolution fatale des quatre systèmes, se contredisant toujours, mais se limitant, et se modérant, par cela même de manière à maintenir l'équilibre, sinon l'harmonie de la pensée humaine.—VACHEROT, *Revue des Deux Mondes*, 1868, iii. 957. Er hat überhaupt das unvergängliche Verdienst, zuerst in Frankreich zu der Erkenntniss gelangt zu sein, dass die menschliche Vernunft nur durch das Studium des Gesetzes ihrer Entwickelungen begriffen werden kann

—LAUSER, *Unsere Zeit*, 1868, i. 459. Le philosophe en quête du vrai en soi, n'est plus réduit à ses conceptions individuelles ; il est riche du trésor amassé par l'humanité.—BOUTROUX, *Revue Politique*, xxxvii. 802. L'histoire, je veux dire l'histoire de l'esprit humain, est en ce sens la vraie philosophie de notre temps.— RENAN, *Études de Morale*, 83. Die Philosophie wurde eine höchst bedeutende Hülfswissenschaft der Geschichte, sie hat ihre Richtung auf das Allgemeine geför-dert, ihren Blick für dasselbe geschärft, und sie, wenigstens durch ihre Vermitt-lung, mit Gesichtspuncten, Ideen, bereichert, die sie aus ihrem eigenen Schoosse sobald noch nicht erzeugt haben würde. Weit die fruchtbarste darunter war die aus der Naturwissenschaft geschöpfte Idee des organischen Lebens, dieselbe auf der die neueste Philosophie selbst beruht. Die seit zwei bis drei Jahrzehnten in der Behandlung der Geschichte eingetretene durchgreifende Veränderung, wie die völlige Umgestaltung so mancher anderen Wissenschaft . . . ist der Hauptsache nach ihr Werk.—HAUG, *Allgemeine Geschichte*, 1841, i. 22. Eine Geschichte der Philosophie in eigentlichen Sinne wurde erst möglich, als man an die Stelle der Philosophen deren Systeme setzte, den inneren Zusammenhang zwischen diesen feststellte und—wie Dilthey sagt—mitten in Wechsel der Philosophien ein sieg-reiches Fortschreiten zur Wahrheit nachwies. Die Gesammtheit der Philosophie stellt sich also dar als eine geschichtliche Einheit.—SAUL, *Rundschau*, February 1894, 307. Warum die Philosophie eine Geschichte habe und haben müsse, blieb unerörtert, ja ungeahnt, dass die Philosophie am meisten von allen Wissenschaften historisch sei, denn man hatte in der Geschichte den Begriff der Entwicklung nicht entdeckt.—MARBACH, *Griechische Philosophie*, 15. Was bei oberflächlicher Betrachtung nur ein Gewirre einzelner Personen und Meinungen zu sein schien, zeigt sich bei genauerer und gründlicherer Untersuchung als eine geschichtliche Entwicklung, in der alles, bald näher, bald entfernter, mit allem anderen zusam-menhängt.—ZELLER, *Rundschau*, February 1894, 307. Nur die Philosophie, die an die geschichtliche Entwickelung anknüpft kann auf bleibenden Erfolg auch für die Zukunft rechnen und fortschreiten zu dem, was in der bisherigen philosophi-schen Entwickelung nur erst unvollkommen erreicht oder angestrebt worden ist. Kann sich doch die Philosophie überhaupt und insbesondere die Metaphysik ihrer eigenen geschichtlichen Entwickelung nicht entschlagen, sondern hat eine Geschichte der Philosophie als eigene und zwar zugleich historische und speku-lative Disziplin, in deren geschichtlichen Entwickelungsphasen und geschichtlich aufeinanderfolgenden Systemen der Philosophen die neuere Spekulation seit Schelling und Hegel zugleich die Philosophie selbst als ein die verschiedenen geschichtlichen Systeme umfassendes ganzes in seiner dialektischen Gliederung erkannt hat.—GLOATZ, *Spekulative Theologie*, i. 23. Die heutige Philosophie führt uns auf einen Standpunkt von dem aus die philosophische Idee als das innere Wesen der Geschichte selbst erscheint. So trat an die Stelle einer abstrakt philosophischen Richtung, welche das Geschichtliche verneinte, eine abstrakt geschichtliche Richtung, welche das Philosophische verläugnete. Beide Richtungen sind als überschrittene und besiegte zu betrachten. — BERNER, *Strafrecht*, 75. Die Geschichte der Philosophie hat uns fast schon die Wissen schaft der Philosophie selbst ersetzt.—HERMANN, *Phil. Monatshefte*, ii. 198, 1889.

[81] La siècle actuel sera principalement caractérisé par l'irrévocable prépondé-rance de l'histoire, en philosophie, en politique, et même en poésie.—COMTE, *Politique Positive*, iii. 1.

[82] The historical or comparative method has revolutionised not only the sciences of law, mythology, and language, of anthropology and sociology, but it has forced its way even into the domain of philosophy and natural science. For what is the theory of evolution itself, with all its far-reaching consequences, but the achievement of the historical method?—PROTHERO, *Inaugural ; National Review*, December 1894, 461. To facilitate the advancement of all the branches of useful science, two things seem to be principally requisite. The first is, an historical account of their rise, progress, and present state. Without the former of these helps, a person every way qualified for extending the bounds of science labours under great disadvantages ; wanting the lights which have been struck out by others, and perpetually running the risk of losing his labour, and finding him-self anticipated.—PRIESTLEY, *History of Vision*, 1772, i., Pref. i. Cuvier se

proposait de montrer l'enchaînement scientifique des découvertes, leurs relations avec les grands évènements historiques, et leur influence sur les progrès et le développement de la civilisation.—DARESTE, *Biographie Générale*, xii. 685. Dans ses éloquentes leçons, l'histoire des sciences est devenue l'histoire même de l'esprit humain ; car, remontant aux causes de leurs progrès et de leurs erreurs, c'est toujours dans les bonnes ou mauvaises routes suivies par l'esprit humain, qu'il trouve ces causes.—FLOURENS, *Éloge de Cuvier*, xxxi. Wie keine fortlaufende Entwickelungsreihe von nur Einem Punkte aus vollkommen aufzufassen ist, so wird auch keine lebendige Wissenschaft nur aus der Gegenwart begriffen werden können. — Deswegen ist aber eine solche Darstellung doch noch nicht der gesammten Wissenschaft adäquat, und sie birgt, wenn sie damit verwechselt wird, starke Gefahren der Einseitigkeit, des Dogmatismus und damit der Stagnation in sich. Diesen Gefahren kann wirksam nur begegnet werden durch die verständige Betrachtung der Geschichte der Wissenschaften, welche diese selbst in stetem Flusse zeigt und die Tendenz ihres Fortschreitens in offenbarer und sicherer Weise klarlegt.—ROSENBERGER, *Geschichte der Physik*, iii. p. vi. Die Continuität in der Ausbildung aller Auffassungen tritt um so deutlicher hervor, je vollständiger man sich damit wie sie zu verschiedenen Zeiten waren, vertraut macht.—KOPP, *Entwickelung der Chemie*, 814.

[83] Die Geschichte und die Politik sind Ein und derselbe Janus mit dem Doppelgesicht, das in der Geschichte in die Vergangenheit, in der Politik in die Zukunft hinschaut.—GÜGLER'S *Leben*, ii. 59.

[84] The papers inclosed, which give an account of the killing of two men in the county of Londonderry ; if they prove to be Tories, 'tis very well they are gone. —I think it will not only be necessary to grant those a pardon who killed them, but also that they have some reward for their own and others' encouragement.— ESSEX, *Letters*, 10, 10th January 1675. The author of this happened to be present. There was a meeting of some honest people in the city, upon the occasion of the discovery of some attempt to stifle the evidence of the witnesses.—Bedloe said he had letters from Ireland, that there were some Tories to be brought over hither, who were privately to murder Dr. Oates and the said Bedloe. The doctor, whose zeal was very hot, could never after this hear any man talk against the plot, or against the witnesses, but he thought he was one of these Tories, and called almost every man a Tory that opposed him in discourse ; till at last the word Tory became popular.—DEFOE, *Edinburgh Review*, l. 403.

[85] La España será el primer pueblo en donde se encenderá esta guerra patriotica que solo puede libertar á Europa.—Hemos oido esto en Inglaterra á varios de los que estaban alli presentes. Muchas veces ha oido lo mismo al duque de Wellington el general Don Miguel de Alava, y dicho duque refirió el suceso en una comida diplomatica que dió en Paris el duque de Richelieu en 1816.—TORENO, *Historia del Levantamiento de España*, 1838, i. 508.

[86] Nunquam propter auctoritatem illorum, quamvis magni sint nominis (supponimus scilicet semper nos cum eo agere qui scientiam historicam vult consequi), sententias quas secuti sunt ipse tamquam certas admittet, sed solummodo ob vim testimoniorum et argumentorum quibus eas confirmarunt.—DE SMEDT, *Introductio ad historiam critice tractandam*, 1866, i. 5.

[87] Hundert schwere Verbrechen wiegen nicht so schwer in der Schale der Unsittlichkeit, als ein unsittliches Princip.—*Hallische Jahrbücher*, 1839, 308. Il faut flétrir les crimes ; mais il faut aussi, et surtout, flétrir les doctrines et les systèmes qui tendent à les justifier. — MORTIMER TERNAUX, *Histoire de la Terreur*.

[88] We see how good and evil mingle in the best of men and in the best of causes ; we learn to see with patience the men whom we like best often in the wrong, and the repulsive men often in the right ; we learn to bear with patience the knowledge that the cause which we love best has suffered, from the awkwardness of its defenders, so great disparagement, as in strict equity to justify the men who were assaulting it.—STUBBS, *Seventeen Lectures*, 97.

[89] *Caeteris paribus*, on trouvera tousjours que ceux qui ont plus de puissance sont sujets à pécher davantage ; et il n'y a point de théorème de géométrie qui soit plus asseuré que cette proposition.—LEIBNIZ, 1688, ed. Rommel, ii. 197.

Il y a toujours eu de la malignité dans la grandeur, et de l'opposition à l'esprit de l'Évangile ; mais maintenant il y en a plus que jamais, et il semble que comme le monde va à sa fin, celui qui est dans l'élévation fait tous ses efforts pour dominer avec plus de tyrannie, et pour étouffer les maximes du Christianisme et le règne de Jésus-Christ, voiant qu'il s'approche.—GODEAU, *Lettres*, 423, 27th March 1667. There is, in fact, an unconquerable tendency in all power, save that of knowledge, acting by and through knowledge, to injure the mind of him by whom that power is exercised.—WORDSWORTH, 22nd June 1817 ; *Letters of Lake Poets*, 369.

[90] I cieli han messo sulla terra due giudici delle umane azioni, la coscienza e la storia.—COLLETTA. Wenn gerade die edelsten Männer um des Nachruhmes willen gearbeitet haben, so soll die Geschichte ihre Belohnung sein, sie auch die Strafe für die Schlechten.—LASAULX, *Philosophie der Künste*, 211. Pour juger ce qui est bon et juste dans la vie actuelle ou passée, il faut posséder un criterium, qui ne soit pas tiré du passé ou du présent, mais de la nature humaine.—AHRENS, *Cours de Droit Naturel*, i. 67.

[91] L'homme de notre temps ! La conscience moderne ! Voilà encore de ces termes qui nous ramènent la prétendue philosophie de l'histoire et la doctrine du progrès, quand il s'agit de la justice, c'est-à-dire de la conscience pure et de l'homme rationnel, que d'autres siècles encore que le nôtre ont connu.— RENOUVIER, *Crit. Phil.* 1873, ii. 55.

[92] Il faut pardonner aux grands hommes le marchepied de leur grandeur.— COUSIN, in J. SIMON, *Nos Hommes d'État*, 1887, 55. L'esprit du XVIIIe siècle n'a pas besoin d'apologie : l'apologie d'un siècle est dans son existence.—COUSIN, *Fragments*, iii. 1826. Suspendus aux lèvres éloquentes de M. Cousin, nous l'entendîmes s'écrier que la meilleure cause l'emportait toujours, que c'était la loi de l'histoire, le rhythme immuable du progrès.—GASPARIN, *La Liberté Morale*, ii. 63. Cousin verurtheilen heisst darum nichts Anderes als jenen Geist historischer Betrachtung verdammen, durch welchen das 19. Jahrhundert die revolutionäre Kritik des 18. Jahrhunderts ergänzt, durch welchen insbesondere Deutschland die geistigen Wohlthaten vergolten hat, welche es im Zeitalter der Aufklärung von seinen westlichen Nachbarn empfangen.—IODL, *Gesch. der Ethik*, ii. 295. Der Gang der Weltgeschichte steht ausserhalb der Tugend, des Lasters, und der Gerechtigkeit.— HEGEL, *Werke*, viii. 425. Die Vermischung des Zufälligen im Individuum mit dem an ihm Historischen führt zu unzähligen falschen Ansichten und Urtheilen. Hierzu gehört namentlich alles Absprechen über die moralische Tüchtigkeit der Individuen, und die Verwunderung, welche bis zur Verzweiflung an göttlicher Gerechtigkeit sich steigert, dass historisch grosse Individuen moralisch nichtswürdig erscheinen können. Die moralische Tüchtigkeit besteht in der Unterordnung alles dessen, was zufällig am Einzelnen unter das an ihm dem Allgemeinen Angehörige.—MARBACH, *Geschichte der Griechischen Philosophie*, 7. Das Sittliche der Neuseeländer, der Mexikaner ist vielmehr ebenso sittlich, wie das der Griechen, der Römer ; und das Sittliche der Christen des Mittelalters ist ebenso sittlich, wie das der Gegenwart.—KIRCH-MANN, *Grundbegriffe des Rechts*, 194. Die Geschichtswissenschaft als solche kennt nur ein zeitliches und mithin auch nur ein relatives Maass der Dinge. Alle Werthbeurtheilung der Geschichte kann daher nur relativ und aus zeitlichen Momenten fliessen, und wer sich nicht selbst täuschen und den Dingen nicht Gewalt anthun will, muss ein für allemal in dieser Wissenschaft auf absolute Werthe verzichten.—LORENZ, *Schlosser*, 80. Only according to his faith is each man judged. Committed as this deed has been by a pure-minded, pious youth, it is a beautiful sign of the time.—DE WETTE to SAND'S Mother ; CHEYNE, *Founders of Criticism*, 44. The men of each age must be judged by the ideal of their own age and country, and not by the ideal of ours. — LECKY, *Value of History*, 50.

[93] La durée ici-bas, c'est le droit, c'est la sanction de Dieu.—GUIRAUD, *Philosophie Catholique de l'Histoire*.

[94] Ceux qui ne sont pas contens de l'ordre des choses ne sçauroient se vanter d'aimer Dieu comme il faut.—Il faut toujours estre content de l'ordre du passé, parce qu'il est conforme à la volonté de Dieu absolue, qu'on connoît par l'évène-

ment. Il faut tâcher de rendre l'avenir, autant qu'il dépend de nous, conforme à la volonté de Dieu présomptive.—LEIBNIZ, *Werke*, ed. Gerhardt, ii. 136. Ich habe damals bekannt und bekenne jetzt, dass die politische Wahrheit aus denselben Quellen zu schöpfen ist, wie alle anderen, aus dem göttlichen Willen und dessen Kundgebung in der Geschichte des Menschengeschlechts.—RADOWITZ, *Neue Gespräche*, 65.

[95] A man is great as he contends best with the circumstances of his age.—FROUDE, *Short Studies*, i. 388. La persuasion que l'homme est avant tout une personne morale et libre, et qu'ayant conçu seul, dans sa conscience et devant Dieu, la règle de sa conduite, il doit s'employer tout entier à l'appliquer en lui, hors de lui, absolument, obstinément, inflexiblement, par une résistance perpétuelle opposée aux autres ; et par une contrainte perpétuelle exercée sur soi, voilà la grande idée anglaise.—TAINE ; SOREL, *Discours de Réception*, 24. In jeder Zeit des Christenthums hat es einzelne Männer gegeben, die über ihrer Zeit standen und von ihren Gegensätzen nicht berührt wurden.—BACHMANN, *Hengstenberg*, i. 160. Eorum enim qui de iisdem rebus mecum aliquid ediderunt, aut solus insanio ego, aut solus non insanio ; tertium enim non est, nisi (quod dicet forte aliquis) insaniamus omnes.—HOBBES, quoted by DE MORGAN, 3rd June 1858 : *Life of Sir W. R. Hamilton*, iii. 552.

[96] I have now to exhibit a rare combination of good qualities, and a steady perseverance in good conduct, which raised an individual to be an object of admiration and love to all his contemporaries, and have made him to be regarded by succeeding generations as a model of public and private virtue.—The evidence shows that upon this occasion he was not only under the influence of the most vulgar credulity, but that he violated the plainest rules of justice, and that he really was the murderer of two innocent women.—Hale's motives were most laudable.—CAMPBELL'S *Lives of the Chief Justices*, i. 512, 561, 566. It was not to be expected of the colonists of New England that they should be the first to see through a delusion which befooled the whole civilised world, and the gravest and most knowing persons in it.—The people of New England believed what the wisest men of the world believed at the end of the seventeenth century.—PALFREY, *New England*, iv. 127, 129 (also speaking of witchcraft). Il est donc bien étrange que sa sévérité tardive s'exerce aujourd'hui sur un homme auquel elle n'a d'autre reproche à faire que d'avoir trop bien servi l'état par des mesures politiques, injustes peut-être, violentes, mais qui, en aucune manière, n'avaient l'intérêt personnel du coupable pour objet.—M. Hastings peut sans doute paraître répréhensible aux yeux des étrangers, des particuliers même, mais il est assez extraordinaire qu'une nation usurpatrice d'une partie de l'Indostan veuille mêler les règles de la morale à celles d'une administration forcée, injuste et violente par essence, et à laquelle il faudrait renoncer à jamais pour être conséquent.—MALLET DU PAN, *Mémoires*, ed. Sayous, i. 102.

[97] On parle volontiers de la stabilité de la constitution anglaise. La vérité est que cette constitution est toujours en mouvement et en oscillation et qu'elle se prête merveilleusement au jeu de ses différentes parties. Sa solidité vient de sa souplesse ; elle plie et ne rompt pas.—BOUTMY, *Nouvelle Revue*, 1878, 49.

[98] This is not an age for a man to follow the strict morality of better times, yet sure mankind is not yet so debased but that there will ever be found some few men who will scorn to join concert with the public voice when it is not well grounded.—*Savile Correspondence*, 173.

[99] Cette proposition : L'homme est incomparablement plus porté au mal qu'au bien, et il se fait dans le monde incomparablement plus de mauvaises actions que de bonnes—est aussi certaine qu'aucun principe de métaphysique. Il est donc incomparablement plus probable qu'une action faite par un homme, est mauvaise, qu'il n'est probable qu'elle soit bonne. Il est incomparablement plus probable que ces secrets ressorts qui l'ont produite sont corrompus, qu'il n'est probable qu'ils soient honnêtes. Je vous avertis que je parle d'une action qui n'est point mauvaise extérieurement.—BAYLE, *Œuvres*, ii. 248.

[100] A Christian is bound by his very creed to suspect evil, and cannot release himself.—His religion has brought evil to light in a way in which it never was before ; it has shown its depth, subtlety, ubiquity ; and a revelation, full of

mercy on the one hand, is terrible in its exposure of the world's real state on the other. The Gospel fastens the sense of evil upon the mind ; a Christian is enlightened, hardened, sharpened, as to evil ; he sees it where others do not.— MOZLEY, *Essays*, i. 308. All satirists, of course, work in the direction of Christian doctrine, by the support they give to the doctrine of original sin, making a sort of meanness and badness a law of society.—MOZLEY, *Letters*, 333. Les critiques, même malveillants, sont plus près de la vérité dernière que les admirateurs.—NISARD, *Lit. fr.*, Conclusion. Les hommes supérieurs doivent nécessairement passer pour méchants. Où les autres ne voient ni un défaut, ni un ridicule, ni un vice, leur implacable œil l'aperçoit.—BARBEY D'AUREVILLY *Figaro*, 31st March 1888.

[101] Prenons garde de ne pas trop expliquer, pour ne pas fournir des arguments à ceux qui veulent tout excuser.—BROGLIE, *Réception de Sorel*, 46.

[102] The eternal truths and rights of things exist, fortunately, independent of our thoughts or wishes, fixed as mathematics, inherent in the nature of man and the world. They are no more to be trifled with than gravitation.—FROUDE, *Inaugural Lecture at St. Andrews*, 1869, 41. What have men to do with interests ? There is a right way and a wrong way. That is all we need think about.—CARLYLE to FROUDE, *Longman's Magazine*, December 1892, 151. As to History, it is full of indirect but very effective moral teaching. It is not only, as Bolingbroke called it, " Philosophy teaching by examples," but it is morality teaching by examples.—It is essentially the study which best helps the student to conceive large thoughts.—It is impossible to overvalue the moral teaching of History.—FITCH, *Lectures on Teaching*, 432. Judging from the past history of our race, in ninety-nine cases out of a hundred, war is a folly and a crime.— Where it is so, it is the saddest and the wildest of all follies, and the most heinous of all crimes.—GREG, *Essays on Political and Social Science*, 1853, i. 562. La volonté de tout un peuple ne peut rendre juste ce qui est injuste : les représentants d'une nation n'ont pas le droit de faire ce que la nation n'a pas le droit de faire elle-même.—B. CONSTANT, *Principes de Politique*, i. 15.

[103] Think not that morality is ambulatory ; that vices in one age are not vices in another, or that virtues, which are under the everlasting seal of right reason, may be stamped by opinion.—SIR THOMAS BROWNE, *Works*, iv. 64.

[104] Osons croire qu'il seroit plus à propos de mettre de côté ces traditions, ces usages, et ces coutumes souvent si imparfaites, si contradictoires, si incohérentes, ou de ne les consulter que pour saisir les inconvéniens et les éviter ; et qu'il faudroit chercher non-seulement les éléments d'une nouvelle législation, mais même ses derniers détails dans une étude approfondie de la morale.—LETROSNE, *Réflexions sur la Législation Criminelle*, 137. M. Renan appartient à cette famille d'esprits qui ne croient pas en réalité la raison, la conscience, le droit applicables à la direction des sociétés humaines, et qui demandent à l'histoire, à la tradition, non à la morale, les règles de la politique. Ces esprits sont atteints de la maladie du siècle, le scepticisme moral.—PILLON, *Critique Philosophique*, i. 49.

[105] The subject of modern History is of all others, to my mind, the most interesting, inasmuch as it includes all questions of the deepest interest relating not to human things only, but to divine.—ARNOLD, *Modern History*, 311.

INDEX

THE END

PRINTED BY R. & R. CLARK, LTD., EDINBURGH